Primer of Electronics and Radiant Energy

THE RADIANT ENERGY SPECTRUM

LOGARITHMIC SCALE

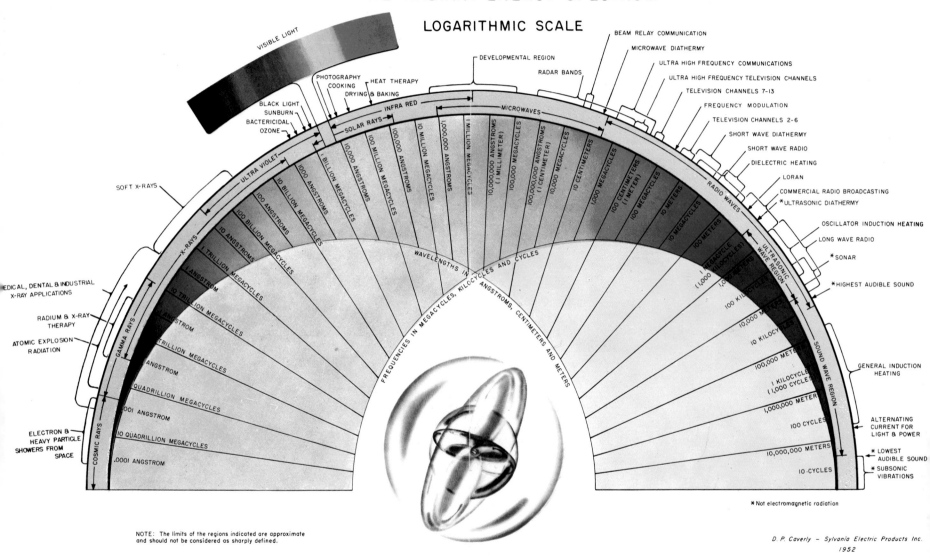

VISIBLE LIGHT

BLACK LIGHT
SUNBURN
BACTERICIDAL
OZONE

PHOTOGRAPHY
COOKING
DRYING & BAKING

HEAT THERAPY

DEVELOPMENTAL REGION

RADAR BANDS

BEAM RELAY COMMUNICATION
MICROWAVE DIATHERMY
ULTRA HIGH FREQUENCY COMMUNICATIONS
ULTRA HIGH FREQUENCY TELEVISION CHANNELS
TELEVISION CHANNELS 7-13
FREQUENCY MODULATION
TELEVISION CHANNELS 2-6
SHORT WAVE DIATHERMY
SHORT WAVE RADIO
DIELECTRIC HEATING
LORAN
COMMERCIAL RADIO BROADCASTING
*ULTRASONIC DIATHERMY
OSCILLATOR INDUCTION HEATING
LONG WAVE RADIO
*SONAR
*HIGHEST AUDIBLE SOUND

GENERAL INDUCTION HEATING

ALTERNATING CURRENT FOR LIGHT & POWER

*LOWEST AUDIBLE SOUND
*SUBSONIC VIBRATIONS

SOFT X-RAYS

ULTRA VIOLET

SOLAR RAYS

INFRA RED

MICROWAVES

RADIO WAVES

ULTRASONIC WAVE REGION

SOUND WAVE REGION

WAVELENGTHS IN CYCLES AND CYCLES

FREQUENCIES IN MEGACYCLES, KILOCYCLES, ANGSTROMS, CENTIMETERS AND METERS

X-RAYS

GAMMA RAYS

COSMIC RAYS

SOFT X-RAYS

MEDICAL, DENTAL & INDUSTRIAL X-RAY APPLICATIONS

RADIUM & X-RAY THERAPY

ATOMIC EXPLOSION RADIATION

ELECTRON & HEAVY PARTICLE SHOWERS FROM SPACE

1 ANGSTROM
10 ANGSTROMS
100 ANGSTROMS
1000 ANGSTROMS
10,000 ANGSTROMS
100 MILLION ANGSTROMS
100,000 ANGSTROMS
10 MILLION MEGACYCLES
1,000,000 ANGSTROMS
1 MILLION MEGACYCLES
10,000,000 ANGSTROMS (1 MILLIMETER)
100,000 MEGACYCLES
100,000,000 ANGSTROMS (1 CENTIMETER)
10,000 MEGACYCLES
10 CENTIMETERS
1,000 MEGACYCLES
100 CENTIMETERS (1 METER)
100 MEGACYCLES
10 METERS
10 MEGACYCLES
100 METERS
1 MEGACYCLE (1,000 KILOCYCLES)
1,000 METERS
100 KILOCYCLES
10,000 METERS
10 KILOCYCLES
100,000 METERS
1 KILOCYCLE (1,000 CYCLES)
1,000,000 METERS
100 CYCLES
10,000,000 METERS
10 CYCLES

1 ANGSTROM
.1 ANGSTROM
1 TRILLION MEGACYCLES
10 TRILLION MEGACYCLES
.01 ANGSTROM
100 TRILLION MEGACYCLES
.001 ANGSTROM
1 QUADRILLION MEGACYCLES
.0001 ANGSTROM
10 QUADRILLION MEGACYCLES
100 BILLION MEGACYCLES
10 BILLION MEGACYCLES
1 BILLION MEGACYCLES

*Not electromagnetic radiation

NOTE: The limits of the regions indicated are approximate and should not be considered as sharply defined.

D. P. Caverly — Sylvania Electric Products Inc.
1952

PRIMER OF ELECTRONICS

AND RADIANT ENERGY

Donald P. Caverly

DIRECTOR OF ENGINEERING AND DEVELOPMENT

SECOND EDITION

McGRAW-HILL BOOK COMPANY, INC.

NEW YORK   TORONTO   LONDON

1952

PRIMER OF ELECTRONICS AND RADIANT ENERGY

Library of Congress Catalog Card Number: 52-5328

FIFTH PRINTING

Preface

There are today, throughout the world, many thousands of people who, through a natural curiosity, would like to know more about some of the things they have been accepting as commonplace. Radio and television, light and heat, ultraviolet and infrared, X rays and other types of radiant energy have been in such wide use that most of us never stop to think of how they are produced and controlled.

The development and use of the atom bomb provided tremendous acceleration to the demand for information about radiant energy—what it is and what it does. But such knowledge is somewhat obscure to the average man or woman. Not being engineers or scientists, they find most of the published information difficult to absorb.

This book is written for them—the salesman, store clerks, lawyers, doctors, housewives, secretaries, and, in fact, almost everyone who, being surrounded by and dependent upon many wonderful things, would like to know a little of the basic principles behind some of them. A deliberate effort has been made to remove the complex technical aspects with which the physicists and engineers must deal and which quite naturally make the non-technically trained person shy away.

There was a big question in the author's mind as to whether the story in the first chapter should be there or whether the information should be condensed and presented later in the book. However, after considerable thought and discussion with others, it was decided to wade right into an explanation of atom structure at the outset, since most people realize that the energy locked up in atoms will probably be the most potent influence on life that has ever appeared. Furthermore, the chapter serves as a fundamental building block for the discussions which follow.

This book is not a first-time presentation of new facts or developments in the fields of electronics and radiant energy and is not intended as a finished and complete treatise on the various subjects discussed. It is, rather, a digest of the very basic principles involved in the study of how electrons, protons, neutrons, and other composite atomic particles behave and are controlled and how the radiant energy attending their release or disturbance in atoms is utilized.

In order to produce such a digest of profound and complex subjects, the author was forced, at times, to make certain mild modifications of scientific data, partly because the data themselves are controversial and partly to accomplish a desirable degree of simplicity. It is hoped that the reader will pursue this book with an interest such as he might show in his newspaper, magazine, or a novel.

Don Caverly

Darien, Connecticut
April, 1952

Contents

Part One: Electricity

1

Energy and Matter

Once upon a time, about 10 years ago, there was a sales meeting. The group of men present were discussing what all business groups discuss—the future progress of their company and what they, as salesmen, would be called upon to sell. The company they represented to the buying public manufactured light sources and equipment, radio tubes, and other types of vacuum and gaseous-discharge tubes for communication, detection, and similar purposes.

The word *electronics* was used freely during conversations until finally someone asked, "Just what is electronics? What does it mean and how can we get to know more about electron tubes and the devices utilizing them?"

During the 10 years since that sales meeting, the average man has learned a great deal about electronics. One of the most significant things among the many that characterize the average person's mind today as compared with 10 years ago is a fundamental concept of atomic energy. Almost everyone has at least some sort of hazy notion of the structure of an atom—with the electron as one of the elements in that structure.

The reason for this general recognition of a most profound and challenging subject is, of course, the atomic bomb which ended the Second World War so abruptly and is today the only man-made factor capable of completely annihilating life on this earth. On the other hand, the energy locked up in atoms could, if released and controlled, create a civilized existence so harmonious that present-day living might be looked upon in the future as almost barbaric.

No wonder, then, that the average man reads about atomic energy, the atom, and the electron whenever he can and whenever something is written he understands.

Basic Substance and Energy

All substances are composed of atoms—infinitely small and frequently complex clusters of matter and/or energy, something more than one one-hundred-millionth of an inch in diameter. They are not necessarily solid spheres or cubes but rather might be considered as dynamic little families of energy—sometimes in a balanced state of stability and sometimes in an active state of instability. To the chemist they are the basic building blocks of his science.

These atoms in turn are composed of a center or core called the *nucleus*. It is made up of a preponderance of positively charged particles around which negative charges, called *electrons*, swarm in orbits or so-called *energy levels*. The study of electrons, their behavior in electromagnetic fields and their ability to absorb and release energy in an atom, establishes the subject matter of the science of electronics. The study of the nucleus makes up our present-day frontier of physics, and it is, in general, called nucleonics. Although the activity in this field has been extremely intense, the results are kept more or less obscure because of the incredible performance of its most widely known product, the atom bomb.

In 1913, Dr. Niels Bohr, a Danish scientist, brought to the attention of physicists a concept or theory of atom structure which today remains the most comprehensible, even though it was conceived long before present knowledge of the atom and its laws of behavior was developed. In his picture of the atom, electrons rapidly revolve around a ball of nuclear particles in much the same way that the planets revolve around the sun.

During the last few years, accelerated study, research, and observation of the results of atom behavior have yielded variations and adjustments in Bohr's original atom picture which probably bring us somewhat nearer to an accurate understanding. It is doubtful, however, whether the human mind can ever grasp completely, in terms of solid things, "particles" and groups

Fig. 1-1. Bohr's basic concept of atom structure as seen in a single atom of hydrogen (left), where one electron revolves around a positively charged nucleus of one proton, and the more complex carbon atom (right), where six electrons swarm around a nucleus of six protons and six neutrons.

of "particles" which are made up of energy, with little or no matter at all.

But regardless of their structure, atoms are very real things. The particles of their nuclei are bound compactly together by tremendous forces resulting in part at least, and as far as is known, from the energies of the particles themselves. The electrons surrounding nuclei are likewise held at certain energy-level distances out from the nuclei by residual nucleonic forces of much less magnitude.

To describe better, perhaps, the meaning of the energy of an atom, let us consider two billiard balls. Each ball is composed entirely of countless billions of atoms, each atom made up of energy and held together by energy about as described above. When the two balls are rolled across the table and strike each other, they click and bounce apart. They are "solid." Now let us suppose that it were possible to remove all the binding forces from all the atoms in each ball and then roll them toward each other. With such a fantastic situation the balls might be expected to meet and roll through each other in ghostly fashion. They might have "form," but there would be no energy binding them together into solidity. Of course, such a condition could not exist, but the description may serve as means of explaining to some slight degree the little-understood phenomenon of atomic *binding energy.*

The Nucleus

When the atom first began to be understood and studied, most attention was given to electrons, since their existence was more certain and the pattern of their behavior more pronounced. More recently, however, the nucleus of the atom has become known as the source of enormous quantities of energy. Sometimes this energy is found to be releasing itself and radiating away, and sometimes it can be knocked out of the nucleus by parts of other atoms which can be made to act like high-velocity bullets.

It has been mentioned that the nucleus is made up of a preponderance of positively charged particles called *protons,* but there are also several other particles in nuclei of different atoms. The most prominent and important of these is the *neutron.* Some of the others are not evident except when they appear at the time of an atomic collision. The probable structure of the nucleus, that is, the arrangement of the particles, is not known with certainty. The most understandable concept is that the particles are arranged in a cluster like a spherical bunch of grapes. There are, however, indications that the protons and neutrons may be grouped in specific shells or orbits much like the system of electron shells surrounding a nucleus. In addition to this, there is definite evidence that the nucleus and/or its particles spin on an axis. With all these factors and others, it becomes apparent that the normally stable atom, and particularly its nucleus, is a highly complex system of energy particles arranged in an orderly structure pattern of shells, levels, or orbits. Some of the nuclear particles are as follows:

Proton: The basic particle of all atomic nuclei. It has a single positive charge equal to that of an electron, which is negative. It is a comparatively heavy particle—an ounce containing over $17\frac{1}{2}$ million billion billion of them. An atom of hydrogen, the lightest of all elements, has a nucleus consisting of one proton only.

Neutron: A particle present in all nuclei except hydrogen. It has a mass slightly larger than that of a proton, but no charge, either positive or negative, a property which allows it, when free, to penetrate all nuclei readily. Neutrons are released or emitted with great speed and energy as a result of particle collisions and may live as long as an hour under such conditions, whereupon they join another particle or nuclear group.

Deuteron: A proton and a neutron bound together by a strong force and exhibiting properties of a single particle under certain conditions.

Alpha Particle: Another composite particle consisting of two protons and two neutrons very tightly bound together and exhibiting the behavior properties of a single particle. An alpha particle is the complete nucleus of a helium atom.

Meson (or Mesotron): The true nature of this particle is not as yet completely clear. Some are known to carry a positive charge, others a negative, and there is evidence of the existence of still others (called *neutrettos*) which carry no charge at all. Their average life span is extremely short—in the order of one five-hundred-thousandth of a second for the light mesons and one one-hundred-millionth of a second for a heavy type. They are created by nuclear activity and collision of particles and at the end of their instant of life become other particles with the release or absorption of atomic energy. Mesons are from about one-tenth to one-seventh as heavy as protons, depending upon the nature of their charge.

Positron: This particle has been called a *positive electron,* since its behavior and characteristics are essentially identical with the electron, except for the fact that it carries a positive charge instead of a negative. Positrons are produced when a quantity of radiant energy (gamma radiation) collides with a nucleus. Each one appears in conjunction with an electron, and the activity is known as *pair production.* Positrons have a relatively short existence, since they combine quickly with an electron again and revert back to energy, apparently vanishing as "particles." There is a recognized theory which proposes that a positron is not a particle at all but is, rather, the vacancy or "hole" remaining when an electron leaves or is ejected from the state of negative energy within its energy level or shell.

Neutrino: The most elusive and difficult to detect of all particles thus far discovered—so much so that its existence has been questioned by many nuclear physicists. The neutrino is admitted in the pattern of nuclear activity primarily because it is needed to explain certain nuclear-energy phenomena involving radioactivity. In other words, it must exist just like the missing piece of a jigsaw puzzle. It would have no positive or negative charge, and its mass is expected to be very small or even zero. The best indication thus far of its influence in the realm of nuclear action is a detectable recoil of the excited atom from which it is ejected during a transitory process of particle and energy change.

Beta Particle: Frequently referred to as beta rays, these particles of energy are electrons, sometimes traveling at extremely high velocities very nearly equal to that of light. Although primary beta particles do not exist in nuclei, they result from a transposition of energy during the breakdown of nuclei under certain conditions (radioactivity). There are slower types called secondary beta particles which have their beginning in the outer electron energy levels of atoms rather than in the nucleus.

Gamma Rays: These rays consist of *photons* of radiating energy and as such are referred to as rays rather than particles, although the difference is primarily in definition, viewpoint, and the properties under consideration. Photons are fundamental units called *quanta* of radiant energy usually identified with the high-frequency, short-wavelength regions of the electromagnetic spectrum, and they, as well as gamma radiation, will be discussed more in detail in Part Three, Chapter 10. While photons of visible light and X rays arise from disturbances in the electron energy shells or levels of an atom, photons of gamma radiation originate in excited (radioactive) nuclei with a consequent shorter wavelength and higher frequency. A quantum of gamma radiation does not carry a charge as do most of the particles described above and therefore is not subject to magnetic-field influences. When a positron vanishes as a "particle," it becomes two quanta of gamma radiation.

The Electron

After this brief glimpse of atomic nuclei and the particles comprising, born within, and emanating from them, let us turn our attention to the satellite electrons. An electron is the fundamental charge of negative electricity, or it might be called the basic "particle" of negative electricity which, as far as is known, cannot be divided or split.

It is difficult as well as unsatisfactory to think of any atomic particle in terms of physical dimensions or size, but measurements have been calculated which indicate that the diameter of an electron (if we consider it as spherical) should be over one six-trillionth of an inch. Its mass is the smallest known—about 1/1,840 that of a proton, which means that it would require more than 28 billion billion billion of them to weigh an ounce. The mass of electrons increases with their velocity. The figure above is the approximate mass of an electron at "rest" as part of an atom (1,500 to 2,000 miles per second), but when accelerated to approach the speed of light (186,000 miles per second) it weighs several times as much.

Another characteristic of an electron which should be mentioned is its *spin*. It is not quite accurate, perhaps, to conceive of a fundamental charge of negative electricity as rotating about an axis like a gyroscope, but since a magnetic field exists around an electron, a spin or *angular momentum* is present in some form.

The electron is basic to all matter. As parts of all atoms they are of equal charge and mass.

The Atom

Now that we have a general idea of both the nucleus and the electrons which swarm around it, let us combine the two and consider the properties of the atom as a whole.

All substances on this earth as well as out of it, whether gaseous, liquid, or solid, are made up of atoms. There are 92 elements comprising all matter as found in nature, and the difference between one element and another is in the structure of its atoms. All normally stable or electrically balanced atoms have one characteristic in common—there are always enough negative electrons around the nucleus to equal the total of positive charges (protons) in the nucleus.

For example, an atom of hydrogen, the lightest element, consists of a nucleus of only one proton, around which revolves one electron. Helium, the next lightest element, is made up of atoms whose nuclei consist of two protons *and* two neutrons, with two electrons encircling it. In this case, it will be remembered, neutrons carry no charge, so that even though four particles exist in the nucleus, only two of them, the protons, carry a positive charge and only two electrons are needed to affect a stable balance.

As we examine more complex atoms, we always find this electrical balance prevailing with stable atoms. Oxygen nuclei have 8 protons and 8 neutrons surrounded by 8 electrons. Frequently, there are more neutrons than protons in a nucleus, as in iron with 26 protons, 29 neutrons, and 26 electrons; gold with 79 protons, 118 neutrons, and 79 electrons; and uranium, the heaviest of all elements, with 92 protons, 146 neutrons, and 92 electrons.

Atomic Number and Weight: The number of protons in the

nucleus of an element designates its *atomic number,* whereas the total of protons and neutrons indicates its *atomic weight.* There are isotopes (which will be discussed more in detail shortly) of all elements which influence the atomic weight, so that the number designating this property is an average of atomic and isotopic nuclei particles. Aluminum, for example, has an atomic number of 13, which means that it has 13 positive charges (protons) in its nucleus, but it has an atomic weight of 26.97. The latter figure is an average of all the particles in the nuclei of both the atoms and the few isotopes which would exist in a quantity of aluminum. Since isotopes will have extra neutrons, the atomic weight is influenced by the few isotopes, so that the average figure is 26.97 instead of an even 26, the total of protons and neutrons in an aluminum-atom nucleus.

Electron Shells: Electrons are arranged around their nucleus in a well-defined and orderly pattern of energy levels called *shells.* Each shell may accommodate anywhere from one to several electrons, and the electrons can be forced from one shell to the next outer one when they absorb the necessary amount of energy. The lowest energy level is the innermost shell which is held in place surrounding the nucleus about one two-hundred-fifty-millionth of an inch (one angstrom) out from the atom center. This is called the *K shell* and will accommodate one electron as in the case of hydrogen or two electrons as in the case of helium.

When three electrons appear as in the atom of the element lithium, the third one takes its place in a second energy level called the *L shell.* This shell occurs outside the first one and will accommodate eight electrons. When it is full, we have, including the two in the K shell, a total of 10 electrons encircling 10 protons and 10 neutrons. This combination is neon—atomic number and weight, 10 and 20.183, respectively. The eleventh electron, which, with another proton and neutron in the nucleus, forms a sodium atom, appears in a third level called the *M shell* which is still farther out from the nucleus. This one can also have 8 electrons (more with heavier elements), and when filled, we have a total of 18 electrons and the element argon. The nineteenth electron occurs in a fourth level known as the *N shell*. This pattern of atomic structure holds throughout all the elements. When we reach uranium we find a nucleus of 92 protons and 146 neutrons, with electrons arranged 2 in the K shell, 8 in the L, 18 in the M, 32 in the N, 18 in the O, 12 in the P, and 2 in the Q—the necessary total of 92 electrons.

Fig. 1-2. A later concept of atom structure, showing electron shells arranged concentrically around the nucleus.

Electrons occupying outer shells of atoms are bound much less firmly in place than in the inner shells and as a result can be displaced much more easily than the inner ones.

Lest the reader wonder about the possibility of collisions within the complex swarms of electrons, it will be well to mention two things. First, since electrons are negative charges, and since like charges repel each other, two electrons approaching

on the same path would go around each other rather than collide. Second, there seems to be some "thickness" to energy shells—
a sort of "strata" situation with groups of electrons circulating
in their own strata of the same shell. For example, the 32 electrons in the N shell of uranium are arranged 2 in the first step,
6 in the second, 10 in the third, and 14 in the fourth. Much remains to be learned about the forces governing atom structure,
and we have taken liberties in explaining it in an effort to present the simplest possible picture.

Thus, in considering the atom as a whole, we find that it is
mostly empty space with a compact nucleus of extreme density
which comprises practically all the weight of the atom and, perhaps, concentric spherical layers in which electron energy moves
around the center. By comparison, if we were to think of a
hydrogen nucleus (one proton only) as the size of a marble, it
might weigh something in the order of a few million tons, and
the electron shell K would be perhaps 600 or 700 miles away
with the electron itself probably somewhat larger, but weighing
1/1,840 as much as the marble.

Isotopes

In our discussion of the atom, it was mentioned that there are
occasional ones in all matter which may contain extra neutrons
in their nucleus. Such atoms are called *isotopes*. They have the
same number of protons and electrons as a normal atom, and
since neutrons have no charge, their electrical equilibrium is
maintained, regardless of the number of extra neutrons found in
the nuclei. Thus, while the atoms and isotopes in a certain
element may be identical with respect to their chemical and
physical characteristics, their atomic weights will differ by the
number of extra neutrons in the isotope.

In hydrogen gas, for example, for about every 5,000 normal
atoms with a 1-proton nucleus and 1 electron, there is usually 1
isotope with a 1-proton–1-neutron nucleus and 1 electron. There-

fore, the atomic weight of hydrogen is not 1.0, but rather the average of the atomic weights of the proportionate number of normal atoms (of atomic weight 1.0) and isotopes (of atomic weight 2.0), or 1.008.

The normal atom of neon gas has 10 protons and 10 neutrons in its nucleus with, of course, 10 electrons. However, neon gas is actually made up of a mixture of normal atoms and isotopes containing 2 extra neutrons, so that its atomic weight has been established at 20.183.

Isotopes are of extreme importance in nuclear physics work as will be pointed out in a later discussion on the release of atomic energy.

Ions

When a normal atom loses an electron for one reason or another, it becomes predominantly positive, since it then has a greater total of protons in its nucleus than electrons surrounding it. It then becomes known as a *positive ion* and responds to magnetic influences the same as any positive particle.

When a normal atom acquires an extra electron from some outside source, it becomes predominantly negative, since it now has more electrons than protons. Such an atom is called a *negative ion* and is influenced by magnetic forces as a negative particle would be.

There are always some ions present in all gases. Even the air we breathe is ionized to a slight degree at all times as a result of a number of influences, among them cosmic radiation from outer space which excites atoms and molecules, causing them to bump each other. Such collisions, if forceful enough, will knock electrons loose from atoms thereby forming ions. When the exciting influences cease, the atoms immediately find an "available" electron and return to their normal state again.

Ionization will be considered more completely later on when we discuss certain types of electron tubes and light sources which depend upon ionized gases for their operation.

Molecules

A molecule is a cluster of atoms—the smallest unit of an element or compound which retains the identity or character of the solid or fluid substance. The water we drink, for example, is composed of two parts of the element hydrogen and one part of the element oxygen; that is, its molecule consists of two hydrogen atoms and one oxygen atom. It is expressed chemically as H_2O.

Ordinary table salt, sodium chloride ($NaCl$) expressed Na for sodium and Cl for chlorine, is made up of molecules consisting of both sodium and chlorine atoms. There are thousands of other compounds, some of them highly complex, with molecules composed of the atoms of several different elements.

The motion of molecules to and fro in gases and liquids, their rotation, and their effect upon each other in bumping about can be studied with considerable accuracy, and much is known about their behavior and the laws governing it.

Crystal Lattice Structure: In crystalline solids such as metals, salt, and others, the atoms arrange themselves in symmetrical, solid geometrical patterns. These molecular arrangements are called *lattice structures.* The simplest of these is a cube with an atom at each of the eight corners. Further development of the cube lattice structure of other crystals finds, in addition, an atom in the center of the cube, atoms at the center of each of the six faces, and so on, in a symmetrical three-dimensional pattern. More complex structures show atoms arranged to form many-sided crystal lattices.

At this point in our discussion of atoms and the make-up of matter, it becomes extremely difficult to present a reasonably accurate picture without recourse to mathematical equations and the involved principles underlying the science of atomic physics. It is also difficult to explain simply how atoms arrange themselves in lattice structure and maintain that arrangement without risk of presenting apparent inconsistencies with previous explanations.

The chemists' concept of the atom—the one which is most

adaptable to his science—permits electron shells to be considered as concentric spheres, one within the other around the nucleus. The metallurgists' concept, however, while it recognizes the same fundamental nucleus and electron shells, is somewhat different and explains many of the phenomena in crystal structure and metallurgy. In it, the electron loses some of its identity as a particle which at one instant is on one side of the nucleus and the next is on the other. Instead we find the basic interest to be in the "solid" or three-dimensional pattern of energy created by the electron in its race around the nucleus.

To draw a simple parallel, the blades of an airplane propeller lose their identity of form and relative location when rotating at high speed. They become blurred into a disk which has not only the essential appearance of solid form but likewise many of the physical effects of a solid. If we spin a hoop rapidly as we might a top, it appears as a sphere and loses its hoop appearance.

Now let us consider an electron circling a nucleus. In one trip around it establishes a hoop-like path. The next trip around is not identical with the first but may be a little to one side or the other. In the third trip, it swings still a little more, and so on, so that, in effect, we have a hoop starting to turn or spin. Since the speed of electrons around the nucleus is tremendous, we see that they lose their identity as particles, and the patterns their paths establish appear (in concept) as three-dimensional clouds of energy and become the prime interest in consideration of atomic structure. We have previously referred to these clouds as energy levels or shells.

But the path of an electron around a nucleus is not necessarily circular. It is more often oval in shape so that its pattern of energy, or cloud, is ovoid or egg-shaped rather than spherical, with the nucleus at the narrow end. The energy patterns of electrons can be almost any shape depending upon what factors influence the path of the electron in its flight. Another electron in the vicinity may, as a result of the repulsive forces of the two negative charges, flatten, depress, or otherwise distort the

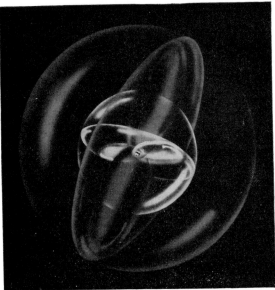

FIG. 1-3. It is difficult to reconcile the various concepts and theories of atom structure in a two-dimensional drawing. The movement of electrons around a nucleus of one atom, or the nuclei of two atoms, forms a complex pattern, and a three-dimensional or stereoscopic picture would be somewhat clearer, if such an illustration could be printed on a flat page. The above rendering presents, perhaps, a reasonably accurate idea of what a carbon atom might look like at a certain specific instant if it were possible to see one. Here we find a nucleus consisting of six protons (black dots) and six neutrons (white dots), around which six electrons swarm in elliptical or oval orbits. As these paths swing around, three-dimensional oval patterns are formed which in turn revolve around the nucleus to create thick doughnut-shaped "solids." These "solids" also spin like hoops, one within the other, to further create concentric spheres which we might consider as shells of energy around the nucleus. The inner or K shell would be formed by the motion of the two electrons whirling in their respective rotating oval paths—one electron for each oval. The outer or L shell would be formed the same as the other except that in this case there would be two electrons for each oval. Thus we "see" a carbon atom with its six protons, six neutrons in the nucleus, and six whirling electrons producing the two spherically concentric energy clouds, as it might appear at one specific instant.

"usual" pattern of energy. Futhermore, the patterns themselves may vibrate or, in a sense, quiver like a ball of jelly, depending upon certain influences.

When electrons get into a path encircling *two* nuclei, the energy pattern generated is elliptically symmetrical rather than ovoid. Two atoms frequently share a common electron, and the energy patterns of electrons in adjacent atoms often overlap with each other. Under these and other circumstances, atoms become

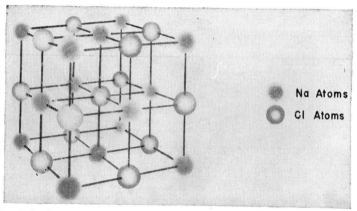

Na Atoms
Cl Atoms

Fɪɢ. 1-4. The crystal lattice structure of rock salt shows a cube arrangement of sodium (Na) and chlorine (Cl) atoms. This is called the *simple cubic lattice*.

bound or fixed in position relative to each other by their own electrostatic attractive forces yet held at fixed distances apart by the repulsive forces of their electrons.

Thus, we begin to see how matter is built up and locked together by energy and how crystal lattice structures are formed. The whole science is extremely complex, and any further exploration of it belongs in the realms of chemistry and metallurgy rather than in a book of this nature. The author has felt, however, that some degree of understanding of the relationship of energy and matter is necessary in preparation for what is to follow.

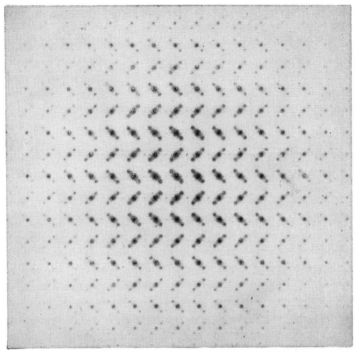

F<small>IG</small>. 1-5. An X-ray microscope photograph of pyrite (FeS_2), looking along the crystallographic a axis, showing the orderly arrangement of atoms in the crystal structure. This photograph, the second made in an apparatus which can indicate individual atoms in any crystal, is the work of Professor Martin J. Buerger in the Geology Department of the Massachusetts Institute of Technology. It shows atoms of iron (large spots) and sulphur (small spots) as they are combined and arranged in the crystal. The magnification is approximately 1 million diameters.

2

Electric Current

Since all substances are made up of atoms, all must contain electrons because they are part of atoms. In a solid, such as metal, glass, or wood, the atoms are relatively close together with many of their outer electron shells intermingled. In some of these materials, the outer electrons are strongly bound to the nuclei, whereas in others, some of the electrons are beyond the nucleonic binding forces and are free to move about in all directions from one atom to another within the limits of the solid. These are called *free electrons*. Their number and speed may be influenced by the application of heat and certain other forces.

Those metallic substances composed of atoms whose electrons can be moved relatively easily from one atom to the next are called *electrical conductors* and include copper, aluminum, iron, and many other metals, compounds, and liquids. Other substances where the electrons are more tightly bound to the atoms and do not migrate so easily are called *nonconductors* because the flow of electrons is greatly impeded. Rubber, mica, paper, oil, porcelain, and similar materials are well-known nonconductors. They are also sometimes called *dielectrics* and when used deliberately to prevent a flow of current are referred to as *insulators* or insulation.

Thus, in a copper wire, electrons move at random in every direction within the metal. When, however, there is a definite drift of electrons through the conductor in one direction, an

18

electric current is said to be flowing. The force that starts this directional electron movement is called an *electromotive force* and is referred to as emf. Electromotive force is comparable to a pressure difference, and its unit of measurement is called the *volt*, a term which will be described more in detail a little later. Since the free electrons are readily moved, only a very slight pressure is required to start them along the wire.

It is not known with certainty just how these electrons move from atom to atom or between atoms from one point in the conductor to another. While it is certain that they do move, it is also probable that energy is transmitted from one to another like a row of toppling dominoes.

Direct current always flows in the same direction. Its flow

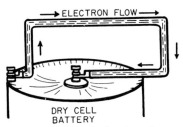

Fig. 2-1. Electrons flowing along a conductor may be compared to the action of water flowing through a pipe. Direct current from a battery flows in one direction through the conductor.

may be compared to the flow of water in a centrifugal pump—through a continuous loop of pipe and back to the pump.

Early Observations and Natural Electrical Phenomena

The Greeks had a word for electricity. It was *elektron*, which translated means amber. Thales of Miletus, an ancient Greek philosopher, is said to have been the first to observe that an amber rod, when rubbed, would attract straws and other light objects. This simple experiment performed 2,500 years ago marks the first time man became aware of electricity. Today, every woman is familiar with a similar phenomenon when her silk slip clings to her dress, and all office workers know how a sheet of paper sticks to the surface of the desk if it is rubbed vigorously a few times and how it will even crackle when lifted from the desk.

When a glass rod is rubbed with dry flannel, friction transfers some electrons from the flannel to the glass rod. The rod becomes *negatively* charged because it

has acquired a surplus of electrons, and the flannel becomes positively charged because of a deficiency of them. If the same thing is done again with another rod and flannel, it will be found that the rods, if suspended on a cord (and insulated from the ground), will tend to repel each other, as will the two pieces of flannel, but that the rods and flannel are attracted to each other. Thus, we find a fundamental law of electricity—that like charges repel each other and unlike charges attract each other. In other words, nature resents having matter thrown out of balance electrically and seeks to regain balance by discharging a surplus of electrons to other

FIG. 2-2. The discovery of electricity by Thales about 2,500 years ago was based on the ability of amber, when rubbed with flannel, to pick up various lightweight objects.

matter having a deficiency of them or at least a more nearly neutral electronic state.

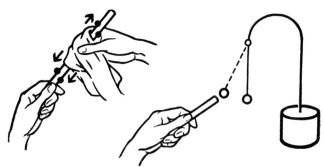

FIG. 2-3. When rubbed with dry flannel, a glass rod becomes negatively charged because it has acquired a surplus of electrons. The rod will then attract a pith ball (right) or it will repel a similar negatively charged rod.

There are a great many visible examples of electron discharges in everyday life. When a lump of sugar is broken, a cat's fur rubbed, or a roll of friction tape unrolled, sparks can be seen if the room is dark enough. The friction creates an electron discharge in each instance. Another example which has caused discomfort and surprise to thousands of people is the result of scuffing feet along a dry rug and then touching a radiator or another person with a finger tip. The friction of scuffing charges

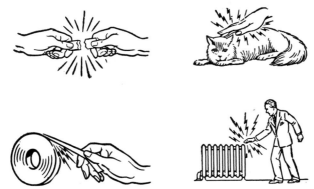

Fig. 2-4. Examples of electronic discharges which are seen in everyday life. Friction causes the spark.

the body with an excess of electrons, which are promptly discharged with a spark upon contact with a noncharged object.

These phenomena are put to many practical uses in industry and commerce. One of the simpler ones is the use of a chain dragging on the roadway beneath a gasoline truck to carry off any charge that may be generated in its metal body while in motion. Another is the use of a vertical flexible rod embedded in the roadway at the approach to the tollgate of a bridge or tunnel. When the rod strikes the bumper or front axle of a car, any charge in the body of the car and its occupants is dissipated so that, when a coin is handed the toll collector, no startling shock is felt by either the driver or collector.

The Ampere—Measurement of Electric-current Flow

It has already been pointed out how the flow of current is somewhat like the flow of water in a pipe. Water flow can be measured in gallons per second. Electric-current flow can be measured if we determine the total quantity of electrical charge
moved and the time involved in moving it.

The flow is measured in terms of its effect upon certain chemicals. The quantity of electricity which will deposit 0.00118 gram
of silver in a standard silver nitrate solution is known as the
coulomb. The total quantity of charge in coulombs may be determined by weighing the negative plate before and after the
time interval of current flow and dividing this weight in grams
by 0.00118. Then by dividing the number of coulombs thus obtained by the total number of seconds for which the current
flowed, the number of coulombs per second can be obtained.
And coulombs per second equals *amperes.*

Of course, such a method of measuring current is inconvenient
and could not be used today except experimentally, so the ammeter has been developed. It is connected in series with the load,
and the current is read directly in amperes on the scale of the
instrument.

Until a few years ago when it became certain that electric
current was the movement of electrons in a wire, the direction
of flow had always been considered as from positive to negative. Certain rules such as the "right-hand rule" and others governing the direction of electromagnetic forces and the direction
of motor or generator rotation were established on this premise.
However, with the development of an understanding of electrons
as basic negative charges, it became evident that they must move
in the opposite direction—toward positive, since unlike charges
attract. Therefore, in this book (Chapter 3), all diagrams and
"hand rules" illustrating the direction of current (electron) flow
or the direction of motor rotation may be at variance with older
textbooks, since they have been drawn to comply with the understanding of electron movement.

In solids such as metals, only the electrons are free to move, but in gases and liquids conducting current, *both* electrons and positive particles can move. Thus, in a column of gas such as in a

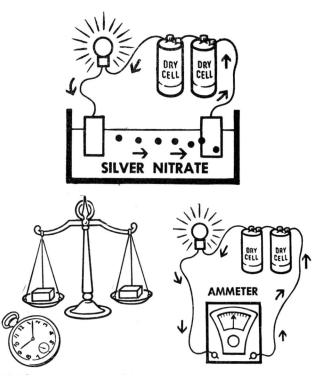

FIG. 2-5. Electricity is measured by the quantity per second passing through a conductor. The unit of quantity is the ampere, established in the laboratory by using a silver nitrate solution (top), scales, and a measure of time (lower left). Commercially, an ammeter (lower right) measures the quantity of electricity passing through a circuit.

fluorescent lamp, the electrons move toward the positive end, but positive ions and any other particles carrying a positive charge move the other way—toward the negative. Resulting collisions ionize the gas and cause a *glow discharge*.

The Volt—Measurement of Electrical Pressure

In discussing current flow in the preceding paragraphs, no account was taken of the electrical pressure forcing it. Of course, some sort of pressure is necessary if current is to flow at all. The unit of such electrical pressure is called the *volt*.

An understanding of voltage may be clearer if the water analogy is used again. If two holes of the same diameter are punched in a water tank, one near the top and one near the bottom, the water will flow more rapidly from the lower hole

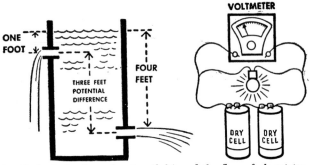

FIG. 2-6. In both the flow of water (left) and the flow of electricity (right) pressure is measured by the difference in potential. The voltmeter measures that there is a 3-volt difference in potential between the ends of the lamp circuit.

than from the upper one. The reason for this is the difference in fluid pressure at the bottom and top of the tank. The weight of water or pressure is greater at the bottom, so the water is forced out more rapidly. The difference in the two pressures is called the difference in *potential*, and it can be easily measured. Electrical pressure or voltage is measured in much the same way. In Fig. 2-6 two 1.5-volt dry-cell batteries are shown connected in series with an incandescent lamp. The voltmeter would show a reading of 3 volts, which means that the difference in potential or electrical pressure between the two ends of the lamp circuit is 3 volts. Electromotive force is the difference in potential which causes a current of electrons to flow in the circuit. Thus, the batteries are like the tank of water being slowly emptied to maintain an emf between the lamp terminals.

One *volt* is the electrical pressure or emf required to produce a current of one *ampere* through a conductor against a resistance of one *ohm*. The ohm, the unit of resistance to current flow, will be discussed shortly.

In electrical calibration work it is essential to have a cell of known and constant emf. The Weston Normal Standard cell has been employed as the International Standard for emf ratings because of its extraordinary constancy of emf. Its emf in standard form at 20° centigrade is 1.0183 volts. Therefore, the legal volt may be defined as 1/1.0183 of the voltage generated by a Standard Weston cell.

A dry-cell battery is based upon the fact that certain chemical or molecular action results in an emf which produces a flow of electrons. The dry cell consists of a zinc container which is the negative side of the circuit. It is filled with ammonium chloride of thick paste-like consistency with a carbon

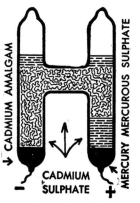

Fig. 2-7. The Weston Normal cell provides a constant and known voltage (1.0183 at 20° centigrade) which is used as a standard in measuring the *legal* volt.

rod immersed in the center which becomes the positive terminal. The ammonium chloride molecule breaks apart under such circumstances with one part carrying a negative charge and one a poistive charge. The latter migrates to the carbon rod and thereupon releases its charge so that a potential or electrical pressure of about one and a half volts is created. When the terminals are connected with a conductor, a flow of electrons takes place which gradually decreases as the battery material is used up and the potential dies out.

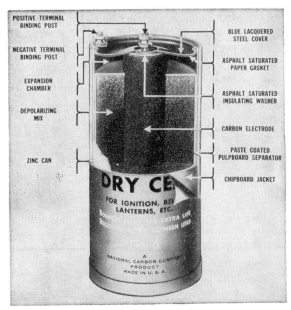

POSITIVE TERMINAL
BINDING POST

NEGATIVE TERMINAL
BINDING POST

EXPANSION
CHAMBER

DEPOLARIZING
MIX

ZINC CAN

BLUE LACQUERED
STEEL COVER

ASPHALT SATURATED
PAPER GASKET

ASPHALT SATURATED
INSULATING WASHER

CARBON ELECTRODE

PASTE COATED
PULPBOARD SEPARATOR

CHIPBOARD JACKET

DRY CE

FOR IGNITION, BE
LANTERNS, ETC.

EXTRA LIFE
EEN USES

A
NATIONAL CARBON COMP
PRODUCT
MADE IN U. S. A.

Fig. 2-8. Cross-sectional view of a dry-cell battery, showing the components and method of construction. (*Courtesy of National Carbon Company.*)

The Ohm—Measurement of Resistance to Current Flow

All movement of matter (except a falling body in a perfect vacuum) is opposed by the resisting force of friction. In the water pipe, the interior walls of the pipe resist the flow of water. In an electrical conductor, a resistance opposes the flow of current. As electrons move along a conductor under pressure through the maze of atoms of the metal which are also moving within themselves, they are bumped about considerably. This means that there is a resistance to current flow through a wire.

This resistance is measured in ohms. When a potential of one volt causes a current of one ampere to flow through a conductor, the conductor is offering a resistance of one ohm. Thus when more voltage is applied, more current flows, and as more resistance is offered, less current flows.

The quantity of flow per second (amperes) which can be forced through a conductor is directly proportional to the push it receives (volts) and is inversely proportional to the resistance

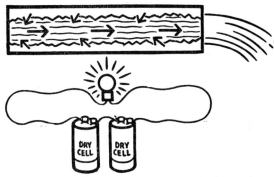

FIG. 2-9. An electrical conductor has resistance which interferes with the flow of electrons. It may be compared with the friction of the interior of the pipe against the flow of the water.

it encounters (ohms). This is known as Ohm's law and is expressed as

$$E = IR \qquad \text{or} \qquad I = \frac{E}{R} \qquad \text{or} \qquad R = \frac{E}{I}$$

where E equals volts, I equals amperes, and R equals ohms.

In electrical circuits, it is frequently necessary to cut down the flow of current deliberately. This is done with resistances or *resistors*, as they are often called. Such resistors may be simple coils of fine wire, carbon or graphite rods, light bulbs, or other devices which will satisfactorily reduce the flow of current through the circuit.

When two or more resistors are connected in series (end to end) so that the same current flows through first one and then the other, the total or combined effective resistance of all is equal to the sum of the individual ones. A common example of this is the so-called series Christmas-tree string of lights. In this case, the current flows through first one and then the next, and so on, until it has passed through all eight bulbs. Thus, when one bulb is removed or burned out, the circuit is broken and none of them receive current and light.

Assuming that the filament in each light bulb offers a resistance of 30 ohms, for example, the total resistance of the eight-bulb string would be 240 ohms. Since normal household voltage

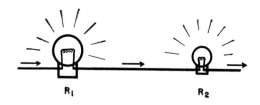

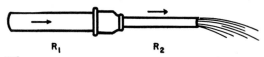

Fig. 2-10. When two or more resistors are connected in series, the total effective resistance will be the sum of the separate resistances.

as supplied by most power companies is about 120 volts, we can apply Ohm's law and find that the total current flowing through the string is half an ampere as follows:

$$\text{Current} = \frac{\text{volts}}{\text{ohms}} \quad \text{or} \quad \frac{120}{240} \quad \text{or} \quad \frac{1}{2} \ (0.5 \text{ ampere})$$

A little later we shall carry this calculation further and determine the wattage of the light string.

In the above example, the resistances are all equal. When unequal resistances are connected in series, the same rules prevail, but it will be helpful to use the water-pipe comparison again, since it will be seen that the action of electrical resistances in series is like the water resistance in two pipes of different sizes coupled end to end. The total resistance to the water flow is equal to the sum of each pipe's resistance. This might be expressed as

$$R_t = R_1 + R_2, \text{ etc.}$$

when R_t equals the total, R_1 the first resistance, R_2 the second, and so on, for any number. Also, the voltage or pressure required to push the same amount of current through the series of resistors is equal to the sum of the pressures required to push it through each one of them. In other words, if R_1 requires 50 volts to push 10 amperes through it and R_2 requires 70 volts to push 10 amperes through it, then both together will require 120 volts. Furthermore, if that much pressure (120 volts) is not available, 10 amperes of current flow will not be able to get through, and Ohm's law will have to be applied to find out just how much will get through.

On the other hand, if, for instance, only 110 volts is available and a current flow of 10 amperes must be obtained for some reason, resistance can be taken out gradually until it is found that the 10-ampere current is getting through. This is the principle of rheostat operation.

To summarize briefly, the current (amperes) in all parts of a *series* circuit is the same, but the pressure (voltage) required to force a given current through is proportional to the amount of resistance offered.

If resistors are connected in *parallel* (side by side), the pressure or voltage drop across each of them is the same regardless of the size of the resistors. However, in this case, the total current flow will be equal to the sum of the current flow in each individual resistor.

Resistances connected in parallel in a circuit are expressed as follows:

$$\frac{1}{R_t} = \frac{1}{R_1} + \frac{1}{R_2}, \text{ etc.}$$

With the two water pipes connected in parallel, the resistance to the flow of water is reduced because in this arrangement it passes through two pipes simultaneously instead of through first one and then the other as in the case of series connection.

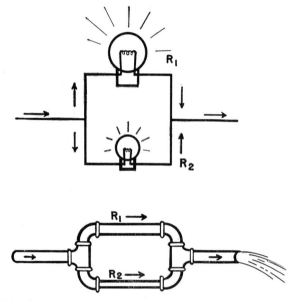

Fig. 2-11. When two or more resistances are connected in parallel the effect is similar to that shown with the two sizes of water pipes. The flow of both the current and the water would be increased as more paths (R_3, R_4, etc.) are added.

Conductor Characteristics and Resistance

The resistance to the flow of current offered by any conductor is affected by any one or a combination of four principal factors, namely, the length of the conductor, its diameter or cross-sectional area, the type of material it is, and its temperature.

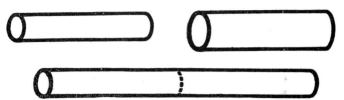

Fig. 2-12. The resistance of any given conductor varies directly with the length and inversely with the cross-sectional area. One unit area of unit length (top left) will have twice the resistance of a unit length of two unit areas (top right) and one-half the resistance of a unit area of two unit lengths (center). Thus, the larger the wire, the less the resistance.

STANDARD WIRE TABLE			
GAUGE	DIAMETER	OHMS PER 1000 FT.	POUNDS PER 1000 FT.
18	.040″	6.39	4.91
20	.032″	10.16	3.09
22	.0253″	16.15	1.94
24	.0201″	25.69	1.22
26	.0159″	40.86	0.77
28	.0126″	64.96	0.48
30	.0100″	103.30	0.30
32	.0079″	164.26	0.19
34	.0063″	261.23	0.12
36	.0050″	415.24	0.08
38	.0039″	660.37	0.05
40	.0031″	1049.7	0.03

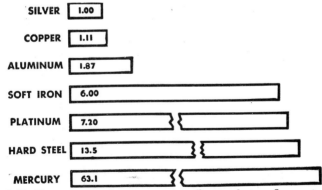

SILVER   1.00
COPPER   1.11
ALUMINUM 1.87
SOFT IRON 6.00
PLATINUM 7.20
HARD STEEL 13.5
MERCURY   63.1

Fig. 2-13. The resistance that copper wire offers to electron flow varies with the size of wire as indicated in the table at the top. The relative electrical resistance of various conducting metals is shown beneath the table.

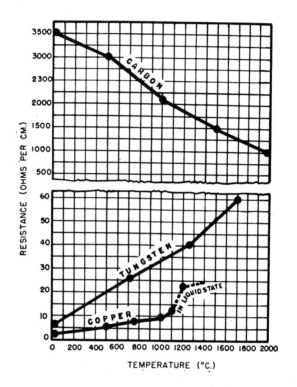

Fig. 2-14. The resistance of a conductor varies with the temperature of the conductor. An increase in resistance is caused by a speeding up in the random movement of the atoms. The chart shows the relationship between temperature and resistance.

First, the resistance of any given type of conductor varies directly with its length. In other words, the longer the wire, the greater its electrical resistance in the same proportion. Second, the resistance of any given type of conductor varies inversely with its cross-sectional area, which means that if the cross-sectional area is doubled, its resistance to the flow of current is cut in half because twice as much room is allowed for it to pass along the wire. Third, different materials offer different amounts of resistance. Since silver has the lowest resistance of all metals, it is established as the basis for comparison with all others with a relative resistance of 1. Fourth, when the temperature of a conductor is raised, it speeds up the random movement of the atoms in the conductor. In all pure metals this *increases* the resistance to current flow. In carbon and a few other substances, however, the resistance decreases as the temperature rises.

The standard or legal unit of resistance (the ohm) is defined as the resistance at 0° centigrade of a column of mercury 106.3 centimeters high, with a uniform cross-sectional area of 1 square millimeter.

The Watt—Measurement of Electric Power

Thus far, none of the units of current-flow measurement discussed has covered the ability of that flow to do work. The ampere is simply a measure of the amount or quantity of current flow, the volt a measure of the pressure behind it, and the ohm a measure of the resistance to flow which must be overcome.

The time-rate of a man, a horse, or a machine to do work (overcome resistance) is called *power*. The average man can lift or raise about 90 pounds a distance of 1 foot in about 1 second. This combination of weight, distance, and time would be called 1 *manpower*. Even if he lifted this weight in two or three pieces of 45 or 30 pounds each, respectively, but lifted them 1 foot each and all in 1 second, he still would be accomplishing 1 manpower of work. If he weighed 180 pounds and stepped up four steps, each 1 foot high, and did it in 1 second, he would accomplish 8 manpower of work.

James Watt, a Scotch engineer for whom the *watt* unit of electric power was named, found by repeated tests and studies

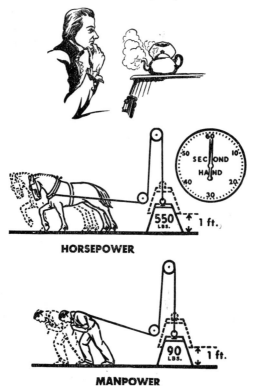

HORSEPOWER

MANPOWER

Fig. 2-15. James Watt, of steam-engine fame, first defined horsepower—the moving of 550 pounds to a height of 1 foot in 1 second. It is compared above to manpower, the moving of 90 pounds to a height of 1 foot in 1 second.

that the average horse can lift 550 pounds at the rate of 1 foot per second. Watt first evaluated and defined the horsepower while developing the first practical steam engine, and his evaluation that

$$1 \text{ hp (horsepower)} = \frac{\text{pounds lifted} \times \text{feet per second}}{550}$$

is the basis of mechanical-power measurement today.

Electric power, however, is measured somewhat differently. The work that a stream of water can do does not depend entirely upon the size of the stream or entirely upon the pressure behind it, but rather upon the combination or product of these two factors. Similarly, the work done by a flow of current does not depend wholly upon the volume or quantity of that flow or wholly upon its pressure, but rather upon the product of the two. Thus,

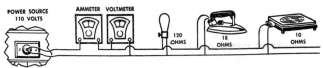

FIG. 2-16. Graphic illustration of how to compute power in watts. $I =$ current, amperes; $E =$ emf, volts; $R =$ resistance, ohms; $P =$ power, watts.

$$I = \frac{E}{R}$$

$$I \text{ (lamp)} = 110/120 = 0.916 \text{ ampere}$$
$$I \text{ (iron)} = 110/18 = 6.11 \text{ amperes}$$
$$I \text{ (grill)} = 110/10 = 11.0 \text{ amperes}$$
$$P = EI$$
$$P \text{ (lamp)} = 110 \times 0.916 = 100.76 \text{ watts}$$
$$P \text{ (iron)} = 110 \times 6.11 = 672.10 \text{ watts}$$
$$P \text{ (grill)} = 110 \times 11 = 1,210.0 \text{ watts}$$

it can be seen that electric power equals the current in amperes times the pressure (or emf) in volts. This is expressed as

$$P = EI \quad \text{or} \quad \text{watts (power)} = \text{volts} \times \text{amperes}$$

(For direct current. Alternating-current characteristics will be discussed later.)

It will be recalled that a few pages back we discussed a Christmas-tree light string and found, by the application of Ohm's law, that, if each of the eight bulbs in series offered a resistance of 30 ohms, the current flowing through the whole string would be 0.5 ampere. Now, we can determine the power or wattage of the string, since we know both the voltage pressure and the current flow in amperes. It would be

Watts = volts × amperes   or   120 × 0.5   or   60 watts

The watt unit of power measurement is the amount of power required to maintain a current flow of one ampere at a pressure

EQUATIONS BASED ON OHM'S LAW

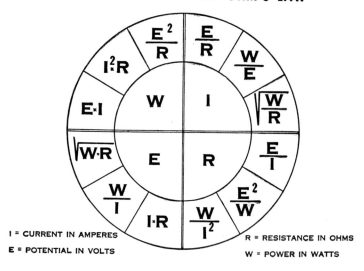

I = CURRENT IN AMPERES
E = POTENTIAL IN VOLTS
R = RESISTANCE IN OHMS
W = POWER IN WATTS

Fig. 2-17. From the chart any one of the four basic units of electrical measurement (inner circle) can be obtained if any two others (outer circle, same quadrant) are known.

of one volt. Since the watt is a relatively small unit of power, the kilowatt (kw), which is 1,000 watts, is used where larger units of power measurement are desired.

Although horsepower is the unit of mechanical-power measurement and watt the unit of electric-power measurement, there is a numerical relationship between the two. One horsepower is equal to 746 watts.

In measuring the amount of work done by electricity, the unit of power (watt) alone is not enough. We must consider also the amount of time required for a quantity of power to do this work. Since a unit encompassing both of these factors, or a *power-time* measurement is needed, the watt-hour or kilowatt-hour (kwh) unit is used to designate the amount of power used over a period. Kilowatt-hour meters are installed by electrical companies in homes, stores, factories, offices, and wherever electric current is used to measure the amount of their power used by the consumer over a period of time such as one month.

Part Two: Magnetism

3

Magnetic Force

No one knows exactly what magnetism is. It is a force which is related in some way to electron flow and one which can be manufactured, or at least made evident at will, as well as accurately controlled. It is present in thousands of devices in everyday use and is as important in the consideration of electricity as electron flow itself. The earth is a gigantic magnet with north and south poles the same as the little U-shaped steel bars with which all children are familiar.

Magnetic force has been known for thousands of years. It is said to have been discovered near the city of Magnesia in Asia Minor, when *magnetite* iron ore was found to have the ability to attract other particles of iron. Early navigators used elongated pieces of the ore as compasses and called them *leading stones,* from which the *lodestone* is derived. When a steel bar is rubbed on lodestone, it becomes *magnetized* and will attract iron.

Just what happens when a steel bar is magnetized is not as yet completely clear. In the generally accepted molecular theory of magnetism, it is assumed that molecules or particles of certain materials, such as steel and others which can be magnetized, are each miniature magnets themselves. That is, each has a north and south pole which might result from the distribution of charges as well as the motion and spin characteristics of the atomic particles in the lattice structure of the material.

38

Under normal conditions, these tiny magnets of the material point in every direction within the metal. However, when the bar of metal is rubbed with lodestone or otherwise exposed to magnetic influences, these small particles turn in one direction with all north poles pointing the same way and all south poles the other. Thus, the whole bar of metal becomes a magnet with a north pole and a south pole. A more precise explanation of magnetism involves consideration of the lattice structure of the metal, which may become distorted under magnetic influences.

Fɪɢ. 3-1. Magnetic iron, or *lodestone,* was the first known magnet.

Fɪɢ. 3-2. One theory of magnetism—a steel bar (left) becomes magnetized (right), and the tiny particles all point in one direction (or normal lattice structure becomes distorted).

In further explanation it should be pointed out that at the center of the bar between poles, the forces counteract each other, but as the ends of the bar are approached, the north or south influences become increasingly pronounced. This is indicated by the fact that, if a bar magnet is cut in several shorter pieces, each piece becomes a magnet in itself with its own north and south pole.

Every magnet has a very definite and consistent pattern of force around it. This pattern is most clearly pictured as lines of force. It is called a *magnetic field.* If a piece of paper is placed over a bar magnet and iron filings are sprinkled on the paper, they will arrange themselves to coincide with the pattern of the field. These lines of force are, of course, imaginary ones along which the attractive or repulsive force of the magnet acts. Their direction is generally assumed to be from the north pole to the south pole and back through the interior of the magnet, forming closed loops called the *magnetic circuit*.

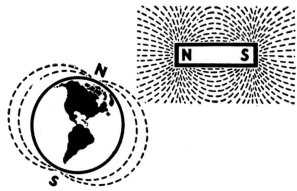

Fig. 3-3. The arrangement of magnetic fields to the north and south poles of a permanent magnet, also to the earth.

Like *unlike* charges of electricity (a negative and a positive), *unlike* magnetic poles attract each other; *like* magnetic poles repel each other as do two positive or two negative electrical charges. The intensity of attraction and repulsion is a function of the pole strengths of the magnets.

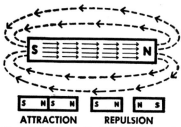

ATTRACTION   REPULSION

Fig. 3-4. Magnetic lines are imaginary lines along which the attractive or repulsive force of the magnet acts.

Electromagnetism

A fundamental similarity in the characteristics of current flow and magnetic lines of force has been indicated in the discussion above. Actually, current flow can be used to produce a magnetic field, or a magnetic field can be used to generate a pressure of emf (voltage), which will cause the electrons to move or flow. As a matter of fact, any conductor through which current is flowing has magnetic force around it and at right angles to it. One way of remembering this relationship is to visualize the operation of driving a screw into a wall. The negative direction of the circuit would be the same as the movement of the screw into the wall—away from the

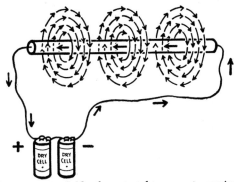

FIG. 3-5. The magnetic field of a straight current-carrying conductor is around the conductor and at right angles to it.

FIG. 3-6. When an electric current flows through a coil of wire, the regions or spaces inside and outside the coil become magnetized.

body so that the electrons would be flowing toward the body out of the negative terminal. The magnetic lines of force around the conductor carrying this current would be in the direction of the twist of the screw driver—clockwise to the person facing the wall.

If a conductor is coiled, the space within as well as around the coil becomes a magnetic field, and an iron bar within the space becomes an electromagnet when current flows through the coil.

André Ampère, a French physicist, discovered a right-hand rule which told us that, with a coil held in the right hand and the

FIG. 3-7. The left-hand rule shown above establishes that when a coil is held in the left hand and the electrons flow in the direction of the fingers, the thumb always points to the north pole of the magnetic field which is set up in the coil.

current flowing in the direction of the curled fingers, the thumb always pointed to the north pole of the magnetic field established within the coil by the current it is carrying. Since we now know that electric current is a flow of electrons and that being negative they must flow toward positive, the *left* hand should be used instead for the application of Ampère's rule.

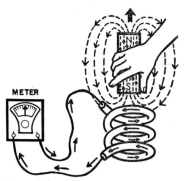

FIG. 3-8. Moving a permanent magnet within a coil or wire causes a current to flow in the electric circuit. This principle is the basis for electric generators.

The other equally important relationship between current flow and magnetic force seems to be the reverse of the production of the magnetic field described above. When a conductor is moved across a magnetic field, an emf is generated which causes current to flow in the conductor if the circuit is closed. To express the same idea another way, if a permanent magnet is plunged into a coil of wire (or removed from it), the magnetic lines of force "cut" the wire and induce an emf or pressure (voltage) which causes current flow in the circuit. Such voltage exists only while the magnet is in motion within the coil and ceases when it is completely removed. This is the basic principle behind the great electric generators in power plants.

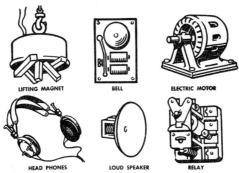

LIFTING MAGNET   BELL   ELECTRIC MOTOR

HEAD PHONES   LOUD SPEAKER   RELAY

FIG. 3-9. There are many practical uses of electromagnetism.

Generation of Electric Power

There are a great many practical uses of electromagnetism in industry and commerce. The most important ones, of course, are those applications involving rotating electric machinery. Electric power can be applied to a device called a *motor,* causing it to turn, or the device can be turned by some other force such as a gasoline engine, a steam turbine, or a water wheel, in which case it produces a flow of current and is called a *generator.* Let us consider the latter situation first.

Michael Faraday, an English scientist, constructed the first electrical generator. It was a simple device as compared with today's massive machines and consisted of a copper disk about 1 foot in diameter which was rotated between the poles of a permanent magnet.

A man supplied the energy necessary to turn the disk. In modern power plants this energy is provided by falling water (hydroelectric generators), by steam produced in boilers using coal or oil as a fuel (steam turbines), or by internal-combustion engines (diesel generators).

The turning copper disk in Faraday's device cut the lines of force of the magnet, and an electric current was generated which flowed from the disk through contact brushes at its rim and shaft and thus into the conductors of the circuit.

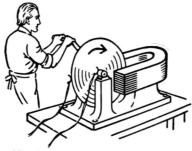

FIG. 3-10. The world's first generator, built by Michael Faraday, had a copper disk in the field of a permanent magnet.

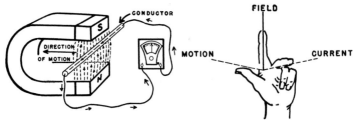

FIG. 3-11. The elementary principle of generation of electric current by cutting the lines of force. The left-hand rule shows the method of determining the direction of the electron flow.

There are three forces involved in the simple generator described above: first, the physical force provided by the man turning the disk; second, the magnetic lines of force between the poles of the magnet; third, the emf or voltage generated in the disk which caused the flow of electric current. The definite relationship between the directions in which these three forces are exerted is best described in another left-hand rule.

It has been previously pointed out that a conductor must be in motion through a magnetic field if a flow of current is to be set up within it. If this conductor is moved in the direction indicated with respect to the north and south poles of the magnet, then electrons will always move in the direction shown by the arrows

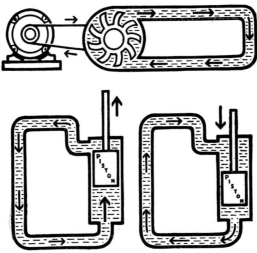

Fig. 3-12. Direct current, in a manner similar to the water from a centrifugal pump (top), flows continuously in one direction. Alternating current changes direction periodically, as does the water in the closed pipe circuit (bottom).

in Fig. 3-11. A left-hand rule demonstrates this relationship by stating that, if the conductor is moved in the direction of the thumb and the forefinger points in the direction of the magnetic force (toward the south pole), then the electrons in the conductor will flow in the direction of the extended second finger—all fingers to be at right angles to each other.

It already has been explained that, when electrons flow along a conductor in one direction only, *direct current* is said to be flowing. This may be compared to a closed pipe circuit through which water flows continuously from a centrifugal pump.

Alternating current, on the other hand, changes or alternates its direction at definite intervals. It might be compared to a closed pipe circuit in which water is constantly circulated back and forth by a valveless reciprocating pump.

Thus far, the source of pressure or emf (voltage) has been generally considered as a battery of established potential. It has just been pointed out, however, that, when a magnetic field is cut by a conductor, current will be caused to flow in that conductor in a direction determined by its relative motion through the lines of magnetic force. Therefore, current also can be produced in a loop of wire being turned in the field of a magnet so that the loop cuts across the lines of magnetic force. This is similar to Faraday's generator except that a loop of wire is used instead of a copper disk.

Alternating-current Generators

As previously explained, the direction of induced emf in the wire loop is dependent upon the direction of its movement through the magnetic lines of force. It can be seen from position A (Fig. 3-13) that, as the loop is turned counterclockwise, the right-hand half of the loop cuts upward through the lines of force. By applying the left-hand rule it is found that the current flow will be in the direction indicated by the straight arrow, or away from the reader. On the other hand, the left half of the loop (shaded half) cuts downward through the magnetic field, and the flow will be in the opposite direction. But since the loop is a continuous one, the current flows on around and out through the brushes into the circuit and back again. Now when the loop reaches position B, no lines of force are being cut, and so there is no emf (voltage) generated at this point.

As the loop continues to turn, position C is reached, and it can be seen that half of the loop which, in position A, was cutting downward on the left (shaded half) is now cutting upward on

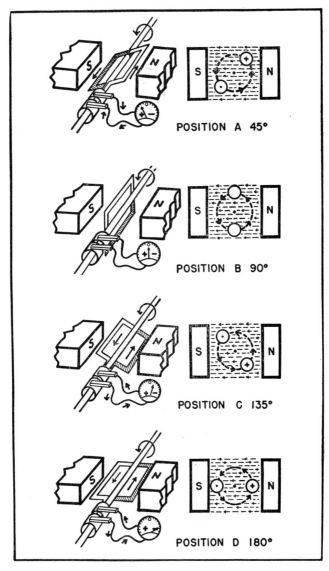

POSITION A 45°

POSITION B 90°

POSITION C 135°

POSITION D 180°

Fig. 3-13. Demonstrating the principle of alternating current.

the right, so that electron current now must flow in the opposite direction through that half as well as through the other half. Thus, we have a complete reversal of current-flow direction in 180 degrees of rotation—or alternating current being generated.

Since at position *B* there was no emf being generated, it follows that at position *D* the maximum value of emf will be found, since in that position the loop is cutting the greatest number of lines of force. This maximum value is reached gradually as the loop approaches a horizontal position *D*. Also, the minimum or zero value is reached gradually as the loop cuts fewer and fewer lines of force and eventually is in a vertical position *B*.

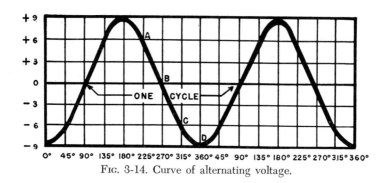

Fig. 3-14. Curve of alternating voltage.

A curve can be plotted for the rise and fall of the generated emf. This curve is called a *sine wave.* Figure 3-14 shows this wave form of a modern a-c generator. The positions *A, B, C,* and *D,* just described, are shown at 45, 90, 135, and 180 degrees. The strength of the emf generated at these positions is indicated above and below the zero value represented by the center horizontal line. Thus the strength of the emf is zero at *B* and maximum at *D,* and it is positive at *A* and negative at *C* or *D.*

When the voltage has gone from zero to one maximum value and back to zero again and then to the other maximum (in the opposite direction) and back to zero—in other words, completed one whole wave from 0 to 360 degrees—it has completed a *cycle.*

The number of cycles completed in one second is called the *frequency.*

The large present-day a-c generators involve the same principle of the wire loop except that many wire loops are used and the process is reversed; that is, magnets revolve inside the wire loops (armature winding), and the magnets instead of being permanent are electromagnets, the field being created by passing an "exciting" current through the coils of the electromagnets. Alternating currents are usually generated at a frequency of 60 cycles, although 25, 40, and 50 are not uncommon.

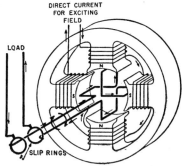

Fig. 3-15. Diagram of a simple generator with a revolving armature and four poles.

Phase Relation

It has just been shown how a simple-loop a-c generator produces its emf in the form of a single rising and falling wave. It is called, therefore, a *single-phase* generator.

If two separate loops at right angles to each other are used and the emf generated pushes electrons out through separate sets of brushes, the resulting two sets of waves would not coincide, because the loops would be cutting the magnetic lines of force at different times. In other words, when one is at its peak emf, the other is at zero, which means that a quarter of a cycle later the opposite condition will exist or that phase 1 follows phase 2 by a quarter cycle. A generator of this type would be called a *two-phase* alternator.

When three single-phase windings are placed on the same shaft with the windings brought out through their respective slip rings and brushes, the voltage waves will occur a third of a cycle apart as shown in the diagram. This manner of generating three-phase current is used to a very large extent throughout the country. Actually, six separate wires are not used, since it is possible to connect all the phases together in such a way that only three wires will serve the purpose.

When a fourth grounded (neutral) wire is introduced, a three-

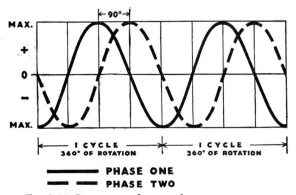

FIG. 3-16. Sine waves of a two-phase a-c generator.

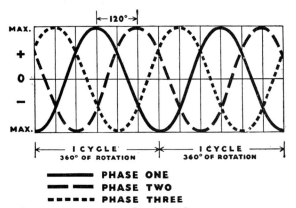

FIG. 3-17. Sine waves of a three-phase a-c generator.

phase, four-wire system results, with approximately one-half as much voltage existing between any one of the phase wires and the ground as between two-phase wires.

Although a greater number of phases is possible in a generator, there is no economic justification for such equipment except in very specialized applications.

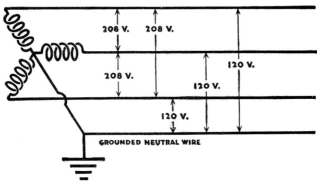

FIG. 3-18. The four-wire, three-phase distribution system.

Direct-current Generators

A d-c generator produces its emf (voltage) in the same way that an a-c generator does. The direct or unidirectional current results from the method of carrying it away from the machine. This method involves the reversal of connections at just the precise instant when the current being generated is changing its direction. In other words, if in position *B* of the simple-loop-generator diagrams (Fig. 3-13) the connections to the meter were reversed, the meter would still show positive instead of negative at positions *C* and *D*. But when the shaded half reached the top in a vertical position, the connection would have to be changed back again to keep the current still flowing in the same direction.

In a d-c generator this changing is done as the generator revolves by means of a device on the shaft called a *commutator*. The brushes in contact with the commutator are so placed that the current always flows away in the same direction.

It might appear that, although the current is direct in a generator of this type, there will be a decided pulsation due to the rise and fall of emf values. This would be true in the simple-loop generator, but in modern multipolar machines, the design of the armatures overcomes this pulsation.

Volumes have been written on the design and various winding methods of generator armatures and fields. They are a study in themselves and an involved one. Therefore, further discussion in this book would be out of place, since it is intended here to present only the fundamental factors and uses of magnetism.

Motors

Basically, an electric motor reverses the process of a generator. If, instead of turning the wire loop through a magnetic field and allowing the generated current to flow out of it, we connect the loop to a source of emf (a battery or generator) and push the current flow through it, the loop will turn by itself. That is, it will turn until it reaches the vertical position B (Fig. 3-13). At this point, it can go no farther because to do so would be contrary to the various forces involved—the magnetic lines of force between the poles of the magnet, the direction of the current flow resulting from the electromotive force (emf) from the battery, and the directional forces of the turning loop.

If the polarity is reversed (connections reversed) and the loop started gently, it will immediately flip around another 180 degrees, where it will stop again for the same reasons noted above.

In a d-c motor this changing of connections is done automatically, as the armature revolves, by means of a split commutator on the shaft which reverses the direction of current flow at each half revolution. The momentum of the armature as it revolves carries it past the "dead point," so that a continuously running d-c motor results. The motor will run as long as current is forced through its armature via the alternating device or commutator on the shaft.

There are many types of motors for both a-c and d-c operation, the differences between them being primarily in the methods of winding the armature and field coils, in the number of poles, and in a few other factors. The selection of the best type of motor for any particular application is governed by the kind of service required. Some applications require high speed, some a constant slower speed, others a readily controlled variable speed, and still others great turning power. Sometimes a motor is desired with a combination of two or more of these characteristics plus other additional ones, and new and better types are constantly being developed.

Like the study of generators, a complete study of motors would require hundreds of pages. Therefore, the discussion here must be limited to the basic magnetic principles and laws involved in motor rotation.

Counter EMF

Lenz, a physicist of the nineteenth century, proved that currents generated in a conductor cutting through a magnetic field produce another magnetic field of their own. This second magnetic field appears around the conductor and tends to oppose the motion of the conductor which produces it. In other words, the forces which make the wire loop turn in the simple motor create other forces around the loop which oppose its motion. It is a sort of conflict between the generating and the motor characteristics of the device. This opposing voltage, generated in the loop by virtue of its cutting magnetic lines of force, pushes a current flow in the opposite direction to the other current flow which is deliberately forced into the loop from a battery or generator in order to make it turn.

The voltage applied from the outside source is usually called the *impressed* emf, whereas the voltage generated in the loop (armature) is called the counter emf. The different between the two may be called the *net* emf.

This distinction is important in motor operation because as a motor gains in speed, its counter emf becomes greater as more and more magnetic lines of force are being cut. This, in turn, means that the net emf becomes less and less, with the result that less current flows in the motor circuit. Thus a motor requires less current when running full speed than when starting.

To compensate for this difference in starting and running currents, starting boxes, which are variable resistors or rheostats, are frequently placed in a motor circuit. If the full line voltage is impressed on the motor while starting and before any counter emf (counter voltage) is generated by the rotating armature, the coils might be seriously damaged or burned out. Therefore, a gradual application of voltage by means of the starting compensator, as the motor gathers speed, will eliminate such damage.

4

Transformers

A conductor moving through magnetic lines of force will have an emf (voltage) set up within it, the strength of which will depend upon the number of lines of force being cut. It follows that any change in magnetic lines of force around a stationary conductor will also generate or *induce* an emf in that conductor. It will be recalled that alternating current is constantly changing its direction, so that the magnetic field produced by a coil through which alternating current is flowing also will be changing. Therefore, it is capable of *inducing* an emf in another coil. This law of magnetism is usually referred to as the principle of *mutual induction* and is the basis of transformer operation.

A simple transformer consists of a ring or open square of iron called a *core*, with two coils of wire wound around it on opposite sides and not connected together. One coil has a current flow pushed through it by a source of alternating emf (a-c generator), so that the magnetic field produced in the core will be constantly changing. This coil is called the *primary*. The second coil on the opposite side will have an emf induced in it by the fluctuating lines of force in the magnetic field of the first coil. If the circuit of the second coil is completed or closed, an induced current will flow in it. The second coil is called the *secondary*.

Thus, in a transformer we have a means of inducing alternating current from one circuit to another by magnetism, the two

55

circuits not being directly connected in any way. Since a reversal of the magnetic field in the primary coil takes place at every alternation of the generator supplying the emf, and since these lines of force generally follow the iron core and pass through the secondary coil, the induced emf in the secondary coil will have exactly the same alternating characteristics or frequency. There is, however, a definite ratio between the strength of voltage in one and in the other, and in this ratio lies the practical use of the transformer.

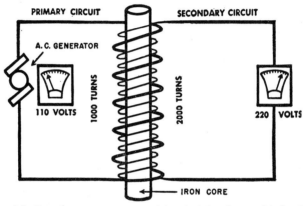

Fig. 4-1. Transformers operate on this principle of mutual induction.

The function of a transformer is to increase (step up) or decrease (step down) the voltage of an alternating current. The voltage in the secondary circuit depends upon the ratio of turns in its coil to the turns in the primary circuit coil. If the primary coil has, for example, 20 turns and the secondary coil 40 turns, the ratio is, of course, 1 to 2, so that with the primary connected to a 120-volt a-c circuit, 240 volts a-c will be produced in the secondary circuit. Conversely, if the 120-volt line is connected to the 40-turn coil, thus making it the primary, only 60 volts will result in the 20-turn or secondary coil.

This relationship holds true in all simple transformers regardless of the number of turns used in either the primary or secondary, and it can be expressed as follows (except for relatively small losses):

$$\frac{\text{Primary voltage}}{\text{Secondary voltage}} = \frac{\text{primary turns}}{\text{secondary turns}}$$

Transformers may be wound in different ways. One common method which saves space and weight is to place one winding over the other on the same core. In some applications such as radio, the power transformer may have two or more secondary

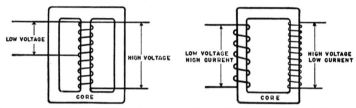

FIG. 4-2. Two types of transformer windings. The one on the left is called an autotransformer, wherein the primary and secondary windings are not insulated from each other. On the right is the conventional types, wherein the primary and secondary are separated and insulated from each other.

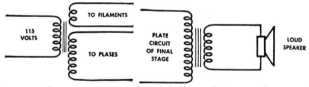

FIG. 4-3. A radio power transformer (left) and the speaker transformer (right) are examples of two types of windings.

windings, each with a different ratio to the primary so that different voltages may be supplied to the different elements of the radio tubes as required.

The transmission of power from generating plants to thousands of homes, stores, and factories would not be feasible without transformers, since they make transmission of high voltages possible over long distances with consequent lower line losses.

Another type of winding is called an *autotransformer.* This

type differs in that only one winding is used. This is divided
into two parts to form both the primary and the secondary. In
this case, the coils are not separated, but the required voltage
change is accomplished.

There is one other factor in transformer design that should be
considered briefly before we leave the subject, and that is the
core construction. When an induced emf is set up in a solid bar
of metal, the resulting flow of electrons will eddy around in the

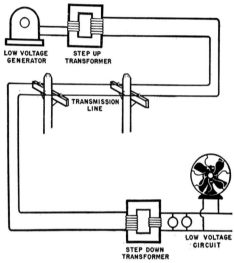

LOW VOLTAGE   STEP UP
GENERATOR   TRANSFORMER

TRANSMISSION
LINE

LOW VOLTAGE
·CIRCUIT
STEP DOWN
TRANSFORMER

Fig. 4-4. Transformers are vital elements in electric power distribution
systems.

metal and develop a magnetic field of their own. These *eddy
currents* will cause a "dragging" or "damping" effect on the main
magnetic field. In order to eliminate this, transformer cores (as
well as the cores of other electromagnetic devices such as
motors) are built up of thin sheets of metal instead of from a
solid bar of metal. This construction, which is called a *laminated
core,* prevents the eddy currents from flowing around but permits
the main magnetic field to be useful.

When there is an increase in voltage in a transformer, there is a *decrease* in current in the same proportion. In other words, the voltage increase is gained at the expense of current. This can be expressed as follows:

$$\frac{\text{Primary current}}{\text{Secondary current}} = \frac{\text{secondary turns}}{\text{primary turns}}$$

But, since wattage or power is the product of voltage and amperage (current), it can be seen that there is no appreciable loss of power in a transformer.

Inductance

It has been explained that, when a bar magnet is plunged into a coil of wire and removed from it several times in quick succession, an alternating current is generated in the circuit of the

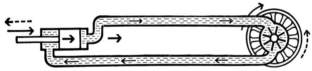

Fig. 4-5. Inductance in an electric circuit is similar to inertia. It is the property in the circuit which opposes any change in the current passing through it. The flywheel in the water circuit above presents a similar opposition to the flow of water through the pipes.

coil as long as the magnet is kept in motion. It has also been pointed out that, if an alternating current flows through a coil around a stationary bar magnet, it amounts to the same thing as moving the magnet. We have, therefore, two distinct emfs— one from the external source as well as one from the magnetic field—pushing current in opposite directions within the coil. The pressure generated by the magnetic field, it will be recalled, is the counter emf, which opposes the start of current flow from the impressed emf and likewise opposes the stopping of it after it is once flowing. This is similar to the inertia of stationary and moving objects.

The property of an electric circuit by which it opposes any

change in the current flow through it is called *inductance*. In other words, the current has a tendency to be sluggish in responding to the rapid alternations of the voltage or emf and may lag behind it. Thus, the voltage may reach its pressure peak before the current reaches its flow peak.

A water-pipe analogy may be used to illustrate inductance. In Fig. 4-5 the piston can be compared to the source of alternating emf, the water in the pipe circuit to the current flow, and the heavy water wheel to the inductance. As the water in the pipe changes its direction, it must start the heavy wheel in motion—first in one direction and then in the other. The sluggishness of the water in changing its direction of flow in the arrangement can be easily visualized. The alternating motion of the wheel will obviously lag behind the motion of the piston.

The unit for measuring self-induction is called the *henry*, named after Joseph Henry, an American scientist. One henry is the inductance which produces an induced emf of one volt when the current is changing at the rate of one ampere per second.

Capacitance—Condensers

The term *capacitance* is used in conjunction with a device called a *condenser;* in fact, condensers are frequently referred to as *capacitors*. Since capacity means *all a thing will hold,* a condenser or capacitor can be thought of as a sort of reservoir in which an abundance of electrons can be temporarily stored, although the meaning is not quite the same as when applied to a full reservoir or tank of water.

A simple condenser consists of two plates of conducting material separated by a dielectric (insulating material), such as mica or glass, or by air. The capacity of such a condenser does not necessarily mean the maximum number of electrons it can hold. It does mean, however, the greatest number in it with relation to the voltage or potential difference existing between the plates.

In a circuit with a condenser connected in series with a source of emf (voltage) such as a battery or generator, the current will flow into the condenser for a moment and then stop. In other words, electrons flow out of the negative terminal of the battery and accumulate on the condenser plate connected to that side. In addition, electrons *leave* the plate connected to the positive battery terminal and flow into the battery. Thus, one plate becomes charged negatively, since it has accumulated a surplus of electrons, whereas the other plate acquires an equal positive charge, since it has lost the same quantity of electrons. This flow of current lasts only a short time until the potential between the plates equals that of the battery; then it stops, and the plates

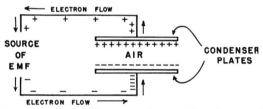

FIG. 4-6. Diagram of a simple air condenser. The electrons flow in the directions indicated only for a short time until the potential difference between the plates equals that of the source of emf.

maintain their charge as long as the battery or generator provides the same voltage or potential difference.

If, however, the plates are brought nearer to each other, the difference in potential between the plates decreases. This causes more electrons to flow into one plate from the battery and out of the other plate into the battery until the potential difference between the plates is brought up again to equal that of the battery as originally. Since the *greater* the distance between the plates, the *less* the quantity of electricity (electrons) is required to maintain the established potential difference between them, it follows that with plates *near* together it is possible to obtain a large charge on a condenser with but relatively small potential difference.

This charge on the condenser is directly proportional to the voltage applied across its terminals. Its capacitance, therefore, can be determined as follows:

$$\text{Capacitance (in farads)} = \frac{\text{quantity of electricity (in coulombs)}}{\text{difference in potential (in volts)}}$$

The unit of capacitance measurement is called the *farad* (named for Faraday), but because it is so large, the microfarad (one-millionth of a farad) is more commonly used. One farad is the capacitance of a condenser in which a charge of one coulomb produces a one-volt potential.

The capacitance of a condenser is determined primarily by three factors: first, the total area of plate surfaces subjected to a potential difference (voltage); second, the space between these surfaces; and third, the dielectric material or substance which separates the surfaces.

When a condenser is charged, it stays that way as long as the voltage or potential difference provided by the battery or generator remains the same. If, however, the voltage source is removed, the electrons will immediately flow back out of the negative plate containing an abundance of them and into the positive plate which had a deficiency in them. Thus, the condenser *discharges* to return to its noncharged state of electron equality in each plate.

There is a water analogy to a condenser circuit. If a centrifugal pump forces water into a closed pipe circuit containing a tank, across which a membrane of rubber has been stretched, the water will flow as a result of the pressure from the pump until the membrane has stretched to a certain point. Then no more water can flow even though the pump continues to provide pressure. When the pump is stopped, the water will flow back again for a short time until a state of equality is reached in the pipe system.

Thus, it should be remembered that current does not flow *through* a condenser, but rather *into* it and then *out* of it.

There are several types of condensers. One type, generally referred to as a *fixed* condenser, is made up of several plates

separated by a dielectric such as mica. Alternate plates are connected in parallel to form one side, and the others also connected
in the same way to form the other. Such condensers have predetermined capacity ratings at established voltages and are used in
hundreds of electrical devices in industry and homes.

Another type is called a *variable* condenser which also consists of alternately connected
plates but separated at specific
distances by air. In these, the
capacitance can be varied by
turning the plates in between
each other. They are used primarily in radio receivers in the
process of "tuning."

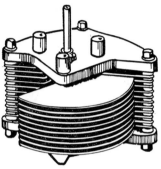

Capacitance in an a-c circuit
has the opposite effect of inductance in that it causes the
current to *lead* the voltage. This
means that the current will reach

Fig. 4-7. A variable condenser
such as is used in radio receivers
for tuning or varying capacitance
in the circuit.

the peak of its flow before the voltage reaches its peak pressure.
Later on, a practical and common use of the capacitance to offset
the lag of inductance in a two-lamp fluorescent circiut will be
described.

Power Factor

Prior to 1939, power factor was a subject which concerned only
power-plant engineers or the manufacturers of rotating electrical
machinery and induction devices. During that year, however, the
use of fluorescent lamps, which have inductance in their circuits,
became quite widespread, and people who used them began to
hear about power factor and ask what it meant.

Many explanations of power factor have been presented to
the general public, but most of them have failed to be completely understood by the layman, partly because he lacked the
necessary knowledge of magnetic inductance. It is hoped that

the reader, having read this far, will have acquired that back-
ground of understanding, because with it the explanation of
power factor is somewhat easier.

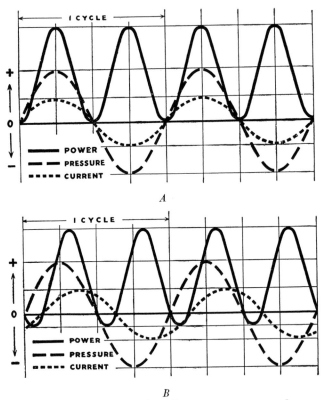

FIG. 4-8. The curves in chart A show the power, pressure, and current flow
reaching 0 as well as the maximum values at the same time. This represents
unity power factor. In chart B the maximum and minimum values occur at
different times, indicating that the power factor in this case is lagging.

It has been explained with a diagram (Fig. 3-14) how the
voltage or pressure of an a-c system builds up from zero to a
maximum value in one direction and diminishes to zero again,
and then does the same thing in the opposite direction to form

what is called a *sine wave*. It also has been indicated that the current flow follows the same schedule of rise and fall. However, it was pointed out under the subject of Inductance that certain characteristics of the system or circuit may cause the current peak to occur *after* the voltage peak or to *lag* behind it. Furthermore, it has been explained how capacitance in the circuit will cause the current peak to occur *before* the voltage peak and to *lead* it.

The power factor of a circuit is said to be 1.0 or unity when the two peaks occur simultaneously. But when inductance is introduced into the circuit as with transformers, induction motors, and similar apparatus and the current peak occurs later than the voltage peak, a *lagging* power factor exists, since the power drawn by the apparatus actually is less than the product of the voltage and current (amperage). The ratio of what it actually is to what it should be is called the *power factor*.

Perhaps a clearer understanding can be obtained by studying the two curves A and B (Fig. 4-8). Curve A represents a condition of unity power factor; that is, the voltage and current peaks occur at the same time so that the power peak, being the product of the two, must also occur along with them and always be positive.

But in curve B, we find the current lagging or occurring later than the voltage, which means that not only do their peaks occur at different times but likewise their zero values. Now, since a figure multiplied by zero gives a product of zero, it can be seen that, whenever *either* the voltage or current is at zero, the power value *must* be there also. Furthermore, whenever the voltage shows a positive value at the same time that the current shows a negative value (or vice versa), the power value must be negative. In effect, this means that the device which is making the circuit inductive should be using more power than it actually is, since a portion of it is negative.

In order to complete an understanding of power factor, it might be well to consider a circuit in which current, voltage, and power readings can be taken for either resistance or induct-

ance devices. Figure 4-9 shows such a circuit, supplied by an
a-c generator, in which an ammeter, a voltmeter, and a wattmeter have been connected. The load can be either a small
motor or an incandescent lamp, depending upon which way the
switch is thrown. Let us assume that the switch is thrown downward to make the lamp light and the meter readings are taken.
First, we see from the ammeter that the current flow is 0.5 ampere. Next, we find from the voltmeter that the a-c generator is
producing a pressure of 120 volts. Then, to find the power or

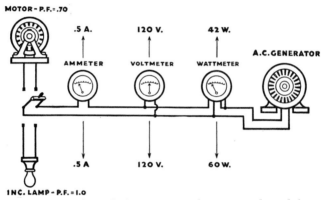

Fig. 4-9. A circuit for calculating power factor as indicated by meter
readings.

load (wattage), the two readings multiplied together will give
60 watts, which we find is also indicated by the wattmeter. There
is, therefore, a 60-watt lamp burning in the socket.

Now let us throw the switch the other way, shutting off the
lamp and starting a small motor. Again we find from the ammeter that the current flow is 0.5 ampere, and that the voltage
from the generator is the same 120 volts, but that the wattmeter
actually shows only 42 watts instead of the product of amperes
and volts as before. This difference of 18 watts of power cannot
be *lost,* because enough current is flowing and enough pressure
is there to produce it. Where, then, does it go? The answer is
found in curve *B* of Fig. 4-8. While the motor draws power

from the line as indicated by the power wave or curve, it will
be seen that part of the wave is below the zero line or down in
the negative region. Perhaps the best way to comprehend power
of negative value is to think of it as being returned into the
circuit by the motor.

The 42 watts, as indicated on wattmeter, is, therefore, the
actual power, whereas the power used ought to be the product
of the volts and amperes. For that reason, the power drawn by a
circuit containing inductance, such as a motor, is measured, as
it should be, in volt-amperes or kilovolt-amperes (kva) for
larger loads, instead of in watts or kilowatts.

Since what the power actually *is* is indicated by the wattmeter,
and what *it ought to be* is the volt-amperes, power factor can
be expressed as:

$$PF = \frac{watts}{volt\text{-}amperes} \quad \text{or for larger loads} \quad \frac{kw}{kva}$$

Therefore, the power factor of the motor in the diagram, as indicated by the readings found on the meters, would be

$$\frac{42}{60} \quad \text{or} \quad 0.70 \text{ (70 per cent)}$$

The *leading* power factor of a circuit containing capacitance is
determined and calculated in the same manner. For commercial
purposes, a meter is used to obtain either lagging or leading
power-factor data directly.

Reactance

Inductive reactance is an opposition to the flow of current in an
a-c circuit which results from the counter emf (explained on
page 53) produced by the self-inductance of a device in the circuit. While resistance also opposes current flow, the opposition is
called inductive reactance when *only* self-inductance is present.
It is measured in ohms.

Capacitive reactance is likewise an opposition to the flow of

current in an a-c circuit, but it is that which is established by a
capacitor or condenser when there is *no* resistance or inductance
It also is measured in ohms.

Total reactance is just what the name implies: that is, it is the
combined inductive and capacitive reactance when the two are
in series and oppose the flow of current in an a-c circuit.

Impedance

When in an a-c circuit there is also a resistance in series with
total reactance, the total opposition to current flow is called the
impedance of the circuit.

The methods of computing reactances and impedance are beyond the intended scope of this book, but they are available in
electrical engineering textbooks.

Resonance

The term *resonance* is commonly associated with sound. Nearly
everyone has had the experience of striking a note on a piano
and hearing a piece of paper on the music rack or on top of

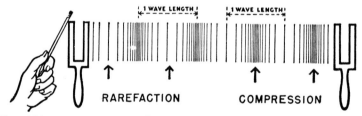

Fig. 4-10. Resonance in sound waves, illustrated by the use of two tuning
forks which have the same frequency (pitch).

the piano vibrate and produce the same tone. Instead of the
paper that vibrates, it may be a vase or dish on the piano or
even elsewhere in the room. The reason these remote objects
vibrate is that their resonating characteristics are the same as
those of the piano string which is struck; that is, they are "in

tune" with each other, and the remote object is said to resonate or be in *resonance* with the sound wave produced by the piano string.

Another example might be two violin strings on the same instrument tuned exactly the same. When the bow is drawn across one of them, the other vibrates and produces the same tone because it is in resonance with the first.

Figure 4-10 illustrates the same thing with two identical tuning forks set up some distance apart. One of them, when struck, produces sound waves which travel to the second and cause it to vibrate, since its natural frequency is the same wavelength as the first. The two are, therefore, in resonance with each other because they vibrate at exactly the same frequency.

Under average conditions (in air at 32° Fahrenheit) sound waves travel at the rate of about 1,088 feet per second.

Resonance in Electrical Circuits

Now, when a charged condenser is discharged by connecting the two plates together, electrons rush over from one side to the other. With an induction coil also in the circuit, too many of them will get over with the first rush because of the inertia characteristics of inductance, thus leaving one side with too few. Consequently, the condenser discharges again, reversed, so that some electrons rush back again. This seesaw action continues a few times and gradually dies out. Such oscillations are very rapid, the frequency being sometimes as high as 2 million a second or more.

An electrical circuit which is made to oscillate in this manner sends out or radiates into space electromagnetic waves that are somewhat similar in characteristics to the sound waves just discussed. They travel at a much higher speed, approximately 186,000 miles per second, however, which is also the speed of light and other types of radiant energy. Furthermore, they do not depend upon air or on solids or liquids as a medium of transmission, as sound waves do. There is a definite relationship be-

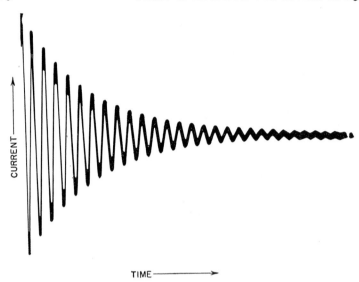

CURRENT

TIME ————————➤

F<small>IG</small>. 4-11. The oscillations of a discharging condenser as shown on an oscillograph. These oscillations show how the electrons rush back and forth from one plate to another and eventually die out, and electrical balance is established.

tween the velocity, wavelength, and frequency of these waves in that the velocity in meters per second equals the product of the frequency (oscillations per second) and the wavelength in meters. This is expressed as

$$V = FX$$

where V = velocity
F = frequency, cycles per second
X = wavelength, meters

It will be recalled that radio-broadcast wavelengths are expressed in meters. Therefore, we must use the metric system also in expressing the velocity in the above equation—186,000 miles per second equals 300,000 kilometers or 300 million meters per second.

Two electrical circuits can be tuned or made to resonate if

they can be adjusted to the same frequency. This is the basic principle of radio transmission and reception. The adjustment is made in the receiver, and we speak of it as *tuning*. The change in tuning or resonance can be accomplished in the receiver by varying either the capacitance (condenser) or inductance.

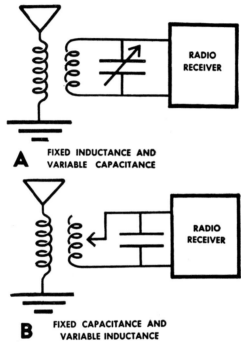

A FIXED INDUCTANCE AND VARIABLE CAPACITANCE

B FIXED CAPACITANCE AND VARIABLE INDUCTANCE

FIG. 4-12. Practically the same principle as the tuning fork is used in radio broadcasting and reception. The receiver is *tuned* or made to resonate to the frequency of the transmitter.

To vary the capacitance it is necessary (as explained previously) only to change the effective area of the condenser plates; the inductance can be changed by varying the effective number of turns in the coil, fewer turns resulting in a decrease in self-inductance and more turns in an increase. Such variable condensers and coils are found in all radios.

Resonance plays an important part in electrical circuits containing gaseous-discharge lamps, fluorescent lamps, and other electronic devices.

Harmonics

Since the electromagnetic waves generated by an oscillating electric circuit can be compared in a general way to sound waves from the standpoint of resonance, it is reasonable to expect that other characteristics of sound waves will be present in electromagnetic radiation.

Any vibrating string produces, in addition to its primary or fundamental tone, several *overtones*, which may be higher pitched and of less volume. Assuming that such a string vibrates at the rate of 220 oscillations a second, there are also several overtones present at 440, 660, 880, and so on, becoming more faint as their pitch becomes higher. This fundamental tone along with its overtones is called a *harmonic* series.

The fundamental frequency of an oscillating electrical circuit also is found to have its electromagnetic overtones, which likewise are called *harmonics.*

Harmonics in an electrical system manifest themselves in a very decided manner and frequently present difficult and involved problems. Further technical discussions of them would be out of place here, but the reader should be aware, at least, of their existence and general character.

Magnetic Recording of Sound

The subject of sound and its production and control is thoroughly covered in a number of excellent textbooks. Acoustics and sound conditioning are familiar terms to almost everyone. Therefore, our brief discussion of sound will be confined to its relationship with specific electromagnetic phenomena.

In a later chapter it will be explained how sound waves *modulate* electromagnetic waves called *radio carriers* and how these carriers are *demodulated* back again into sound waves which are then amplified and reproduced in headphones or speaker. This chapter, however, seems to be the logical place to discuss electromagnetic recording of sound on wire or tape.

Sound recording and reproducing with ordinary phonograph records are fundamentally mechanical processes, even though amplifiers and other electrical apparatus may be employed before we hear the sound. The actual sound record results when a recording needle cuts wavering grooves in the soft record ma-

VIBRATORY MOTION OF NEEDLE

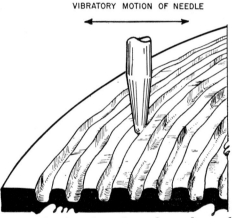

Fig. 4-13. The principle of mechanical sound recording and reproduction. Grooves in the record, placed there by the recording needle, waver in accordance with the sound which made the needle vibrate from side to side as the record turned. In reproducing the sound, the reverse process takes place. As the record turns, a needle follows the wavering grooves. The rapid vibratory motion of the needle is transferred to a diaphragm where the vibrations set up compressional waves in the air which advance through a tone arm and horn for amplification and are heard as sound.

terial. When these lateral "waves" are large, deep tones result, and when small, high tones are reproduced by the pickup needle exactly as the recording needle put them down. Regardless of the type of recording or pickup, crystal or otherwise, the process is one of mechanical vibration at the point of record contact.

With wire or tape recording and pickup, however, there are no grooves, needles, or any mechanical devices used. The wire or tape records by means of thousands of tiny magnetic fields around it and closely packed along its length.

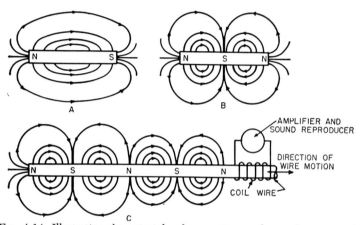

Fɪɢ. 4-14. Illustrating the principle of magnetic sound recording on a wire or tape. *A* shows a simple permanent bar magnet having a north and south pole at opposite ends, with the lines of magnetic force indicated. *B* is a magnetized dipole with a north pole at each end and a common south pole in the center. *C* shows how the principle is applied to a continuous wire or tape with magnetic fields of varying strength occurring along the length of the wire or tape. As it passes through the coil, shown on the right, current is induced in accordance with the magnetic field strength passing through the coil at the moment. This current is amplified and sound is reproduced by more or less conventional methods through a loud-speaker. The reverse of this process, with a microphone and other apparatus in place of a sound reproducer, creates the chain of magnetic fields along the wire or tape to make the recording.

While the fact that a steel bar can be magnetized so that one end becomes a north pole and the other a south pole is well known, it is not generally realized that a bar of the same proportions can also be magnetized so that it has a north pole at each end with a common south pole at the center. It is called a *magnetized dipole.* Furthermore, a bar or rod can be magnetized to have almost any number of poles alternating along its length. This is the principle of recording sound on wire or tape.

The wire is permanently magnetized (until erased or demagnetized) as it passes between the poles of an electromagnet. The field strength of this magnet is caused to vary in accordance with the sounds coming into a microphone, so that we have along the length of the wire a closely packed pattern of successive magnetic fields varying in strength, length, and other properties in accord with the sound fluctuations which created them.

The pickup and conversion of these magnetic fields back into sound are essentially the reverse processes of recording them. It will be recalled from Chapter 3 that, when a magnet is plunged into a coil of wire, an electric current is induced to flow in the coil as long as the magnet is in motion. Similarly, the wire or tape on which has been created the continuous string of magnetic fields is passed through a coil of wire. An a-c voltage is induced in this coil which varies in strength in accordance with the sounds which produced the magnetic fields on the wire.

This voltage passes through more or less conventional radio circuits and emerges from the speaker as a reproduction of the tones and sound amplitudes that went into the microphone and onto the wire. When it is desired to clear the tape or wire of a recording, it is passed back through another electromagnetic device called the *erase head*. The pickup process does not destroy or affect the magnetic record. The erasing operation, however, consists primarily of impressing a conflicting magnetic field which destroys those comprising the record, so that the tape or wire is ready to receive another record.

There are many more factors, of course, identified with wire and tape recording and reproducing, but we are concerned only with principles here.

Part Three: Electromagnetic Radiation

<hr>

5

Electromagnetic radiation is *radiant energy;* that is, it is energy radiating away from a source of electromagnetic disturbance. In order to obtain a clear concept of energy which radiates away in waves, let us first consider energy in forms which are most familiar and then correlate them with a discussion of waves and their behavior.

Energy

Potential energy is just what its name indicates. It is energy which is stored up and ready for release under the right conditions at any time. The storage of water behind a dam is a typical example of potential energy. It is ready to turn the mill wheel and do useful work when the gate is opened.

Coal, oil, and natural gas, hidden deep in the earth, are also examples of potential energy. Created millions of years ago from vegetable and animal matter under terrific heat and pressure, these three fuels are tremendously important today as sources of power when burned in diesel-engine generators or in the boilers of the great steam-turbine power plants.

The storage battery is another illustration of potential energy. Gaston Plante, the inventor, found that two plates of lead placed in a dilute solution of sulphuric acid would become *charged* if connected for a short time to a voltaic cell. Thomas A. Edison spent many years developing and perfecting a slightly different type of storage battery. At present, storage batteries are the heart

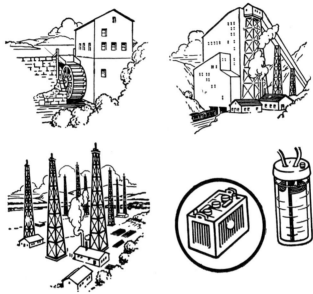

FIG. 5-1. Potential energy is common in everyday life—the weight of the water above the wheel, the coal from the mines, the oil from the wells. Also, in electricity, the storage battery when *charged* holds potential energy.

of automobile-ignition systems and have countless uses in industry and transportation. The charging is accomplished with a low-voltage d-c generator, and the potential energy stored is in the form of chemical energy.

One other form of potential energy which might be mentioned is that evidenced in a flat spiral steel spring which is wound tight. In this case, the potential energy is the result of displacement of the steel molecules. In a relaxed condition the steel molecules are in what might be called a normal relative position. But when the spring is wound, these little particles are forced out of place, and their tendency to return to their original positions supplies the potential energy of a tightened spring.

This example of the wound spring is an ideal place to turn to the consideration of kinetic energy because while the spring is

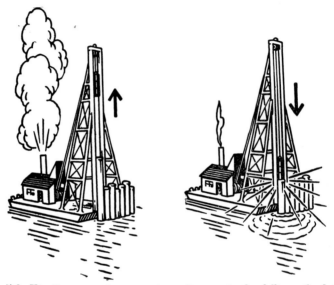

FIG. 5-2. Kinetic energy is energy in motion, as in the falling pile driver (right). The turbine that drives an electric generator imparts the same kind of energy.

unwinding, either rapidly or slowly as in a clock, it is a source of kinetic energy.

Kinetic energy is energy in motion. In a pile driver, for instance, potential energy is present while the weight is held at the top, but, upon release, this energy has been transformed from potential to kinetic as the weight falls to drive the pile into the river bottom.

The energy in explosives results from the relative positions of atoms rather than from molecules as in the steel spring. Here the atoms which were in their "normal" positions in the solid form of the explosive are suddenly and violently disarranged when the solid undergoes an abrupt chemical change by becoming a gas. The consequent large increase in volume is what we call the explosion. Thus, the potential energy of the solid (or liquid) explosive becomes kinetic energy during a split second, whereas the clock spring may require days to unwind.

The source of all energy lies locked up in the atom and/or its particles, as discussed in Chapter 1. Atomic energy is "raw" energy and, in a sense, both potential and kinetic. However, in terms of things which manifest themselves to us most clearly, atomic energy can be considered as potential. When it is released, however, as in an atomic explosion, the energy becomes kinetic and has the ability to destroy or, if in a fuel, the ability to create heat and do work.

As far as is known, or at least within the scope of present average human conception, energy itself, like matter, can be neither destroyed nor created. Even though energy appears to become matter and matter energy in the disruption of atomic nuclei, the law of the conservation of energy is one of the great scientific generalizations. If it is true that energy can be changed only in form or from one location to another, then there is no more energy (and/or matter) in all the universe today than there was in the beginning—and no less.

Simple Waves

It may be well to consider for a moment the simplest and most familiar of all waves—those produced on the surface of water.

Everyone knows how a stone tossed out upon a calm pond sets up a disturbance on the surface of the water which radiates in ever-widening circles away from the point where the stone fell. This disturbance we call *waves*. Further study of such waves reveals that they travel at a fairly constant rate of speed and that they are reflected away from a wall or other rigid surface at the edge of the pond and will start back out toward the center again.

It should be remembered that the water itself does not move toward the shore with the waves but that it merely rises and falls as the energy from the disturbances passes through it. The

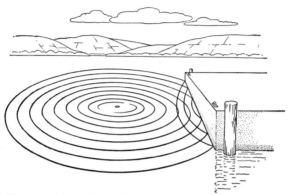

FIG. 5-3. Waves on the surface of calm water radiate away from the source of disturbance and are reflected from the surfaces they strike.

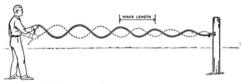

FIG. 5-4. Waves travel along a slack rope and are reflected back from the fastened end.

movement of the water might be indicated by a floating object such as a stick. As the wave approaches, the stick moves upward to the crest and slightly forward, and then as the crest passes, it descends again and moves back to its approximate original position.

The distance between the crests of two successive waves is called the *wavelength,* and the vertical distance between the crest and the level surface of the water (or one-half the vertical distance between the crest and the trough) is called the *amplitude*. Those two terms are applied in a similar manner to electromagnetic waves.

Waves travel through solids as well as liquids. A slack wire or rope will transmit the energy of a disturbance from one end to the other and back and forth several times before it finally dies out. If a long beam of wood or metal is tapped at one end with a hammer, the disturbance can be felt as it travels from one end to the other. The rates of speed of waves vary with the material through which they pass.

Sound Waves

Sound waves are transmitted through air, liquids, and solids in much the same maner. They are, however, somewhat different in character in that they are *compressional* in form. This form

Fig. 5-5. Like the waves in a coiled spring, sound waves are compressional. However, they do not follow one direction as in the spring.

may be illustrated fairly well with a long coiled spring. If the spring is stretched out to moderate tension between two rigid points and three or four of the coils are squeezed together at one end and then suddenly released, this compression will traverse the length of the spring, be reflected back from the opposite end, and so on, back and forth for a few times.

While sound waves are compressional, they do not follow one direction like those of the spring or move in a plane as do the waves on the surface of water, but rather they radiate in all directions like a rapidly expanding balloon. Sound waves are created by some disturbance just as the stone on the quiet pond creates the water waves. If a rifle is fired in the woods a half mile away, the disturbance caused travels outward in spherical waves so that about 2 seconds later when it reaches our ears we *hear* the waves and interpret the disturbance as a sound.

It has been mentioned previously that sound waves travel 1,088 feet per second in air at 32° Fahrenheit. In water they travel more than four times as fast and in steel about fifteen times as fast, but they are not transmitted at all through a vacuum. They also are reflected from surfaces as water waves are reflected from the wall. This reflected sound we call an *echo*. The study of how sound waves behave in their reflection from flat and curved surfaces and how they can be amplified and diminished is called *acoustics*.

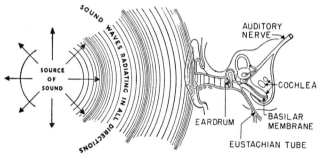

F⊤ıɢ. 5-6. Sound waves radiate spherically from a disturbance and, when striking the eardrum, cause it to vibrate, producing the sensation of sound.

During the First World War the presence and location of a submerged submarine were determined by a means of sound detectors called *hydrophones*. These instruments were placed on shipboard and connected to delicate sound receivers on the underside of the ship's hull. Since then, a much more accurate and extensive method of detecting enemy undersea craft has been developed and is used at present. It involves electron tubes and ultrasonic waves instead of audible sound waves. Surface craft and airplanes are located many miles away through fog, haze and in total darkness by means of electromagnetic waves produced and received with radar equipment. Both types of radiation will be discussed more fully later.

Electromagnetic Waves

About the only similarity between sound waves and electromagnetic waves is that they both radiate spherically from the source of disturbance. Otherwise, they are quite different. The disturbance which starts electromagnetic radiation has to do with the movement of atomic particles and a consequent release of energy. While it is known that electromagnetic waves are moving electric and magnetic fields, it is not as yet completely clear just what such fields actually are.

A study of the frontispiece, giving the range of electromagnetic radiation, shows that, while these waves all radiate from the source of disturbance (at the speed of about 186,000 miles per second), there is a tremendous difference in their frequency and wavelength characteristics even though the speed is constant. At the extreme right end, for instance, we find waves which are 10 million meters (over 6,000 miles) from crest to crest and which vibrate only 30 times per second (30 cycles). At the opposite end the wavelengths are so short and the frequencies so high that it is difficult to conceive of them at all. The distances between the "crests" of these waves are in the order of one ten-thousandth of an *angstrom*, an angstrom being a unit of length approximately equal to one two-hundred fifty-millionth of an inch (100 million angstroms equals 1 centimeter), and they vibrate at a frequency of over 30 thousand quintillion times per second (30,000,000,000,000,000,000,-000 cycles—usually expressed as 3×10^{22} cycles or 3×10^{16} megacycles). Another unit of wavelength measurement is called the millimicron (mu) and is equal to 10 angstroms, a micron being one-millionth of a meter.

Although, as has been stated, the true nature of electromagnetic waves is not completely understood, we do know how to start them and how to detect them. In some regions of the scale it is much simpler than in others. Nature has endowed all men and animals with two senses which detect or respond to certain bands of wavelengths and frequencies falling about midway between the two extremes. These senses are *sight* and *touch*. Electromagnetic radiation between 4,000 and 7,800 angstrom units in wavelength we *see* as visible light in colors ranging from deep violet to deep red. Beyond the red for some distance we *feel* the waves as radiant heat, and beyond the violet the radiation is known as *ultraviolet*, which acts upon our skin to cause sunburn.

Other than this, so far as is known, we recognize no sense which interprets naturally the vast range of other wavelengths and frequencies. But science has developed many types of electron tubes which can generate, detect, and control the electromagnetic waves in many of those regions which nature has closed to us and thus place them at our disposal by changing the radiant energy of the waves into a form that we can see, feel, or hear.

The diagram of the range of electromagnetic radiation shows the major divisions or regions which can best be discussed as individual units. Some of these are vital to everyday life, while others are undergoing development and scientific investigation. There are also a few regions of frequencies and wavelengths about which very little is known except that they must exist to fill in the gaps between the more developed and understood regions. Therefore, rather than starting at the low or right-hand end of the scale and considering each bracket in order all the way up, it will be better, perhaps, to discuss them in accordance with their apparent importance to human life, comfort, and happiness.

6

Light

Solar radiation sustains practically all life on earth. As shown in the electromagnetic-range diagram, the sun radiates its energy in a band which includes ultraviolet, visible light, and infrared or heat. Some of the energy coming from the sun to the earth never reaches its surface, however, because the envelope of air surrounding the earth filters it out, but the most important radiations get through and permit us to live.

Within the band of solar radiation there is a relatively narrow section of electromagnetic waves having wavelengths ranging between about 4,000 and 7,800 angstrom units and frequencies of around 500 or 600 billion kilocycles. Nature has provided us with two receiving sets for electromagnetic waves of these characteristics. The receiving sets consist primarily of a group of nerve fibers ending in rods and cones which are sensitive to the wavelengths and frequencies and in front of which are lenses to focus the radiation upon them. We call these receivers our *eyes*. When the electromagnetic waves pass through the lens and strike the nerve ends, the pulsation set up proceeds along the optic nerve to the brain and we experience the sensation of seeing light; that is, we see an object from which light is being reflected or an object which is emitting light.

Just how the eye and brain work together in transmitting radiant energy of these wavelengths and frequencies into the sensation of sight no one knows with certainty. It involves an electrochemical process in which a flow of electrons to and from the brain takes place, but beyond that, the working of the mind is known only to its Maker.

Radiation having wavelengths from 4,000 to 5,000 angstrom units we see as violet to blue light, whereas with wavelengths from 6,500 to 7,800 units the sensation is red. Between these limits we see all the other colors as in a rainbow. The wavelength of green colors is around 5,300 angstroms, and yellow is between 5,500 and 6,000. Orange obviously falls between yellow and red, that is, between 6,000 and 6,500 angstrom units. Above the

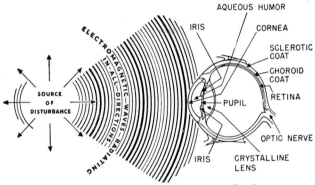

FIG. 6-1. Electromagnetic waves radiate spherically from a source of disturbance and pass through the lens of the eye which focuses them on the retina, producing the sensation of sight.

violet limit in one direction and below the red limit in the other we see nothing, but we know that radiations exist because we can feel them and produce, control, or measure them with devices and instruments designed for the purpose.

Like water waves, electromagnetic waves are energy being radiated (in bundles called *quanta*—see Chapter 1, Gamma Rays) from a source of disturbance. The source of electromagnetic radiation, it has been stated, involves the movement of electrons which were described at the beginning of the book as negative elements in the little knots of balanced energy called atoms. Light, therefore, being electromagnetic radiation of definite wavelength and frequency is radiant energy and as such must result basically from a disturbance of electrons in which this energy is released and radiated.

It will be recalled that, in an electrically neutral atom, electrons revolve about the nucleus, each in its own energy level. But when something disturbs an electron and bumps it momentarily out of its sphere, it releases energy while falling back. If a length of wire or a solid block of metal is heated sufficiently, thus agitating countless billions of atoms, their electrons become abnormally active, and the released energy emanates in electromagnetic waves or quanta of radiant energy which we know as *light*. The color of light depends upon the predominant wavelengths of the radiation. As more heat is applied, increased electron energy results in a consequent shift of wavelength or color from red hot to yellow and white hot. Since the atomic structure of each metallic element is different, different metals burn with characteristic colors of their own.

There are other ways of producing light without the application of heat. In chemistry, for instance, phosphorescent light can be produced by mixing together solutions which result in a disturbance of their molecules to the extent that electromagnetic waves will radiate as visible light without heat. This is found in nature when fireflies and many types of sea creatures do the mixing within themselves.

Another method involves the deliberate knocking about of atoms with free electrons to release the energy from the atoms (their electrons) and thus obtain electromagnetic radiation of wavelengths which the eye can collect and send to the brain to interpret as light. This method is the basic principle of today's most efficient gaseous-discharge and fluorescent-light sources. In nature we see the same phenomenon many miles up in the rare atmosphere of the earth and call it *aurora borealis* or *northern lights*. For the present, we are concerned only with a discussion of light as radiant energy. A more complete description of the characteristics of light from ionized gases will be presented later.

Control of Light

Any discussion of light, no matter how brief, would be in-
complete without mention of its control by *reflection* and *refraction* or an explanation of its measurement. Light waves may
be compared with water waves again when considering their
reflection, but it should be remembered that, while water waves
may be anywhere from an eighth of an inch or so to several
feet in wavelength, light waves are in the order of one fifty-

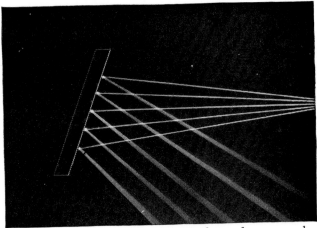

FIG. 6-2. Angular reflection of diverging light beams from a specular (mir-
ror-like) plane surface. (*Courtesy of the Museum Committee, Massachusetts
Institute of Technology.*)

or sixty-thousandth of an inch in wavelength and furthermore
that light waves are vibrating at the rate of about 500 or 600
trillion times a second whereas water waves may reach the shore
anywhere from three or four per second to one every few
seconds. Therefore, in making a mental comparison, we must
appreciate that our eyes do not distinguish minute waves of such
extremely rapid vibration but rather give us a concept of light
as a steady or "solid" flow in all directions, spherically.

A beam or ray of light can be compared to a segment of a

water wave or rather to a whole series of segments, one after the other. Both travel in a straight line from their source. Both are reflected away from a smooth surface at the same angle that they strike it. If the surface is rough or uneven, the reflected beam or succession of waves is diffused in both cases. If the surface is circular or parabolic in shape, the pattern of reflection is essentially the same for both.

In either instance, reflection means that the energy of the waves

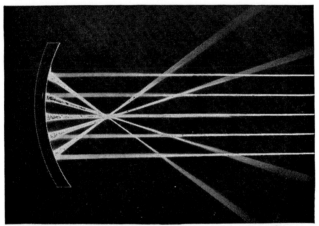

Fig. 6-3. Reflection of parallel light beams from a concave specular surface. (*Courtesy of the Museum Committee, Massachusetts Institute of Technology.*)

"bounces" back from the surface after some is absorbed by the surface. The ratio of the energy which bounces back to that which strikes the reflector is called the *efficiency* of the reflector. For example, if 100 units of light strike a reflecting surface such as a white plaster ceiling and 20 units are absorbed by the ceiling with 80 coming back, the reflection factor or reflecting efficiency of the ceiling would be 80 per cent.

The water-wave analogy cannot be used in discussing light refraction because water waves are not transmitted through a solid such as glass. A comparison with the transmission of sound

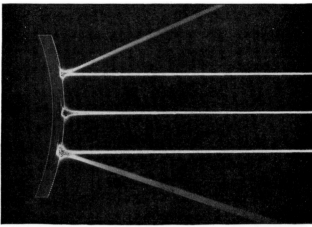

FIG. 6-4. Reflection of parallel light beams from a convex specular surface. (*Courtesy of the Museum Committee, Massachusetts Institute of Technology.*)

waves might be more accurate, but it is not a particularly satisfactory analogy, since sound waves cannot be seen except with laboratory apparatus.

FIG. 6-5. A stick thrust into shallow water appears to be broken where it enters the water. This is one example of light refraction.

Light waves travel at a different rate of speed through transparent solids and liquids than they do through air or a vacuum. As a matter of fact, they travel slightly slower in air than in space beyond the earth's atmosphere (vacuum). In water the speed of light is about three-fourths that in air or approximately 140,000 miles per second.

In passing from one medium to another, light is bent or refracted as a result of this velocity change. Nearly everyone has noticed the broken or bent appearance of a rigid stick thrust into shallow water at an angle. At the surface where the stick enters the water, it seems to abruptly change its direction to the bottom. A shallow pool always looks

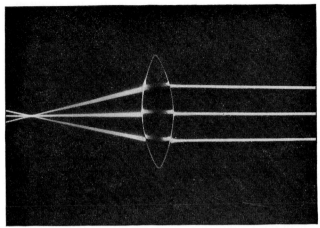

FIG. 6-6. Refraction of parallel light beams through a condensing or converging lens. (*Courtesy of the Museum Committee, Massachusetts Institute of Technology.*)

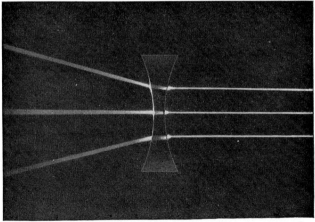

FIG. 6-7. Refraction of parallel light beams through a concave or diverging lens. (*Courtesy of the Museum Committee, Massachusetts Institute of Technology.*)

shallower from above than it actually is, and the depth appears to decrease as the distance away from the bottom area, directly below, increases.

At sunrise and sunset the sun seems larger than at noonday because its radiation comes to us in rays tangent to the earth's surface and therefore must pass through more and denser air than when directly above. The air in this case refracts or bends the rays, causing the same visual effect as the water in the shallow pool when it makes the bottom look nearer.

The refraction of light through glass is the basic principle of all optical instruments. The varying thicknesses of lenses result in the high-power magnification which brings the sun, moon, planets, and other heavenly bodies, as well as the realm of bacteriology and the physical structure of material, within the range of our vision.

The study of light reflection and refraction is called *optics,* and to cover it completely would require many volumes. Some consideration of the prism is necessary, however, to complete our discussion of light.

The Prism

As previously pointed out, electromagnetic waves producing the visual sensation of deep-red light have a wavelength nearly twice as long as those producing deep-violet light. In passing through a liquid medium such as water or a solid medium such as glass, the shorter wavelengths (higher frequencies) are retarded more than the longer ones (lower frequencies), so that they are bent or refracted to a greater degree. Thus, when a beam of light of all wavelengths, which appears to us as white light, enters these media at an angle and passes through and out again, the colors separate in the order of their respective wavelengths and we have a pattern of colors with red at one end and violet at the other. This occurs in nature when sunlight passes through raindrops or mist and we see a rainbow.

A prism is simply a short length of glass which is triangular

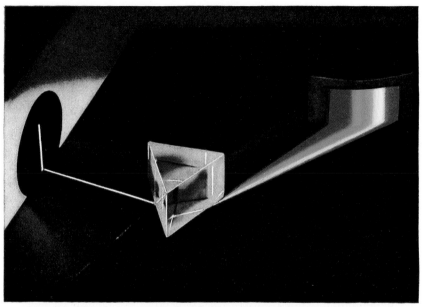

Fig. 6-8. The dispersion of white light into its component wavelengths or colors by means of refraction through a prism. This "rainbow" of colors is called the prismatic or visible spectrum, since our eyes do not see the ultraviolet radiation, which lies beyond the violet, or the infrared, which lies beyond the visible red. (*From Alpheus W. Smith, "The Elements of Physics," 5th ed., McGraw-Hill Book Company, Inc., New York, 1948.*)

in cross section. White light passing through two of its plane surfaces is *dispersed* or broken up into the component colors. Prisms may be cut to produce different results when light enters at different angles. If the cross section is an isosceles right triangle and a light beam is made to enter normal (perpendicular) to one of the short sides, the beam will be refracted

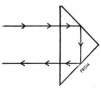

back out through the other short side without dispersion, by being totally reflected from the hypotenuse or long side. Since in this case the light enters and leaves the glass perpendicularly, there is no bending of rays and, therefore, no breaking up into colors. The same prism will refract a light beam back in the direction from which it came if the beam enters the hypotenuse perpendicularly, so that no dispersion occurs. Fresnel lenses, which are used extensively in airport beacons, lighthouses, and a great

Fig. 6-9. Total re-fraction of light oc-curs with an isosce-les - right - triangle prism as shown in the above diagram.

many other similar applications, utilize the refraction of multiple prisms (as well as spherical or cylindrical sections) to control the light in well-defined patterns. Certain types of commercial and industrial lighting fixtures and lenses depend entirely upon the refraction of many small prisms for their diffusion and light distribution.

Spectra

The light-refracting characteristics of glass are such that, when prisms are cut cross sectionally as equilateral triangles (all sides and angles equal), they will only refract light beams with dis-persion. In other words, if a beam cannot both enter and leave the glass perpendicular to the surfaces through which it passes, the light is broken up into its component wavelengths or colors. Prisms of this type are used in the *spectroscope*, an instrument specifically designed to separate light into its colors for analysis.

Spectra and their infinite value to science deserve much more

space than can be devoted to them here. Briefly, spectrum
analysis is a means whereby the presence of any of the elements
can be detected, even in the most minute quantities. The spectra
(color dispersement) of incandescent or burning solids or liquids,
or of ionized gases and metallic vapor discharges, contain lines

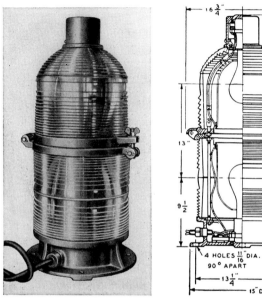

Fig. 6-10. An airport code beacon utilizes two circular Fresnel lenses which
produce a thin, horizontal disk of light 360 degrees around the unit. The
unit pictured above distributes light in a disk 4 degrees wide above the
horizontal. In addition to airports it is used as a light on antenna towers
and other aircraft obstructions over 200 feet high. (*Courtesy of Crouse-
Hinds Co., Syracuse, N.Y.*)

(light or dark, depending upon the method of analysis used)
which always appear at the same place for the same element.
They are different and characteristic for each element. These
lines may occur singly or in groups and appear deep in the
regions beyond the range of visible light as well as within it.

For each element there are always the same characteristic lines identified with the element, appearing at precise wavelength positions in its spectrum.

This being the case, light emanating from sources of unknown make-up can be analyzed in a spectroscope, and by the characteristic lines appearing at certain wavelengths it can be determined of just what elements the emitting source is composed. This has been done with the sun and other celestial bodies many times, as well as with countless compounds in the laboratory. New elements have been discovered through the appearance of unfamiliar lines at new wavelength positions.

Since light is electromagnetic radiation or energy quanta resulting from a disturbance in the normal electron orbits around the nucleus of an atom, and since the number of electrons is different in the atoms of each element, it follows that there is a relationship between the released electron energy causing light radiation and the lines appearing in the spectrum. This correlation of atomic structure in terms of the spectrum lines of a substance has been a fruitful field of science during the last three decades. From it has come most of our basic understanding which has developed into the science of modern physics.

Color

Color is a sensation involving a chain of mental and visual processes. To understand how we see it, it is necessary to examine the eye and its physiological activity, the light source and the components of its radiating energy, and the reflecting characteristics of the object at which we are looking.

As has been pointed out, the sensation of light is the result of electromagnetic radiation between about 3,800 and 7,800 angstroms in wavelength. In the laboratory when the spectrum is examined, the wavelength of each color can be measured by instruments.

Our eyes discriminate or are sensitive to many thousands of separate and distinct color differences. When all or a large number of the wavelengths are present in the radiation, we "see" them as white light, or when equal parts of "pure" red, green, and blue radiation are mixed, the result appears as white light. But when all the radiant energy is at one end or the center of the band, we experience the sensation of color. If, for example, the energy is all radiated at wavelengths around 4,000 angstroms, we see it and the mind interprets it as blue. Red, on the other hand, is made up of radiations around 7,500 angstroms in wavelength. In other words, what is seen as white light is actually the presence of colors perceived in a certain proportion, and if the combination changes, the light acquires a predominant color.

The basic colors in the rainbow or spectrum are violet, indigo, blue, green, yellow, orange, and red. Many of the colors which we see and use regularly are not in the rainbow or spectrum at all but are combinations of the colors at each end of the spectrum, such as lavender and purple, or they result from the addition of black and white pigments to basic reflecting surface colors, such as with brown and gray.

Color as it is applied in commerce and industry every day is a complex and profound subject involving the psychological likes and dislikes of individuals. No material or object has a "color of its own" unless, of course, it is actually producing its own radiation. An object or pigment which has the property of reflecting only red radiation is said to be red. Similarly, one which can reflect both red and blue wavelengths will appear purple, providing the source of light falling on it has both red and blue in its radiation.

There are four basic terms used in color work and analysis. *Hue* refers to a color family—a basic color as it appears in the spectrum. A dark red and light pink are the same hue. *Value* refers to the total quality of a color from light to dark. It is determined by comparisons with a graduated scale from black to white. In the natural order of the spectrum, yellow is the lightest in value and blue-violet the deepest. *Chroma* is a term used to designate the strength of a color as it extends from a gray of the same value to the greatest saturation of the color. *Finish* applies to the surface reflecting the color. It either may be a rough or matte finish or have a glaze or specular surface.

Incandescent lamps, fluorescent lamps, and other sources which produce light of specific color characteristics will be discussed in a later chapter.

Color Temperature

While *color temperature* would not be considered one of the basic units of light measurement, it has become quite well known to the general public as a result of the widespread application of fluorescent-light sources. In scientific illumination work, use is made of a theoretical object or substance which, when heated sufficiently, will radiate energy in colored light just as a hot stove lid will first become deep red, then orange, and so on, until it reaches white heat and eventually its melting point. This theoretical object is called a *black body* and is assumed to have perfect characteristics for emitting all the colors of the visible spectrum from red to violet as it becomes hotter. A light source is said to have a certain color temperature when its radiation has the identical color characteristics as the theoretical black body at this given temperature.

Color temperature is indicated in degrees Kelvin, which is a temperature scale (sometimes called *absolute* temperature) having its zero at —273° centigrade or —459.4° Fahrenheit, a temperature at which no heat exists and all molecular motion ceases. Thus, when an incandescent lamp is said to have a color temperature of 2700° Kelvin, it means that the filament is the same color as the black body would be at 2700° Kelvin, or yellow-white hot.

Color temperature should be applied only to light which is generated by heat, but it has become more or less customary to apply it to the colors of some fluorescent lamps for the sake of simplicity in distinguishing one color from another. The Standard Cool White fluorescent lamp, for instance, was formerly designated as 4500° white, but actually a black body at this temperature would be slightly different in color. The lamp, however, will be nearer to the color of the black body at 4500° than at any other temperature.

Noon sunlight will average between 5000 and 6500° Kelvin, but if the total light from the sun and the clear blue sky is considered, the average will be somewhat higher.

Polarization of Light

It has been explained that light is made up of electromagnetic waves which radiate spherically in packets of energy called quanta from a source of electron disturbance. If we can imagine these waves passing through a fine grating such as a comb, the teeth of which are no farther apart than the waves are to each other (approximately one fifty-thousandth of an inch), it can be seen that, after passing through, the waves will be sliced into thin "sheets," each of which will be only the thickness of the space between the teeth of the "comb." Thus, the waves can continue to radiate up and down only if the teeth are vertical, from side to side only if they are horizontal, or in any other direction the teeth will permit. Light having undergone this fine "slicing" process is said to be *polarized*.

If a second comb is placed in front of the first, the radiating light will pass through it also only if the teeth point the same way. If they point at right angles and in a parallel plane to those of the first comb, the slices are sliced again or "diced," as it were, into dimensions smaller than their actual wavelengths, so that the radiation is completely absorbed. This should not be confused with louvering of light, which merely effects a cutoff by reflecting or absorbing the radiation.

Light will be polarized by reflection if it falls upon a surface at a certain angle and may result in what is commonly called *reflected glare* if viewed at the same angle from the opposite side. Other angles will only partly polarize the light, and different materials have slightly different angles of polarization. If an observer sees this reflected polarized light through glasses made of material which serves the function of a second comb at right angles, a large amount of the annoying and harmful reflected glare can be eliminated.

There is another method of polarizing light by passing it through multiple layers of transparent media such as glass or certain plastics. If, for example, 15 or 20 thin layers of the medium are stacked to form a laminated sheet, the sheet will polarize a large percentage of light passing through it. Since the optical and physical principles involve *angular* reflection from each surface as radiation strikes it and multiple refraction as it passes through from one lamina to the next with an imperceptibly thin layer of air in between, the light is not polarized perpendicularly to the sheet. In other words, if a laminated transparent medium as described above is suspended horizontally beneath a light source, the light directly under it is not polarized, but as the angle from the vertical is increased, a higher degree of polarization is obtained with the maximum taking place between 35 and 70 degrees from the vertical.

Polarization of light in this manner can be used to advantage in certain commercial lighting applications where the veiling effect or sheen of reflected glare is a problem. Such applications include the lighting of oil paintings in art museums and the illumination of drafting rooms, certain types of displays, and similar locations where it is important to minimize the veiling effect of reflected glare for an accurate appraisal of color and detail.

Both methods of polarizing light have been known and accomplished in laboratories for many years. Certain types of crystals have, in their natural structure, the necessary minute grating characteristics to polarize light in the manner of the combs described above. A few years ago a manufacturing process was developed to produce a material having polarizing properties much like the crystal grating method. It is available commercially today in sunglasses and other forms.

Polarized light also plays a vital part in many industries in the examination of various materials for stresses and strains. Under polarized light the strains appear as symmetrical color formations which change their shape to conform with the shifting of the load under which the material is placed.

Measurement of Light

The word *light* is frequently used in conjunction with the word *flux,* so that the combination *light flux* more properly describes, perhaps, the flow of light in electromagnetic waves from its source. Physicists measure light flux, that is, the flow of radiant energy, in ergs per second, just as the layman might refer to water flow in gallons per minute. Since the flow of light is so rapid, however (186,000 miles per second), the general concept of it is as a static quantity like gallons, with no reference to time involved. Illuminating engineers speak of the total light flux of a source or of the flux in a certain direction, but the common units of light measurement disregard the elements of time because there obviously can be no visual sensation of light-wave movement at such a velocity.

The first basic unit of light measurement applies to the power of the source and is called *candlepower.* This unit was established in 1909, when an agreement was reached between the standardizing laboratories of the governments of the United States, Great Britain, and France that a standard light-source power unit should be the luminous intensity of a candle flame— the candle itself to have certain dimensions as well as definite specifications as far as the tallow and wick were concerned. Since then, these laboratories maintain the original standard candlepower with incandescent lamps of precise operating characteristics.

Some light sources are rated in accordance with their luminous power. We purchase automobile headlight lamps, for example, by their candlepower size, whereas ordinary incandescent lamps for use in home, store, or industrial illumination are rated according to their electric-power requirements—in watts.

Large searchlights have a unit called *beam candlepower* applied to them, which, as the term indicates, is the luminous intensity of a beam of light in any specified direction within the confines of the beam.

The second fundamental unit of light measurement is the *lumen*. It is a unit of light-flux quantity, that is, the amount of light falling upon an area of surface. When a one-foot square of any flexible material, such as paper, is placed one foot away from a one-candlepower source and so that all points of the square are one foot away or equidistant from the source, the square has one lumen of light upon it. It intercepts this amount radiating from the source. Obviously, such a square would be part of the area of a sphere 1 foot in radius. Since a sphere with a 1-foot radius will have 12.57 square feet of surface ($4\pi r^2$), a source of 1 candlepower must always emit 12.57 lumens. A 2-candlepower source will emit twice as many or 25.14; 3-candlepower, three times as many, and so on.

It should be remembered that the size of the sphere or the area upon which the light falls has nothing to do with the lumen rating of the source. Areas intercept some of the lumens (or a portion of one) emitted by the source. Certain types of street-lighting lamps are size-designated in lumens rather than in watts, so that a true measure of their light output will be indicated. All light sources except those in the process of commercial improvement have published lumen ratings in order that their actual light output will be known to the purchaser. The efficiency of any electric-light source is the ratio of its light output in lumens to its power input. This efficiency is expressed in *lumens per watt*. In other words, if a standard 100-watt incandescent lamp emits 1,620 lumens, its efficiency will be 16.2 lumens per watt.

The third basic unit of light measurement, called the *foot-candle*, is quite well known. The foot-candle is no direct indication of the power of the source or the amount of light it emits (except through calculation) but rather is a measure of the intensity of light at a point on any illuminated surface. It can be defined as the illumination at a point one foot distant from a one-candlepower light source. Since a lumen is the amount of light on a one-foot square one foot distant from a one-candle-power source, it can be seen that every point on that square will be illuminated to an intensity of one foot-candle.

A study of the diagram should clarify the relationship between these three units of light measurement as well as illustrate the principle of the *inverse square law*, which states that the illumination on any surface perpendicular to the direction from which

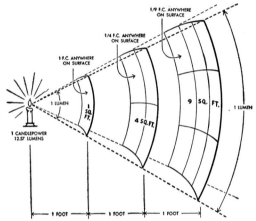

FIG. 6-11. A diagram which illustrates the inverse square law of light and the units of light measurement.

the light flux is traveling varies inversely as the square of distance of the surface from the source.

The science of illumination involves many terms relating to brightness, brightness contrasts, relative visibility, and a number of other factors having to do with optics and vision. It is a science which vitally affects the health and comfort of all mankind. For that reason, considerable space has been devoted here to those electromagnetic waves in the spectral region which we sense as visible light.

7.

Infrared Radiation

Referring again to the diagram of the range of electromagnetic radiation (frontispiece), we find a rather wide band of wavelengths between the limits of about 7,800 and 1,500,000 angstrom units called *infrared* radiation. The frequencies of these electromagnetic waves range from about 400 billion to somewhere around 700 or 800 million kilocycles.

As previously mentioned, wavelengths longer than deep red (at 7,800 angstroms) we cannot see, but we do feel them as radiant heat. It is not quite correct to refer to infrared radiation only as heat radiation, however, because all wavelengths of radiant energy generate some heat when they are absorbed. But since infrared energy does little else but produce the sensation of heat as far as we know at present, it is always closely associated with it.

Heat is a relative term. A red-hot stove is cool when compared with molten steel. An ice cube is warm as compared with carbon dioxide snow (dry ice), and carbon dioxide snow (at about 180° below zero Fahrenheit) is warm as compared with other liquefied gases. All matter, therefore, radiates heat or infrared radiation at some wavelengths whenever the surrounding medium is cooler. When the medium is warmer, matter absorbs heat from the medium. Thus we see that nature is again trying to seek a balance, just as with the discharge of electrons from a charged object to one which is more nearly in an electrically neutral state.

It is interesting to recall and associate two facts that have been pointed out: that the movement of electrons in a solid is stimulated by heat and that absolute zero ($-273°$ centigrade) is a condition wherein *no* heat exists and all molecular motion ceases. This condition and temperature (or rather lack of it) are believed to exist in outer space where there is no matter in any form to absorb any of the electromagnetic waves.

The infrared band is usually split into two regions for the sake of analysis. The region adjacent to visible light extending from the 7,800-angstrom wavelength to about the 30,000-angstrom wavelength is called *near* infrared. Almost all the practical applications of infrared radiation utilize wavelengths in the near region, so most of what will be discussed here will deal with those shorter wavelengths. The other portion of the infrared band is called *far* infrared. The shorter wavelengths of this far portion, that is, those above 30,000 but below 50,000 angstroms, are produced by ordinary ovens at around 300° Fahrenheit. Uses for the longer ones ranging between 50,000 and about 1,500,000 angstroms are being developed but as yet have no widespread application.

Near infrared energy for commercial and industrial use usually is produced by incandescent lamps so designed that some of their visible-light output is sacrificed in order that infrared radiation will be produced with greater efficiency. Another efficient method utilizes gas-fired infrared units called *gas radiants*. Like other wavelengths of electromagnetic radiation, infrared waves travel through space at the 186,000-mile-per-second speed until they strike a surface where they are absorbed and heat is generated in the material they strike. Most nonreflective substances will absorb and convert into heat a large percentage of the radiant infrared energy striking them, whereas reflecting surfaces redirect and control it just as visible light waves are reflected and controlled.

The heat energy thus absorbed by a substance such as iron will be transferred from one iron atom to another until within a short time the whole body of the object is warm even though the infrared radiation is falling upon only a part of it. This transfer of heat within the object itself is called *conduction*. The most familiar example of conduction is found in a steel rod or poker. The handle can become unbearably hot even though only the opposite end is thrust in the fire. Some materials conduct heat much less rapidly than others, which explains why wooden handles are placed on metal pots and pans used on the kitchen stove and why aluminum, being an excellent conductor of heat, makes highly satisfactory cooking utensils.

When an object is hot or even warm, it radiates its heat into the cooler air until it eventually reaches the temperature of the air. The surrounding air thus absorbs the heat energy, and if air circulation exists, this warmer air around the hot object rises and circulates away. This type of heat transfer is called *convection*.

All three types are present in heating the average home. Combustion of coal, oil, or gas fuel produces radiant heat (infrared energy) which is absorbed by the boiler pipes and transferred to the water in them by conduction. This hot water is circulated through the radiators so that they become warm and heat the air surrounding them. Normal air circulation within the room carries this warm air about so that the heat is transferred by convection and the house is warm and comfortable. A fireplace is a good example of infrared radiation at home. While some air is heated and circulated through the house, we must sit before the fire to really feel its heat. The same is true with electric sun bowls, which are quite widely used for "spot" heating.

Industrial Applications of Infrared

Aside from providing heat to make us comfortable, infrared is put to work in many industrial processes. These include paint and enamel drying, baking, preheating, and dehydrating.

Basically, these processes are the same. Banks of incandescent infrared lamps are used, each lamp being equipped with its own reflector. The reflector can be applied as an "aluminized" surface to the glass bulb itself or as a separate element in back of a lamp. Gold-plated steel reflectors, while they are not so efficient as other surfaces for visible light, do reflect the greatest amounts of useful infrared and are used extensively in industry. Such reflectors control the infrared flux just as do those used for visible light. An opaque object placed in the "beam" of radiant

Fig. 7-1. This infrared oven bakes the prime and finish coats of paint on army tanks. It requires only a few minutes for this method as compared with approximately 1 hour in convection ovens. (*Courtesy of Amplex Corp.,* New York, N.Y.)

heat will cast an invisible "shadow" by absorbing the radiations that strike it.

The one pronounced advantage of using radiant infrared energy for drying paints, lacquers, and similar finishes or for dehydrating and baking materials is the reduction in time involved to accomplish the task. Near infrared radiation is penetrating, that is, the heat is absorbed *within* the object being treated, so that a film of paint tends to dry from the inside out rather than from the surface inward as with oven drying or baking. Processes that formerly required as much as 15 or 20 hours normal drying time are frequently completed with infrared in a matter of 15 or 20 minutes. Others may require no more than 1 or 2 minutes as compared with over an hour for oven drying.

Obviously, there can be no established drying-time rule to cover all applications. Different materials, such as iron and wood, have different heat-conducting characteristics, as was pointed out earlier by the mention of wooden handles on kitchenware. In addition, the types of finishes to be dried or baked vary widely in their composition, so that more time will be required for some than for others. The color of a finish also affects its drying time. Light finishes usually take longer to dry thoroughly because some of the infrared will be reflected, whereas darker paints or lacquers dry more rapidly by virtue of more rapid infrared absorption. The same time differences occur in dehydrating operations. A hard wet surface of metal can be dried more quickly, for example, than a wet rug or a water-soaked piece of wood, but in either case the drying time would be less than with heated air as the only drying medium.

Radiant heat requires no air for its transmission, and the air present between an infrared source and the object is heated only to a comparatively negligible extent. Thus, with infrared radiant drying it is not always necessary to exclude air circulation or to provide insulation to keep the heat in. Some ovens are enclosed, however, in order to heat the air and, therefore, aid the drying action, while others may be left open to allow the escape of fumes and smoke resulting from paint drying.

These factors result in speed and economy in a great many processes. It is apparent that the technique of utilizing these wavelengths of electromagnetic radiation is just crossing the threshold of a much wider range of industrial application than is generally appreciated.

Infrared Therapy

Infrared radiation also serves in the field of medicine. The sun, producing more than an abundance of infrared, has been considered and recognized as a great healing agency since the dawn of civilization. The same radiations as those of the sun, produced artificially in therapeutic lamps, have the characteristic warming effect, so that heat is generated in the body tissue directly beneath the skin and transmitted more deeply by conduction. Bruised and strained muscles and ligaments can be relaxed and soothed with a consequent decrease in pain by infrared therapeutic application. Lamps and reflectors for this purpose are found in all gymnasiums and doctors' offices where athletic injuries are treated, and many thousands of them have been sold through drugstores and other retail outlets for home use.

There is evidence which indicates that visible light of different colors possesses a healing or tonic effect upon the human system; that blue or green light, for instance, has definite curative powers for some ailments while red light will produce healing results for others. It is quite likely, however, that such effects, where evident, are largely psychological rather than physiological, since the nervous reaction to color is quite pronounced in most individuals.

Infrared Photography

The use of infrared radiation in photography has made it possible to extend that art beyond the limits of normal vision. Objects can be photographed in absolute darkness or through a haze which makes them visually obscure.

It has been explained that we see an object by virtue of the visible light it reflects and that most objects reflect infrared as well as light but that infrared is beyond the limit of eye sensitivity. A camera, however, equipped with film sensitized to infrared radiations by means of special emulsions will capture objects or landscapes which the eye cannot see. Thus, an object in the kitchen can be photographed at night and without light merely by heat from a stove which is not even red-hot.

Since infrared possesses far greater penetrating power than

FIG. 7-2. Photograph on panchromatic film, without a filter, taken from a mountain top in New York State. Because of atmospheric haze, few or no details are shown of the horizon or mountains in the distance. (*Courtesy of Walter Clark, Kodak Research Laboratory, Eastman Kodak Company.*)

visible light, and since all objects reflect infrared, it is possible to photograph landscapes through a haze so thick that they cannot be seen. After considerable research work, film has been developed which is sensitive to infrared radiation as long as 12,000 angstroms in wavelength. If used in the daytime, special lens filters, which are opaque to visible light but not to infrared, must be placed over the lens.

Black-and-white photographic prints from an infrared film have a somewhat unusual reversed appearance due to reflection factors of objects which are different for infrared than for visible light. A blue sky or lake, for instance, will appear quite dark, whereas, red, green, or yellow objects will show up much lighter than in a regular photograph.

Fɪɢ. 7-3. A photograph of the same scene shown in Fig. 7-2, but using infrared film and the Wratton No. 25 red filter. Note that in this case infrared radiation penetrates the haze so that the horizon line and distant mountains are clearly visible, as well as additional details in the middle distance. (*Courtesy of Walter Clark, Kodak Research Laboratory, Eastman Kodak Company.*)

Conversion of Infrared to Visible Light

Since infrared radiation is invisible but behaves much like visible light, that is, can be reflected and controlled in a beam pattern, it has served as a means of communication for specific wartime applications. Signaling in code with infrared radiators was accomplished during the Second World War, and the development of equipment which would receive the invisible signals and convert them into visible light was the foundation for the design and successful use of some highly important weapons.

For signaling purposes, infrared radiation adjacent to the red end of the visible spectrum is used, since the most satisfactory sources (cesium-vapor lamps) radiate an abundance of energy at 8,521 and 8,944 angstroms in wavelength. In addition, they can be rapidly "flashed" as compared with a filament source which requires a moment to reach full "brilliancy" and a further time lag to cool sufficiently for the next impulse to be effective.

In other applications where the sources are required to operate for periods of time, filament lamps similar to those used in the industrial processes mentioned previously prove satisfactory, since the equipment needed to operate them is simpler with less weight—an important factor in portable-weapon design.

In the most effective sources of infrared, some visible light is produced and filters of special glass or plastic are necessary to absorb and eliminate the visible light while transmitting the infrared. Such filters must be able to withstand considerable heat, since they are placed in front of a focused infrared beam in a completely light-tight enclosure.

The conversion of infrared energy into visible-light energy is comparatively simple in the signaling operations, since it is only necessary to perceive a "flash" or impulse. This is accomplished, basically, with an infrared sensitive cell or phosphor button which is excited by the invisible signal and reradiates it as visible light, similar to the way a stove lid absorbs heat or infrared from the fire and reradiates some of it as visible light when the lid becomes red-hot. In the case of the signal receiver, however, this conversion is essentially instantaneous.

When an actual and detailed image of a scene or subject "illuminated" with infrared is required, the receiver and converter to visible light are much more involved.

During the Second World War, a rifle sometimes referred to as the *sniperscope* was developed and used most effectively. It is equipped with an infrared source and reflector which focuses a rather concentrated invisible beam for some distance in the direction of aim. In this way, an area in the line of sight is "spotted" with invisible radiation and reflects this radiation back toward the rifleman. To receive and convert this reflected energy from the target back into a visible scene that the rifleman can see, an *electron image* tube is placed on the gun in combination with a lens at the rear gun sight. Thus, it is possible for a man to see a target in complete darkness and fire with normal accuracy without the enemy's even becoming aware of his presence.

The electron image tube which makes this weapon possible will be discussed briefly in Chapter 15.

Food Cooking with Infrared

There is nothing new about cooking food with infrared. In fact, it has always been cooked this way, whether over an open campfire, a coal stove, or an electric range. Oven baking which is accomplished with hot-air convection results from infrared radiating from oven walls, gas burners, or heating coils.

A relatively new source of infrared for cooking has been developed, however, which does offer certain advantages over other types of heating elements and burners. It is an incandescent filament bulb in which the filament has been designed specifically to produce an abundance of infrared radiation. This source is equipped with its own gold reflector and is constructed of a heat-resisting glass. It will be described in detail in Chapter 14.

Basically, this source provides some of the advantages of both gas and electric burners in that the production of heat is instantaneous as with gas, and clean and odorless (no products of combustion) as with the conventional electric stove burners. In addition, it has certain physical features which make it ideal for domestic range use.

Fɪɢ. 7-4. A kitchen range utilizing an infrared bulb surface-cooking unit. In the left foreground under the coffee maker is shown the large 2,100-watt unit, whereas the one at the right foreground is 1,250 watt. (*Courtesy of Life magazine.*)

Induction Heating

It has been indicated that the heating of a material results when the molecules or atoms of that material are agitated sufficiently to be jostled around against each other. We have just seen that electromagnetic waves of the infrared region will cause this agitation as the material absorbs radiant energy.

Molecules in metals will also be jostled violently when the metal is subjected to strong magnetic fields. Such fields are produced by alternating current flowing through coils placed around the metal. When subjected to this magnetic-field influence, eddy currents (see Chapter 4, Transformers) flow in the metal and are opposed by resistance, as in a wire. In overcoming the resistance, heat is generated within the metal. Since the currents and consequent heat are induced in the metal by the magnetic field created within it, we call this method of heating *induction heating*.

This process is used extensively in industry for heat-treating of metal parts. It provides extreme flexibility in that the metal parts can be heated either to a mild degree or to the melting

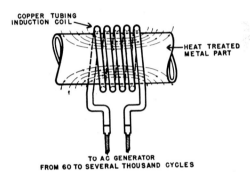

Fig. 7-5. Illustrating the principles involved in induction heating. The induction coil is supplied by a high-frequency generator, and the metal part inserted in the magnetic field created undergoes a rapid temperature rise as a result of the consequent agitation of molecules in the metal part.

point. In addition, the heat can be made to penetrate either completely through the piece or only a very slight distance in from the surface.

There are several variable factors which may be adjusted to accomplish exactly what is desired. These include the time of exposure to the magnetic-field influence, the strength of the field as produced by the a-c generator, and the frequency of current-flow alternations. The first two are determined more or less by the metallic nature of the part being treated, that is, whether it is copper, nickel, iron, or some other element or alloy, and also by its size and shape. Changes in frequency, however, will affect the depth of heating within the part.

Low frequencies from 60 to 5,000 cycles as produced by rotating generators are used for low-temperature annealing, for deep penetration, and sometimes for melting. Higher frequencies between 10,000 and 500,000 cycles are produced by electron tubes and are used for heat-treating the surface of metals to some depth. Frequencies between 500,000 and a million cycles result from certain types of electron-tube oscillators and are used for the "skin" heating of metallic ribbon and similar metal parts. In other words, the higher the frequency, the less depth there is to the heating process with, of course, proper correlation of time and power.

The heat produced in the object or part undergoing treatment is *not* the direct result of current from the a-c generator, since current does not flow through the part. Nor is it the result of heat conducted to the part from the exciting coil or *inducer*. The latter does not touch the part. If the coil is a hollow tube coil, it may be cooled by a forced flow of water through it. Coil design is extremely important in the technique of induction heating, since it serves to create a magnetic-field pattern best suited to the size, shape, and character of the workpiece or part.

Frequencies upward of a million cycles (*one megacycle*) are used for heat-treating nonmetallic materials.

Dielectric Heating

Materials such as wood, plastics, fabrics, rubber, and fibers are nonconductors of electricity and are called *dielectrics*. Frequencies which are effective in heating metals as in induction heating have little, if any, effect on dielectrics. In some induction-heating applications the metal part is covered by or separated from the inducing coil by glass, wood, or some other dielectric, and the process will have no effect whatever on the dielectric, even though it may heat the metallic part to a high temperature.

However, dielectrics can be heat-treated by high-frequency

alternating currents in the order of from 1 to 50 megacycles or more. Furthermore, such high frequencies have little or no effect upon metals, so that each type of material, metal or dielectric, is characterized by the frequency ranges which will generate heat within it.

Since dielectrics are nonmetallic and, therefore, nonmagnetic, the heating of them cannot and does not result from a magnetic field created within them. It does result from an electric field such as is produced between the plates of a condenser.

Materials such as wood, rubber, plastics, and other noncon-

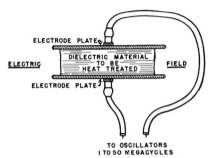

Fig. 7-6. Illustrating the principles involved in dielectric heating. The dielectric material is placed in a rapidly oscillating electric field which exists between the two electrode plates. The consequent agitation of molecules in the material results in a quick temperature rise.

ductors are, of course, composed of atoms. When placed in an electric field, the electrons of these atoms tend to be attracted to the positive electrode or side of the field. The fact that they are tightly bound to their atoms and are not free to move makes the material a nonconductor. Nevertheless, the force of the electric field has some influence on them in that it tends to distort their normal movement in shells around the nucleus. Thus we have here also a condition of agitated atoms and molecules in a dielectric which is placed between two plates carrying charges of opposite sign—one positive and one negative.

When current is applied to these plates which alternates its direction a few million times a second, the high degree of agitation of particles comprising the material placed between the plates can be imagined. Such particle "excitement" causes a temperature rise in the material and is called *dielectric heating*.

This method of heat-treating nonmetallic materials is widely used in industry for curing, bonding, drying, dehydrating, and similar processes.

Diathermy

Diathermy or thermotherapy is, in a sense, the dielectric heating of body tissue for the treatment of certain ailments and the relief of pain, and it is accomplished in a similar manner to the heating of dielectric materials. There is a relatively recent development involving the use of a much higher frequency (2,450 megacycles) wherein the generation of heat in body tissue is based upon somewhat different phenomena. It will be discussed in some detail shortly.

When the atoms and/or molecules comprising living cells in tissue are agitated, heat is developed the same as in materials such as metals or dielectrics. In diathermy, the electrodes are referred to as *space plates* and are placed at different parts of the body. When alternating current is applied, the electric field produced between the plates excites the atoms or molecules and heat is produced.

The Federal Communications Commission has established three frequencies for this purpose at 13.56, 27.12, and 40.98 megacycles. Since diathermy equipment radiates energy which can cause radio interference in the vicinity of the equipment, FCC control and frequency assignment are necessary in order to avoid the widespread radio difficulties which would result from random use of different frequencies. Even with such control, occasional interference prevails in television channels in some localities under certain conditions.

There is a wide difference in the heat-generating properties of different types of tissue. At lower frequencies, heat is produced in fat much more rapidly than in muscle tissue, but with higher frequencies, the difference becomes much less pronounced. Diathermy of this sort has been used for several years with considerable success in certain types of physiological disorders.

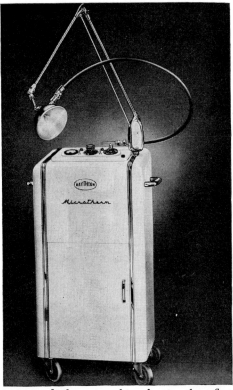

Fig. 7-7. A microwave diathermy machine showing the reflector from which the microwaves advance. This reflector is readily adjustable for all types of microwave therapy. (*Courtesy of Raytheon Mfg. Co., Waltham, Mass.*)

More recently the use of much higher frequencies, or a "beam" of microwaves, has been found to produce excellent therapeutic results. In contrast to the electric-field type of thermotherapy which is referred to as *shortwave diathermy*, the newest tech-

nique is called *microwave diathermy*. In either case, the fundamental purpose is to excite the atoms or molecules of cells in
order to produce heat within the tissue. The atoms absorb energy
from either the electric field or the microwave radiation as the
case may be, become excited, and release the energy as heat.

In order to avoid random use of the higher frequencies for
diathermic purposes, the FCC also assigned the frequency band
between 2,400 and 2,500 megacycles for diathermy equipment
of the microwave type. While this region of the radio spectrum
is well above either existing (or proposed) short-wave radio or
television (black and white or color) channels, the frequency
of other types of radio communication is in the vicinity.

Certain advantages appear for microwave diathermy. The fact
that energy absorption and consequent heat generation are essentially equal to either fat or muscle tissue permits a more precise use of such therapeutic treatment.

The penetrating properties of microwaves at a frequency of
2,450 megacycles are particularly favorable to thermotherapy in
that they cause a more even heating from the surface to the
deep tissues, with the result that the latter can be adequately
treated without the development of uncomfortably high surface
(skin) temperatures.

Microwaves is a name applied to a band of frequencies at the
upper or short-wavelength limit of the range of radio waves.
Their wavelengths are in the order of a few centimeters. A more
complete discussion of them will be found in Chapter 11.

The Undeveloped Infrared Region

In between infrared radiation of a million angstroms (one two-
hundred-and-fiftieth of an inch) in wavelength and the shortest
microwaves used at present, which are an inch or less in wavelength, lies an unexplored or at least undeveloped region in the
electromagnetic spectrum. This wide band is generally referred
to as *Hertzian waves.*

At present, it seems questionable whether these waves will

ever be of much use in distant communication, since the structure of air is such that they tend to attenuate or be absorbed very rapidly when radiating through it. The Hertzian wave region is being studied in the laboratories, however, and it is quite possible that during the next few years more will be discovered about their generation and control for use in biological, medical, or allied fields.

8

Ultraviolet

Beyond the violet limit of the visible-light band in the diagram of the range of electromagnetic waves and in the opposite direction from infrared, the radiations are called *ultraviolet*. The long-wavelength limit of the ultraviolet band is established at about 4,000 angstroms or where visual color sensation ceases, but the short-wavelength extreme is somewhat indefinite. It is generally considered as around 100 angstroms, which is a decided overlap with another band known as *X rays*.

The frequencies of ultraviolet radiations are, of course, higher than those of either infrared or visible light, since the wavelengths are much shorter. These vibrations range from 800,000 to 900,000 billion per second to somewhere in the order of 200,000 or 300,000 trillion per second—an almost inconceivable frequency, but still not so high as others to be considered later.

Like infrared, the ultraviolet region is split into *near* and *far* portions for the sake of analysis, the near being adjacent to the violet end of the light spectrum and the far encompassing the shorter wavelengths. Sometimes a *middle* portion extending between 2,000 and 3,000 angstroms is referred to in textbooks, but since the limits are more or less arbitrary, we can, for the sake of simplicity here, avoid the middle designation and consider the border between near and far ultraviolet as being at the 2,000-angstrom wavelength. With this border line established, most of our discussion will involve the near portion or wavelength between visible violet light and ultraviolet at 2,000 angstroms.

As with visible light and infrared, nature's most abundant source of ultraviolet is the sun. Although the sun radiates a great amount of ultraviolet energy into space, only a relatively small amount of it (the longer wavelengths) reaches the earth. The atmosphere filters out or absorbs nearly all the radiation of a wavelength shorter than 3,000 angstroms. This is indeed fortunate because these shorter wavelengths, even in amounts much less than the longer wavelength energy which we do receive, would cause burns and injuries so severe that life could not exist, at least in the open.

Careful study and analysis of the sun's spectrum indicate that its temperature is around 10,000 or 12,000° Fahrenheit at its "surface" or atmosphere and as high as 20 million degrees at the center. Its maximum energy is radiated in the visible region at a wavelength of about 4,700 angstroms. At the earth's surface from 1 to 5 per cent of the energy is ultraviolet between 3,000 and 4,000 angstroms, from 41 to 45 per cent is visible light, and from 52 to 60 per cent is infrared. This is the sun at average height in the sky under average seasonal conditions. As the afternoon passes and the sun sinks lower, the energy is absorbed to greater extents by increases in the thickness of air through which it must pass. Obviously, the reverse takes place during the forenoon hours as the sun approaches the zenith.

It also has been found that, while the noonday summer sun is only 10 per cent more potent in infrared radiation than in winter, it is about 1,000 per cent richer in ultraviolet in summer. In view of this, it can be seen that between these two extremes the additional visible-light energy in the summertime will become increasingly greater for each successive color from violet to red.

Sunburn

Almost everyone has experienced a severe sunburn after exposure to midsummer sun. The physiology of sunburn (erythema) is somewhat complicated for a complete discussion here, since it involves a study of several layers of skin, various parts of the body, and subjects having different complexions. In general, blondes will sunburn more rapidly than brunettes, and as a rule the nature of the latter's skin is such that they "tan" more readily than blondes. Wavelengths between 3,000 and 3,200 angstroms will penetrate the skin deeply enough to reach the pigment-producing cells and cause a tan, but those between 2,800 and 3,000 angstroms merely burn at the surface with but very little tanning effect.

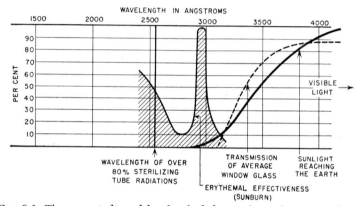

Fig. 8-1. The curve indicated by the shaded area shows the region of sunburning radiation in the ultraviolet spectrum. The maximum effect is found at 2,900 angstrom units.

While sunburn (tanning and burning) is produced by ultraviolet radiation between the wavelengths of 2,800 and 3,200 angstroms, the maximum effect is at about 2,970 angstroms (in nature). It will be recalled that very little ultraviolet energy shorter than 3,000 angstroms reaches the surface of the earth owing to atmospheric absorption, but it should be remembered also that the sun is an abundant producer of all wavelengths, so that those longer than 3,000 angstroms which penetrate the atmosphere are amply potent to cause severe and painful burns with sufficient exposure time. In other words, if the air were thinner, as at very high altitudes, so that the maximum sun-burning wavelengths around 2,970 angstroms could pass through, we would suffer terrific burns in a matter of a very few minutes.

Unlike infrared, ultraviolet is not penetrating as compared with other wavelengths of electromagnetic radiation. We do not become sunburned while sitting by a closed window because the rays will not pass through ordinary window glass. There are certain types of glasses, however, which are specially made to permit the transmission of ultraviolet. One such glass, called *Corex*, is used in certain types of ultraviolet sun-lamp bulbs and transmits wavelengths as short as 2,900 angstroms. Certain other materials, such as cellophane and sodium silicate (water glass), also transmit ultraviolet in amounts depending upon their thickness. Special glasses are manufactured which allow much shorter wavelengths (2,000 angstroms) to pass through.

Ultraviolet radiant energy behaves much like visible light and infrared. It has just been indicated how it is transmitted by some glasses and other materials. These materials also refract ultra-violet as they do light, and since quartz has a high transmission factor for ultraviolet, quartz prisms are frequently used for the purpose of wavelength study. Ultraviolet is also reflected by various surfaces, the most efficient ones being metallic.

There are a great many more phenomena connected with ultraviolet radiation than can be covered here, but we can dis-cuss the most important ones. These phenomena occur at differ-ent wavelengths. In nature, where ultraviolet is practically all above the 3,000-angstrom wavelength, the sunburning effect is the most prominent and has already been briefly covered. Below 3,000 angstroms we must deal with radiations produced arti-ficially, since they are not present in solar energy reaching the earth.

Ultraviolet Sources

Ultraviolet radiation is produced by some materials when they are heated to brilliant incandescence. Today, such heating is accomplished electrically, but a hundred years or so ago it was done chemically with an oxyhydrogen flame and a piece of rare-earth oxide or lime. Such a device was called a *limelight,* or sometimes a *calcium light,* and was used to illuminate theatrical stages, since it produced visible light of high brilliancy as well as relatively long-wavelength ultraviolet radiations.

Although such sources have the advantage of burning without an enclosure in the open air, they are cumbersome for commercial application and are not rich enough in ultraviolet to be of practical use.

A high-voltage electric spark or an arc between metallic electrodes, such as iron or carbon, is also a producer of ultraviolet in the open air, but mercury-vapor arcs created in an inert gas such as argon are widely used at present for the commercial generation of ultraviolet. Of course, such mercury-vapor discharges must be confined within a sealed glass or quartz envelope.

It has been explained how ordinary window glass will not transmit any except the very long wavelengths of ultraviolet adjacent to the visible light region, so that although the discharge itself may be extremely rich in ultraviolet, the potency of the source is wholly dependent upon the transmission characteristics of the glass envelope.

Quartz is perhaps the best commercially available transmitter of ultraviolet and will pass radiations having wavelengths as short as 1,850 angstroms, depending upon its thickness. As that approximate limit is approached, the oxygen in the air itself undergoes certain chemical changes, and the production of ozone, which results from the absorption of far ultraviolet radiations by the air, creates an envelope of ozone around the source through which short radiations cannot pass. The sun, radiating ultraviolet of all wavelengths, creates a protective layer of ozone high above the surface of the earth in the outer limits of the atmosphere, thereby absorbing the short, harmful rays.

In the laboratories, equipment is used which permits the

study of extremely short-wave ultraviolet. This equipment utilizes fluorite and other substances which allow far greater transmission of short-wave ultraviolet than quartz. For several years, there remained an unexplored gap between the shortest ultraviolet radiation and the longest X rays, but comparatively recently this region has been penetrated to the extent that ultraviolet and X rays are found to overlap at their respective extremes. This is indicated in the diagram of the range of electromagnetic waves (frontispiece).

Below the quartz-transmission limit at about 1,850 angstroms, the radiations have little or no commercial value at present. Small fluorescent bulbs have been successfully made and sold for decorative purposes which do utilize such radiation within the bulb to excite certain phosphors to fluorescence. Instead of mercury vapor, which is used in standard tubular fluorescent lamps, these small bulbs contain neon gas which, when ionized, produces considerable ultraviolet energy in the region of 1,000 angstroms, and it is this radiation which excites the phosphors to radiate visible light. Since these lamps contain no metallic vapor, they have the advantage of starting at extremely low temperatures.

Future development in the technique of generation and control of very short-wavelength or far ultraviolet will, no doubt, bring many benefits to mankind in the fields of surgery, bacteriology, and medicine.

In the near region of ultraviolet radiation, particularly that portion sometimes referred to as *middle* ultraviolet, between 2,000 and 3,000 angstroms in wavelength, great progress has been made during the past few years.

Much of this progress is due to Corning Glass Works' development of glasses which pass ultraviolet at different wavelengths. Many of these glasses can be looked upon as protective glasses, since they transmit those wavelengths desired and shut out the shorter ones, which are damaging to the eyes. Some of them, however, must be used with extreme care, since they are de-

liberately designed to transmit short wavelengths for bactericidal and other purposes.

Physiological Effects of Ultraviolet

Quartz lamps, lamps made of glass transmitting wavelengths
shorter than 3,000 angstroms, and open arcs such as are used in
welding will cause serious damage to the eyes and skin unless
they are properly shielded. The skin injury is an inflammation
similar to sunburn, and the eye injury is an inflammation of the
conjunctiva, a mucous membrane covering part of the eyeball
as well as the inside of the lids. *Conjunctivitis,* as the inflammation is called, is usually indicated by the feeling that the eyes
are full of sand and the lids stuck together. It is frequently quite
painful and may be of several hours' duration. Prompt treatment
by a physician may avoid permanent damage and in extreme
cases even blindness.

There are a great many physiological effects of ultraviolet
energy, besides those on the skin which are evidenced by sunburn and tanning, although sun-bath treatments (heliotherapy)
are looked upon as the major function of ultraviolet. Of recent
years, however, the general public seems to have acquired a
respect for ultraviolet and has avoided excessive exposure to the
hot summer sun.

Ultraviolet penetrating the thin outer layers of skin is absorbed by the blood stream and enables it to accumulate more
phosphorus and calcium. These two elements are essential for
the building and maintenance of sound bones and teeth and
consequently result in the avoidance or cure of a bone disease
called *rickets.* Vitamin D, which is abundantly present in fish-
liver oil and milk, aids in the same purpose and is frequently
referred to as the *sunshine vitamin.*

The healing of some types of skin diseases has been found
to be hastened by ultraviolet radiation. When the disease is of
such a nature that deep wounds exist, it is probable that infrared, which is, of course, more penetrating than ultraviolet, may

be more effective if used in conjunction with the ultraviolet. In natural sunlight exposure, the increased blood-circulation and toning effect of the infrared is present along with the bactericidal and cauterizing action of the ultraviolet.

Extensive analysis of the action of certain wavelengths of ultraviolet has been carried on by several investigators. The published works of Dr. Henry Laurens and of Ellis and Wells are particularly complete and cover a great many effects on the blood, skin, circulatory system, metabolism, respiration, heartbeat, and human diseases. In general, it can be said that ultraviolet radiation of wavelengths no shorter than found in nature can be beneficial and curative in moderate amounts and that a lack of sufficient radiation can be at least partly made up with a diet properly regulated to include the necessary additional vitamin D and A components.

The effective wavelength for the production of calcium and phosphorus in the system is in the region of 3,020 angstroms. Since the effect is on the blood stream, it is obvious that irradiation of only one part will affect the whole body as the blood circulates through it.

A comparable result can be accomplished through the irradiation of several types of foods instead of the body itself. Irradiated milk is readily available and is perhaps the best known of irradiated foods, although the vitamin D content of certain cereals, starch foods, and vegetable oils can be appreciably increased through ultraviolet irradiation.

Experiments with other vitamins and with diseases other than rickets have met with little success. It seems, at present, that the primary function of ultraviolet radiation upon the human system is to assure sound, healthy bones and teeth.

Considerable successful work has been done in conjunction with the raising of poultry and the production of eggs. Calcium and phosphorus are vitally important in this industry, since they have as much effect upon the egg-laying capacity of hens as upon the development of their bones. Incandescent tungsten-filament lamps having special ultraviolet-transmitting glass bulbs have been developed specifically for application to poultry. These lamps are called *CX lamps,* and although the amount of ultraviolet produced is relatively small, their consistent use has been a means of some increase in egg production and improvement in the health and sturdiness of chickens. More recently, the application of standard germicidal lamps—which are much richer in ultraviolet—and also lamps with special ultraviolet-producing phosphors have proved much more successful when properly used and controlled.

Radiant Energy and Plant Growth

As far as the effect of radiant energy on plants is concerned, considerable investigation shows that, as a rule, plants grow best under light of all wavelengths as found in nature. The elimination of solar ultraviolet (or infrared) does not seriously curtail plant growth, but excessive amounts of either will cause severe damage. Plants can be "forced" with light up to a certain point, after which a leaf injury may appear and increase until the leaves completely wither and drop off. Experiments with apples indicate that ultraviolet has a marked effect upon the pigment-producing cells in the skin and is essential to produce attractive red apples. Infrared, on the other hand, is not needed to develop color and will, in fact, cause injury to the fruit in amounts much in excess of normal autumn sunlight.

Plant growth is a rather complicated and delicate process which is not wholly understood. It is also one which is very carefully regulated and controlled by nature. As with any living matter, leaves are composed of cells. In those cells which are exposed to light, a green coloring matter called *chlorophyll* is developed. This pigment, with the help of carbon dioxide which the leaves obtain from the air, makes it possible for leaves to absorb radiant energy in the visible-light region. The energy then combines with mineral salts in the water which has been drawn from the ground by the plant's roots, and the result of the combination is the formation of starch and certain carbohydrates which are essential to plant growth and life.

The ability of a plant to thus convert radiant energy into the food upon which it lives is called *photosynthesis.* While animal life requires oxygen for the manufacture of blood and exhales carbon dioxide as the waste product of metabolism, plants, in a

FIG. 8-2. Three petunia plants. The one on the left was exposed to the natural complete spectrum of sunlight; the center one received only the violet and blue light (the longer wavelengths were filtered out); the plant at the right received only infrared, red, orange, and yellow light from the sun. (*Photograph and data from Boyce Thompson Institute for Plant Research, Yonkers, N.Y.*

reverse process, absorb carbon dioxide and liberate oxygen as a waste product of photosynthesis. As indicated above, all wavelengths of light in about the proportion found in nature produce the best results. All violet and blue light, in some instances, causes short, stubby plants, whereas all red, orange, and yellow radiation results in tall, spindly growth, with short-lived, unhealthy plants in either case.

Complete studies on the correlation between radiant energy and plant growth have been carried out at the Boyce Thompson Institute for Plant Research at Yonkers, New York. An accurate generalization covering all plants is difficult because different plants may vary in their response to different wavelengths of visible light, ultraviolet, and infrared.

Fig. 8-3. Tomato plants. The one at the left is the normal control plant. The center one was taken from a greenhouse and exposed to a mercury-vapor arc in quartz for 3 minutes. The plant at the right was deprived of all light for 4 days, then similarly exposed to a mercury arc. (*Photograph and data from Boyce Thompson Institute for Plant Research, Yonkers, N.Y.*)

Bactericidal Ultraviolet

The bactericidal effect of ultraviolet has been known for many years but was not commercially applied until a glass with adequate transmission characteristics at the most potent wavelength (2,537 angstroms) was developed a few years ago. The sun has long been considered as a germ-killing medium, and virtually all types of bacteria can be killed or at least weakened by it if sufficient exposure time is allowed.

Since practically no ultraviolet radiation of a wavelength shorter than 3,000 angstroms reaches the surface of the earth, it is evident that at least some of this radiation must be bactericidal.

Extensive research shows that, while there is a slight bactericidal effect in the extreme lower limits of solar radiation, there is a tremendous bactericidal potency in radiations in the region of 2,537 angstroms, a wavelength not present in solar energy. Obviously, therefore, the sun's germicidal values lies in the fact that it is a powerful source of the less effective wavelengths. Of course this is fortunate because, as has been explained, wavelengths shorter than 3,000 will seriously damage the skin and eyes.

In order to apply bactericidal ultraviolet successfully, the

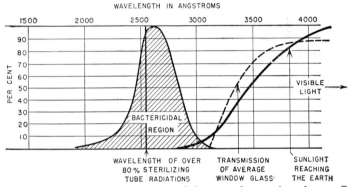

FIG. 8-4. The curve enclosing the shaded area indicates the relative effectiveness of ultraviolet wavelengths in killing bacteria. The 2,537-angstrom mercury line falls at the approximate peak of the region, and germicidal lamps are made to produce an abundance of radiation in that wavelength.

most potent wavelengths should be employed. Therefore, a lamp which is rich in 2,537-angstrom-wavelength ultraviolet is necessary. There were a number of difficult problems involved in the development of such a lamp before it could be applied commercially. While the carbon arc produced an abundance of 2,537-angstrom ultraviolet, it also produced brilliant light and considerable heat (infrared), so that it was extremely awkward to handle. Likewise a high-voltage disruptive spark presented problems, so that the most likely remaining source was a mercury-vapor arc discharge within a glass envelope which would permit the transmission of the 2,537 energy through it.

Such a glass was produced a few years ago, and today there are several types of sterilizing or germicidal lamps available for use in hospitals and other locations where sterilization of the air and exposed surfaces is essential. A description of these lamps and their operating characteristics will be presented in Chapter 14.

Ultraviolet as Applied to Food

In addition to bacteria killing, the 2,537-wavelength ultraviolet will arrest the development of many types of molds and fungi by killing the spores of these organisms which float about in the air. The author has conducted several tests with common bread mold and has concluded that, if properly irradiated bread is enclosed in an airtight wrapper (which also must be irradiated), it will not become moldly over an extended period. It may become dehydrated and unpalatable, however, as the moisture condenses on the inside of the wrapper. These tests were conducted in a large bakery where special ultraviolet equipment was applied to irradiate the automatic slicing knives and all surfaces touching the bread as well as the bread itself and its wrapper. Control loaves (not irradiated) showed mold colonies in from 3 to 4 days, whereas irradiated loaves did not show indications of mold for over twice that period even though the wrappers were not airtight. Since cellophane transmits some amount of ultraviolet, several loaves were irradiated after being wrapped in it, but the results of this test could not be considered conclusive. It must be added that mold spores are much more resistant to the lethal effect of ultraviolet than are bacteria, and at least one type of mold appears to thrive under it.

There are a great many possible applications for ultraviolet irradiation to kill microorganisms, many of which are in successful operation today. There are also many installations of ultraviolet sources wherein the actual value is rather dubious. Their use in refrigerators, particularly in the large walk-in type used for meat storage, appears to have considerable merit from the standpoint of reducing trimming losses by arresting the growth of slime on the surface of meats. In order to avoid an excessive accumulation of such slime, low humidity is maintained in the refrigerator with a consequent amount of dehydration or drying of the meat surface. This dry and hardened meat must be trimmed off before sale. With ultraviolet lamps in operation, however, a higher humidity can be maintained without an exces-

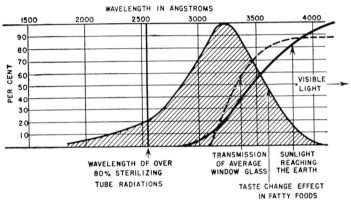

FIG. 8-5. The curve indicated by the shaded area shows the ultraviolet wavelengths that cause a taste change in certain foods.

sive formation of slime, resulting in less dehydrated-meat-trimming losses.

Whenever such foods as milk, butter, and fatty acids are exposed to ultraviolet, care must be used to avoid overexposure, since a taste change occurs which may render these foods extremely unpalatable. This change in taste results from oxidation of proteins as well as the de-emulsification of fats and is not to be confused with the souring of milk or the rancidity of butter. The effect occurs at long wavelengths of ultraviolet as well as at shorter ones, since it can be detected in a sealed bottle of milk left standing for some time in the sunlight. The thickness and type of glass used in the bottle would be such that only very near ultraviolet in the order of 3,700 or 3,800 angstroms in wavelength could be transmitted to the milk itself.

Ultraviolet Production of Ozone

Before leaving the subject of ultraviolet radiation it might be well to discuss ozone again briefly, since as the use of sources producing shorter wavelengths of ultraviolet becomes more common in industry and commerce, the problem of ozone control may reach critical proportions.

Ozone is a rather unstable and active form of oxygen which results when the oxygen atoms making up an oxygen molecule are torn apart and reformed under unusual conditions. This reforming occurs most often when air, of which oxygen is a large part, is circulated through a high-voltage spark gap. Such a spark produces, in addition to visible light, considerable ultraviolet, some of which may be shorter than 2,000 angstroms in wavelength. Ultraviolet energy, radiating at such short wavelengths, also is produced by a mercury-vapor arc enclosed in a tube of quartz or special glass designed to transmit it. When these radiations pass through (or attempt to pass through) the oxygen in the air, the tearing apart of the normal oxygen molecules takes place and the ozone is formed. But being active in this form, the ozone molecules quickly join together again and revert to oxygen, particularly if water vapor is present in the air.

Ozone has a characteristically clean odor and is frequently noticed in nature after a nearby stroke of lightning occurs. It may be temporarily stimulating when inhaled, but the nitrogen compounds usually formed when ozone is produced in air may cause serious damage to the respiratory system if inhaled for a period of time. The odor of ozone can be detected if it is present in only a few parts per million of air, and even in this quantity the nitrogen products may be harmful. Therefore, in laboratories where work with apparatus producing ozone is in operation, precautions are always (or should be) taken to exhaust or absorb it so that workers will not be required to inhale it constantly.

Strangely enough, when methods of generating ozone were first developed a few years ago, its initial stimulating effect was considered beneficial to health, and "ozonators" were placed on the market to produce it deliberately. Now, however, much more is known about the results when it is formed in air and inhaled. Ozone is sometimes used in laundries with special apparatus to impart a clean, fresh, and absolutely harmless odor to laundered articles before they are sent back to the owner.

As far as its application to destroy odors is concerned, there is some question as to whether it actually destroys such odors or merely covers them up with its own. Possibly it is a combination of both.

There are many other effects of a chemical or biological nature which occur throughout the entire range of ultraviolet waves and frequencies, and the volumes devoted entirely to the subject are suggested to those who wish to pursue the study further.

9

Slow Oscillations

At the extreme right end of the electromagnetic-wave-range diagram (frontispiece), we find radiations of extremely long wavelength and very low vibration frequency. Although the slowest frequency indicated is 10 per second or 10 cycles, it is possible to produce slower ones, since such oscillations are generated by a coil of wire rotating in a magnetic field and the rotation can, of course, be made slow enough barely to move the coil. Such very low-frequency and long-wavelength electromagnetic radiations, however, are very difficult to obtain, requiring a long antenna and special equipment. They have little, if any, practical commercial value at present, but they do serve in certain experimental work.

It was indicated in Chapter 5, in the general discussion of electromagnetic waves, that such waves are moving electric and magnetic fields and originate with the movement of electrons. Since electric current involves the flow of electrons from negative to positive, and since a magnetic field is produced around a wire through which electrons are flowing, it follows that pulses or waves can be made to radiate away from a wire with every alternation of the generator. Alternating current is most frequently generated at 60 cycles, although 50, 40, and 25 cycles are occasionally found in this country and more often in foreign countries. Frequencies higher than 60 cycles are usually generated for special purposes. Thus, we may have electromagnetic waves of 25-, 40-, or 60-cycle frequency, whichever the case may be, or of some intermediate or higher frequency, depending upon the generator design and speed.

These waves can be detected mechanically, electrically, magnetically, or through certain thermal effects of alternating currents. The upper or higher frequency limit of the slow-oscillation region is established, more or less, by the ability to rotate a coil mechanically in a magnetic field. This ability is restricted by friction and other natural laws, so that the upper limit of 10,000 alternations per second (10 kilocycles) is an arbitrary one. The top speeds of practical centrifuges used in medical work are in the order of only about 2,000 revolutions per second, although experimental devices (ultracentrifuges) have been developed which are designed to whirl in a vacuum at enormous speeds approaching a million revolutions per second. It is clear, however, that to obtain higher frequency oscillations a method other than the mechanical rotation of a coil of wire in a magnetic field must be employed.

During the discussion of resonance in Chapter 4, it was pointed out that a condenser or capacitor can be made to charge and discharge back and forth from one side to the other and that such seesaw oscillations are very rapid as compared with those produced mechanically. This method provides the higher frequencies and will be discussed more in detail later.

Subsonics

Slow oscillations called *subsonic* are not electromagnetic radiations at all but are sound waves too low in pitch to be audible. Although they may have the same frequency as slow electromagnetic oscillations, they should not be consfused with them, as there is a vast difference in the character of each.

The average human ear is capable of hearing the deep sound produced by vibrations as low as about 20 to 25 per second or 20 to 25 cycles. Below that, the motion of a vibrating object or string may be seen and felt, but no audible sound is produced, and the frequencies are termed *subsonic*.

Ultrasonics

The upper limit of audible sound is somewhere in the order of 20,000 vibrations per second or 20 kilocycles. In acoustics and ultrasonic work this is sometimes called 20 kilo Hertz (kH_z), but since kilocycles is a more familiar term, it will be used here. At about 15 kilocycles the sound is so shrill as to be most annoying, at 18 kilocycles it begins to fade from audibility, and at 20 kilocycles there is no sound at all that the human ear can detect although the hearing organs of animals, birds, and insects may be able to do so. This region of sound waves too high in pitch to be heard is called the *ultrasonic* region.

Strictly speaking, the subject of ultrasonics (or subsonics) does not belong in a discussion of electromagnetic waves. Ultrasonic waves are sound waves of a vibrating frequency (pitch) too high to be heard, and, as such, require a medium such as air or water through which to travel, whereas electromagnetic radiations require no medium. In air, water, and solids ultrasonic frequencies parallel the region of slow oscillations and radio waves up to 500 megacycles in the radiant-energy spectrum. In solids, they can be produced experimentally at wavelengths approaching those of visible light. Since electron tubes are involved in ultrasonic wave production and control, we can consider the subject briefly here.

Production of Ultrasonic Waves

Ultrasonic waves can be produced mechanically up to certain limits, but beyond those, the higher frequencies are generated electronically. Small tuning forks, for example, can be made to produce vibrations up to about 90 kilocycles, although the amplitude is so small that they have no practical use. A type of whistle called the Galton whistle will produce vibrations as high as 100 kilocycles with constant frequency and amplitude if a constant air pressure is maintained.

There are other methods of generating ultrasonic waves which involve the longitudinal vibration of rods by mechanical or magnetic means. The latter method is called *magnetostriction* and is based on the fact that a metal rod placed in a magnetic field parallel to its length will be either lengthened or shortened depending upon the character of the metal, its temperature, the degree to which it has been previously magnetized, and certain other factors. The linear variations, of course, are very small— in order of one-millionth the length of the rod. However, when the magnetic field alternates at high frequency as a result of electron-tube oscillators, it can be seen that there will be corresponding high-frequency mechanical change in the linear characteristics of the rod.

There is a relationship between the length of a rod and the fundamental ultrasonic frequency of the waves which will advance from its end. When there is resonance (see Chapter 4) between a rod of certain dimensions and the a-c frequency applied, the amplitude of the ultrasonic waves will be at maximum.

Thus, it is possible to produce ultrasonic frequencies as high as 300 kilocycles and some considerable degree of amplitude with magnetostriction generators.

Piezoelectric Crystals

When higher ultrasonic frequencies are to be attained, the method of generating them requires the application of *piezo-electric* phenomena. The word piezoelectricity is derived from the Greek and means "pressure electricity."

Piezoelectric effects were first noted by Pierre Curie, who is identified with the discovery of radioactive elements. These effects are the result of the natural arrangement of atoms in the lattice structure of quartz crystals (see Chapter 1). The crystals are cut from the mother crystal in wafer and other forms with a high degree of accuracy, and the angle of cut with respect to various axes of the mother crystal determines their piezo-electric characteristics.

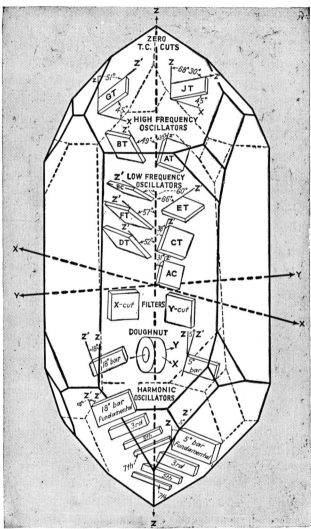

Fig. 9-1. Diagram showing how oscillator plates are cut from the mother crystal with specific angular relationship to the axes of the mother. The angle of cut, thickness, and other basic characteristics are extremely critical. (*Courtesy of Crystal Products Company.*)

When the wafers are subjected to either mechanical or electrical distortion, the effects occur. If one side of a quartz plate is compressed or deformed mechanically, electric charges will occur on the opposite face, or if one side is subjected to an electric charge, the plate will become physically distorted. Thus, when such crystal plates are influenced by alternating voltages, they will oscillate along certain axes in accordance with the frequencies being applied.

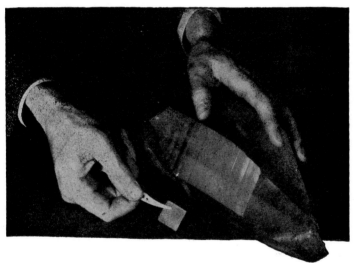

FIG. 9-2. A large mother crystal from which has been cut a small square oscillator plate, shown in the foreground. (*Courtesy of Crystal Products Company.*)

Quartz oscillator plates are placed in vacuum-tube circuits to stabilize or *fix* the frequencies of the oscillations, since a circuit of this sort will oscillate only at the frequency permitted by a quartz plate which has been cut at a carefully predetermined angle from the mother crystal. Their physical dimensions and angular cut determine their resonance of oscillating-frequency characteristics, so that extreme care and accuracy must be used in the cutting and grinding technique.

If a quartz rod is set in vibration longitudinally, the "sound" emanates from the ends as with metal magnetostriction, but with quartz crystal plates, it is emitted perpendicular to the plate surface.

Thus we have in quartz a means of attaining very high-frequency ultrasonic vibrations, the upper limit being in the order of 50,000 kilocycles before the crystal breaks down. Tourmaline crystal plates, however, can be made to produce fundamental ultrasonic frequencies as high as 150 megacycles, which is comparable to the ultrahigh-frequency radio region in the electromagnetic spectrum.

Fig. 9-3. A bowl-shaped piezoelectric ceramic generator which focuses the ultrasonic energy as indicated by the arrows. Elements similar to this one are designed for specific applications of ultrasonic work. (*Courtesy of Brush Development Co., Cleveland, Ohio.*)

There are certain materials other than natural crystals which can be made to exhibit piezoelectric effects. One of these is a ceramic material having barium titanate as a basic ingredient. This material is not naturally piezoelectric, but when combined with small percentages of other compounds, compressed into forms of carefully predetermined shape and thickness, and polarized, it yields electromechanical conversion properties which may be superior to quartz crystals in many ways for specific purposes.

This product, when formed into bowl-shaped oscillators, will "focus" a large amount of its ultrasonic energy at the focal point of the "bowl." Manufactured elements of this sort have been widely used in ultrasonic submarine work.

Detection of Ultrasonic Waves

It is quite as important to be able to detect or receive ultrasonic impulses as it is to produce them. Our ears, of course, cannot hear them, and the usual acoustic devices used for audible sound do not respond satisfactorily to the higher frequency vibrations.

On the other hand, their shorter wavelength characteristics make it possible to render them visible for experimental and observation purposes in the laboratory. While this can be done with audible sound waves, the process is not accomplished so readily. For example, certain fine metallic powders spread out on a smooth surface will arrange themselves in a pattern of ridges corresponding to the waves when exposed to ultrasonic vibrations emitted from the end of an oscillating quartz rod. When powders are suspended in liquids, they also tend to compress in accordance with the standing ultrasonic wave compressions, the degree of compression depending upon the amplitude of vibrations. There are several other methods of observing the effect and pattern of high-frequency ultrasonic waves in solids, liquids, and gases.

Vibrations above the limit of audibility can be focused or sent out in a beam similar to the way audible sound waves can be directed with a megaphone. Ultrasonic waves, however, being of shorter wavelengths than audible sound waves, can be controlled much more sharply, particularly if traveling through water, since they are not dispersed or spread out so readily by the medium through which they are passing.

In practical applications of ultrasonic waves, the reception of them is accomplished with piezoelectric elements in a process which, in effect, reverses that of their production. In other words, a crystal plate, when subjected to such vibrations traveling through air, water, or some similar medium, will physically vibrate when in resonance with the frequency of the ultrasonic impulses. As explained a moment ago, such plates when caused to vibrate in this manner develop charges on their surfaces. These can be amplified and measured so that the detection of ultrasonic frequencies is accomplished with accuracy.

Application of Ultrasonic Waves

Low-pitched sounds travel farther in air than high-pitched ones. We usually hear the bass drum of a band as it approaches before we hear the high-pitched fifes. Similarly, after the parade passes, the fifes fade from audibility first, while we may still hear the bass drum several blocks away. The deep boom of an ocean liner's whistle can be heard for miles, but the shrill blast of a busy tugboat carries only about the harbor, and its tone is recognized by all captains. Although this may be due in part to the relative amplitude of the instruments' sound, as well as to the nature of our hearing mechanism, part of the effect, at least, is due to a greater absorption of high tones by air.

Thus, it follows that vibrations in the ultrasonic region attenuate (are absorbed) very quickly in air. This is the result of slow molecular thermal transmission in air. Gas molecules become thermally excited in absorbing the pressure of an ultrasonic wave, but this thermal energy is not transmitted fast enough from one molecule to the next, so that the wave rapidly loses its ability to advance. As the frequencies become higher, the attenuation becomes greater, and at the upper limits, ultrasonic waves travel effectively only a small fraction of an inch, if at all, beyond a few molecular layers. At 500 kilocycles, for example, an ultrasonic impulse which will travel about 175 yards in water will travel only about ½ inch in air before it is completely absorbed.

It is apparent that media other than air must be employed wherein the transmission of thermal energy is more rapid if the successful use of ultrasonic frequencies is to be accomplished.

It was mentioned in Chapter 5 (Sound Waves) that audible

sound travels more than four times faster in water than in air. Water, therefore, becomes the medium in which ultrasonic waves find their most widespread use. Oil and a few other liquids as well as some solids are used in certain industrial processes and testing of materials.

Sonar

During the Second World War ultrasonic devices were used extensively by surface craft for detecting and locating submerged submarines. Ultrasonic waves can be generated and focused or sent out in a beam similar to the way audible sound waves can be directed with a megaphone. Since they are not dispersed so rapidly in water, however, their control is much more accurate and sharp.

Underwater location of reefs and other submerged objects, depth finding, and the detection of submarines are called *sonar* (sounding and ranging) and involve the sending of an ultrasonic pulse to the floor of the sea or in the direction of the submerged object where it is echoed back to a receiver. The ultrasonic generators and receivers are usually recessed or otherwise fastened to the underside of a ship's hull. They can be made to turn in all directions and from horizontal to vertical, if necessary, so that a wide area beneath the ship can be scanned ultrasonically.

The technique of determining location and depth requires the calculation of distance in accordance with the time it takes for an ultrasonic pulse to reach its destination and echo back. The speed of the pulse in water is a known factor but must be corrected for salt or fresh water as well as for temperature to obtain accurate data on obstacles or submarine location. Furthermore, pulses of extremely short duration are necessary. Otherwise, if the duration were long, a blurring reception would result with consequent inaccuracies.

The instantaneous packets of ultrasonic waves are sent down at regular intervals and echo back to the receiver, so that the

Fig. 9-4. An ultrasonic marine depth-finding head (left), called a *trans-ducer*, shown with its principle elements, as compared in size with an ordinary pair of pliers. The oscillating element (center) is neither a quartz nor ceramic plate, bowl or rod. It is, rather, made up of a "pile" or "pack" of nickel lamination rings which are magnetized when high-frequency alternating current passes through the coil which is toroidally wound around them as shown. The result of this rapid magnetic oscillation is a slight physical change in the diameter of the rings each time they are magnetized, so that ultrasonic waves are produced which radiate out sideways from the pack. At the right, this element is shown in its reflector, which directs the waves in a beam-like pattern approximately 15 degrees each side of the center. These parts are assembled in the heavy bronze housing (left) having a thick bronze protecting face plate, which is transparent to the radiating ultrasonic energy. The whole unit is bolted to leveling rings, flush on the underside of a ship's hull, so that a beam of ultrasonic pulses can be sent to the ocean bottom from which they are echoed back to be received by another similar unit. Equipment such as this is used on the "Queen Elizabeth" and many other passenger, freight, and naval vessels. (*Courtesy of Bludworth Marine Division of National, Simplex, Bludworth, Inc., New York, N.Y.*)

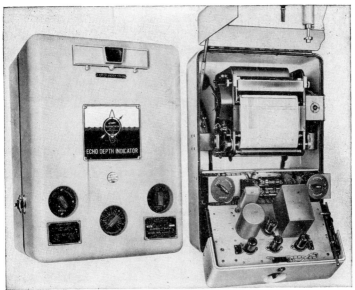

Fig. 9-5. Indicating instruments used in ultrasonic depth finding. At the left is a depth indicator. The depth of water beneath a vessel, in either feet or fathoms, is shown accurately through the viewing port at the top. The depth thus shown directly is in large, easily read numbers. At the right is a depth recorder, shown opened to reveal some of the mechanism and electronic equipment used. This instrument accurately and permanently records depths on dry paper tape in continuous true profile as a ship proceeds along its course. Two hundred separate soundings per minute can be obtained, and the resulting chart indicates various objects and conditions such as weed growth, rock pinnacles, sandy bottoms, and even compact schools of fish, as well as the depths (in feet or fathoms) at which they are located. (*Courtesy of Bludworth Marine Division of National, Simplex, Bludworth, Inc., New York, N.Y.*)

time interval required is in direct proportion to the distance they travel. Electron tubes which control the duration of the impulse and also the frequency with which they are released are called *strobotrons*. These act as "trigger" tubes for the ultrasonic wave-beam generator. They will be described in more detail in Chapter 15.

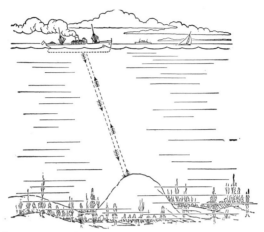

FIG. 9-6. Ultrasonic impulses sent to the ocean floor travel down and echo back at a constant speed so that the depth may be calculated accurately.

Ultrasonic Communication

In addition to detecting and locating underwater objects, ultrasonics are used for communication between submerged submarines up to a distance of approximately 20 miles. Distance and location can be determined in a manner similar to that described above to an accuracy of about 1 degree.

Code signaling between craft may be used, or the ultrasonic waves as produced by the vibrating quartz or ceramic plate can be modulated by the audio frequencies of speech. In this manner, underwater conversation can be maintained with ultrasonic waves as the carriers.

There are many more phenomena identified with ultrasonics, some of which have practical application, but we cannot dwell too long upon them here.

There is a system of television called *scophony* which is based upon the fact that ultrasonic vibrations will diffract light in a liquid. This system has certain features and advantages which hold some promise for specific purposes, and the development

is continuing. The possibility of its application to stereo television is an intriguing one.

Ultrasonic Effects in Liquids and Solids

Ultrasonics can be applied to advantage in chemistry and metallurgy. Vibrations of high intensity will emulsify oil and water
and/or similar combinations for practical purposes. They will
also coagulate smoke, vapors, and dust under proper conditions—
the most effective ultrasonic frequency for a specific condition
being governed primarily by the size of particles suspended.
There are other interesting phenomena in the application of
ultrasonic waves to various elements and compounds, but they
are mostly for laboratory investigation.

In metallurgy, mechanical stress is known to affect the crystalline structure of metal. Ultrasonic vibrations provide such mechanical stress, with a resulting molecular change. In certain
steel-hardening processes, for example, these vibrations will enhance the penetration of nitrogen, with a consequent saving
of time.

Ultrasonic Therapy

Biological applications of ultrasonic waves are quite well advanced. While there appears to be little or no effect upon bacteria, some thermal effect is always present when ultrasonic
vibrations penetrate solids and liquids. In some instances and
under some conditions this thermal effect is extremely pronounced, while in others it is rather obscure. Since this effect
occurs in living tissue, it provides a means of *ultrasonic therapy*
which is not wholly unlike the forms of diathermy discussed in
Chapter 7.

The principles involved in ultrasonic therapy are about the
same as in other apparatus. A quartz piezoelectric crystal generates the waves at a frequency of around 1,000 kilocycles and
is located in a "head" or applicator. The surface emitting the

ultrasonic "ray" is a little less than a square inch in area, and the focused "ray" advances perpendicular from the surface.

The applicator is held directly against the skin, and since frequencies in the order of 1,000 kilocycles attenuate very rapidly

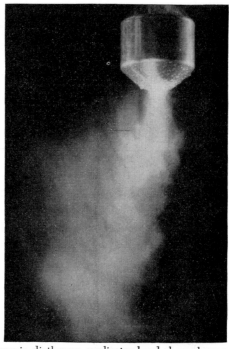

Fig. 9-7. Ultrasonic diathermy applicator head shows how a drop of water which has been suspended from it is instantly vaporized when ultrasonic energy is applied. (*Courtesy of Ultrasonic Medical Equipment Co., New York, N.Y.*)

in air, treatment is accomplished either with a layer or cushion of oil or water between the applicator surface and the skin or with the part to be treated totally submerged in water.

The therapeutic effect results partly from the heat generated and partly from a so-called "micromassage" which takes place within the tissue among the cells. The heat is generated primarily at the boundary surfaces of flesh and bones or wherever tissue differences occur, because it is here that the effects of friction are most pronounced.

Ultrasonic therapy should be applied only by those physicians who thoroughly understand it. As with any treatment of this nature there are certain conditions which would preclude its use, but where indicated, there are definite benefits reported.

Fundamentally, all mechanical and physiological effects of ultrasonics are the result of actual physical vibrations of particles comprising the liquid or solid. With this in mind, it should be remembered that, if violent agitation of the particles takes place, severe damage can be done. Small creatures living in water such as fish and frogs can be killed in an ultrasonic beam, and aquatic plant life either blighted or ruined when exposed to such vibrations.

The science of ultrasonics is destined for much more exploration in the future, particularly in biological fields. We may find in it a partial answer, at least, to many of our most puzzling problems of controlled and uncontrolled cell growth.

10

Radio Waves

Now that we have discussed ultrasonic waves and their characteristics in passing through media such as air, liquids, and solids, let us turn our attention back again to electromagnetic waves, which, as previously pointed out, require no medium for their propagation and travel at a much higher rate of speed (186,000 miles per second).

The electromagnetic waves used in radio extend from the slow-oscillation region to an indefinite limit which approaches infrared radiation. The frequencies range from about 10 kilocycles to the region well over 30,000 megacycles (thus far), and the wavelengths from about 40,000 meters to a small fraction of a centimeter. Different bands in this radio-wave portion of the electromagnetic spectrum are used for different types of radio communication depending upon how their characteristics can best be utilized.

When commercial radio communication first became practical, it was believed that the longer wavelengths and lower frequencies could be transmitted farther and more reliably than the shorter ones, and transoceanic wireless utilized a band embracing wavelengths from 3,000 to 30,0000 meters and frequencies from about 10 to 100 kilocycles. Amateur radio operators, at that time considered of secondary importance by some, were assigned a band of shorter wavelengths and higher frequencies so as not to interfere with commercial communication. The amateurs, however, proved their worth by determined and persistent work,

154

and it was soon found that their communications of short-wave-length high-frequency energy were extending farther around the globe than the commercial stations using the longer wave-lengths.

Investigations as to the reason for this resulted in the discovery that high above the earth there exists a multiple layer of ionized (electrically charged) gas which acts as a refractor for radio waves, bending them back to the earth. If the frequencies are too high, however (above about 45 megacycles), and the wave-lengths too short (less than about 8 or 9 meters), the radiations are not readily bent back but pass on out into space. A similar

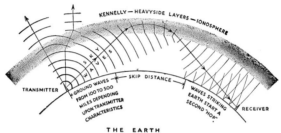

Fig. 10-1. The behavior of radio waves in passing over the earth's surface depends upon their refraction from the layers of ionized gas high above the surface.

layer was referred to in Chapter 8, where it was explained that short-wavelength ultraviolet from the sun produced a protective envelope of ozone around the earth so that damage to animal and vegetable life would not result from exposure to it.

The layers of electrically charged gas may be found sometimes as low as 30 miles above the earth during the daytime or as high as 200 miles or more at night. They are called the *Kennelly-Heaviside layers* after those two scientists showed independently of each other that the existence of such layers was highly prob-able. They are also known as the *ionosphere*. There have been many interesting phenomena observed in conjunction with the ionosphere, but we cannot dwell too long upon them here. The effectiveness of the ionosphere as a refractor of electromagnetic waves varies quite widely from time to time. Since the ionosphere is produced by radiations from the sun, changes in the sun's surface (sunspots) will affect its ability to send radio waves back to the earth. While long-distance, long-wavelength transmission is usually not so good during the day as at night, the reverse is often true with short-wavelength transmission. Since the layers are not always consistent as far as thickness or density is concerned, their effectiveness as a refractor of radio waves continually fluctuates, which accounts to some extent for the fading of short-wave transoceanic signals. It is interesting to note also that short-wave transmission is often less effective at relatively short distances than at greater distances of several hundred miles. This circular band of poor or no reception around a short-wave transmitter has been referred to as *skip distance* and results from the fact that radiations traveling nearly straight upward from the transmitting antenna are not refracted back to the earth so readily as those striking the layers at an angle farther away. This phenomenon is similar to the behavior of light waves when they are passing through a refracting medium. Since lower frequency long-wavelength radiations are refracted to an extent that they can almost be considered as reflected, skip distances are much less pronounced with such transmission.

Commercial broadcasting of entertainment programs is carried on within a band of wavelengths from about 600 to 150 meters and from 500 to 2,000 kilocycles. In order to avoid confusion and interference with others, each broadcasting station is assigned a specific wavelength and frequency at which it may operate. By tuning our radio to the same frequency and wavelength at which a station is broadcasting, we can transform the electromagnetic waves it is sending out into sound without interference from other stations broadcasting at different frequencies at the same time.

Many radios have facilities for receiving short-wave signals which have been allocated to specific frequency bands throughout the radio-communication region of the spectrum. Such allocations are necessary to avoid interference with commercial broadcasting and with one another. Within these short-wave bands thousands of amateur radio operators talk with each other across oceans, police officers cruising about a bustling city in their cars talk with and receive orders from the station, air-line pilots learn about weather conditions at a distant airport where they are scheduled to land, and ship captains obtain and give out information essential to the safe and expeditious conduct of their cargoes and passengers. All this can reach our ears at home in a fraction of a second without interference because each uses a different frequency to which we can tune our radio, excluding the others.

Before passing along to the uses of still shorter wavelengths and higher frequencies of electromagnetic radiations, which are used for television, radar, and other purposes, it may be well to consider for a moment the basic operating principles of radio transmission and reception.

Production of Radio Waves

A circuit containing only a battery and resistance, as shown in Fig. 10-2, cannot be tuned because, while there will be a magnetic field around the wire, it does not oscillate with any frequency or radiate away in waves but rather might be considered as a stationary field of force around the wire coil. In such a circuit the electrons flow continuously in one direction until the circuit is broken or the battery exhausted. But if a condenser is substituted for the resistance, the electrons will flow out of condenser plate 2 through the battery and into plate 1 in a number depending upon the pressure or voltage provided by the battery and the capacity of the condenser. If the battery is suddenly replaced by a short length of wire, the electrons which had left plate 2 for plate 1 will rush back to plate 2, so that there will again be a balanced equal number in each plate as before. Now if the battery is replaced by an inductance coil instead of by the length of wire, as indicated in C, the electrons, although they will get started more slowly, will keep moving back to plate

2 until it has more than the normal balanced amount and becomes negative (electrons being negative charges) instead of positive, as originally, and plate 1, having too few electrons, becomes positive. This inertia or tendency of current to stay in an inductance coil is explained in the discussion of inductance in Chapter 4.

With the two condenser plates again electronically unbalanced, the electrons rush back again to plate 1, with a few too many getting over this time also. Thus a few pulses of current will alternate back and forth through the circuit until they fade

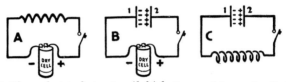

Fig. 10-2. Three electrical circuits: (left) battery-resistance circuit; (center) battery-condenser circuit; (right) condenser-coil circuit.

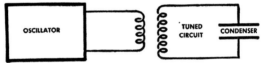

Fig. 10-3. An oscillating circuit, providing undamped high-frequency oscillations, is basic in the production of radio waves.

into a condition of balance again. When this fading occurs, the pulses are said to be *damped* out. Such damping takes place very rapidly as a result of resistance losses in the circuit unless new energy is supplied.

Energy may be supplied to such a circuit and thus provide *undamped* high-frequency oscillations by coupling the circuit to an oscillator, as shown in Fig. 10-3, so that a pulse through the oscillator circuit will induce a pulse through the other one (see Chapter 4). An oscillator may be a high-frequency a-c generator, or it may be a vacuum tube having its elements so designed that controlled pulses of energy will be released. Such tubes will be described more in detail in Chapter 13.

A certain amount of time is consumed in getting a pulse under way through either a condenser or an inductance—the larger the capacitance or inductance, the longer the time required. Any combination of a condenser and inductance is responsive to some one frequency only and is, therefore, *resonant* to that frequency (see Chapter 4).

Thus, we have in the circuit a continuous alternating current which oscillates at high frequency and radiates or broadcasts electromagnetic energy (via an antenna) in wavelengths and frequencies as determined by the characteristics of its condenser and inductance.

The transmission of code messages by radio quite naturally preceded the broadcasting of the sounds of voice and music. In order to transmit code signals it is necessary simply to break up the electromagnetic wave train produced by the oscillating current into dots and dashes of the Morse code by means of a contactor or key.

The transmission of sounds as in radio broadcasting, however, employs a different principle. In this case, the train of electromagnetic radiations is not broken as with code signals. Rather, it is continuous but modulated by the much lower frequency oscillations produced by the microphone. In other words, although the higher frequency waves are continuous, they are made to increase or diminish in amplitude (see Chapter 5, Simple Waves) in accordance with the current from the microphone, which, in turn, is determined by the sound waves of voice or music that enter it.

Ordinary telephone transmitters contain a thin disk or diaphragm behind which is packed a quantity of small carbon granules. Sound striking the diaphragm causes it to vibrate in accordance with fluctuations of the sound waves. Such vibration results in varying degrees of compression of the carbon particles, so that, when electric current is passed through them, the resistance encountered changes in accordance with the compression of the particles. Thus a telephone transmitter is, in effect, a device to make the electric current passing through it fluctuate almost exactly in accord with the fluctuations of the sound waves which strike it.

The microphones used for radio broadcasting require a more accurate transposition of sound waves into electric-current variations, and different methods have been developed—some for extreme fidelity, some for sensitivity, and others for ruggedness. One type, called the *induction microphone,* utilizes induction coils and a metallic ribbon, another makes use of carefully cut and adjusted crystals, and a third method utilizes the principle of a condenser and is called a *condenser microphone.* In the last device two parallel diaphragms are used, separated by an air gap in the order of a thousandth of an inch. One of them

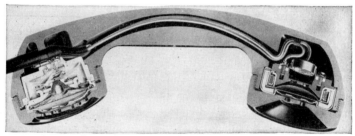

Fig. 10-4. A modern telephone handset showing the internal construction of the carbon transmitter (left) and the receiver (right). (*Courtesy of Bell Telephone Laboratories.*)

vibrates in accordance with the sound waves striking it, just as the telephone transmitter does, but in this case, instead of carbon granules being compressed, the distance between the diaphragms fluctuates. With the two diaphragms acting as the two plates of a condenser, it can be seen that the capacitance will vary in accord with the vibrations of the sound waves (see Chapter 4, Capacitance), so that a changing current is caused in the circuit connected to the two plates.

It is this changing current from a microphone which *modulates* the continuous train of higher frequency electromagnetic waves produced by the oscillating current of the radio-transmitting equipment. The high-frequency (radio-frequency current) oscillations are called the *carrier waves,* and when they are modulated or made to vary in amplitude in unison with the variations of audio-frequency current from the microphone, they are called *amplitude-modulated waves.*

The Reception of Radio Waves

The modulated or broken, whichever the case may be, electromagnetic waves radiate out into space from the antenna and travel at the same speed as light, infrared, ultraviolet, X rays, and all the others of the electromagnetic spectrum—186,000 miles per second.

At the receiving point the incoming train of waves sets up an oscillatory current in the receiving antenna. Since the wavelength of the waves has been established at the transmitting station by adjusting or tuning its inductance and capacitance to a certain frequency of vibration, the reverse must be done at the receiver; that is, the inductance or capacitance of the receiving circuit must be made to match or resonate with the frequency of the transmitter (see Chapter 4, Resonance). This matching is called *tuning* a radio. When we turn the dial, we change the capacitance of a variable condenser or change the inductance of coils in our radio set so that it will respond to or pass the same frequency of oscillations radiating from the station to which we wish to listen.

The method of changing the modulated electromagnetic waves back into sound waves via a loud-speaker or headphones involves electron tubes (radio tubes) or a crystal detector and will be covered in detail in Chapter 13. The pickup circuit not only must be tuned to the frequency of the transmitter but must also provide means of separating the modulating wave from the carrier before the headphones or speaker will vibrate to produce sound waves like those entering the microphone in the broadcasting studio.

The basic operating principle of a telephone receiver, radio headphones, or a radio loud-speaker is essentially the same for each. The function, of course, is to change the fluctuating current back into sound waves. This is done in a manner similar to the reverse of a transmitter; that is, a diaphragm is made to vibrate in accordance with the current variations coming to it from the receiver. A magnet is used around which coils are wound, and the fluctuating current passed through them. The strength of magnet changes with each fluctuation of the current, and the diaphragm, which is placed in front of the poles of the magnet, is pulled back and forth, thus vibrating rapidly in ac-

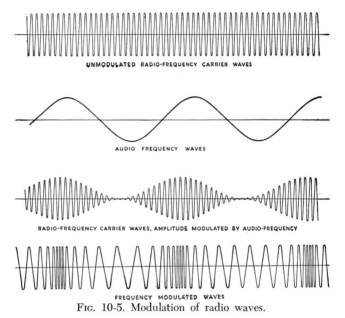

UNMODULATED RADIO-FREQUENCY CARRIER WAVES

AUDIO FREQUENCY WAVES

RADIO-FREQUENCY CARRIER WAVES, AMPLITUDE MODULATED BY AUDIO-FREQUENCY

FREQUENCY MODULATED WAVES

FIG. 10-5. Modulation of radio waves.

cord with the current variations and producing the sound waves which we hear.

Radio, therefore, is a means of changing sound waves into modulated electromagnetic waves, broadcasting them, and then changing them back into sound waves again.

Short-wave Radio

It has already been indicated that, as the wavelengths of electromagnetic waves used in radio become shorter and as the frequencies become higher, their characteristics and behavior change somewhat. Short-wave radio is successful in long-distance transmission as long as refraction from the layers of ionized gas high above the earth takes place. But when the wavelengths become much shorter than 10 meters, we find that they have different characteristics.

One reason why later developments in radio, such as frequency modulation and television, are placed in the short-wave, higher frequency regions is to keep them out of the crowded longer wavelength bands where commercial broadcasting is carried on.

Frequency Modulation

Frequency modulation is, basically, a method of transmitting and receiving radio waves which are modulated in frequency (or wavelength) rather than in amplitude, as previously explained. Amplitude modulation can be compared to sound waves producing one tone of a certain pitch which is modulated or varied in its degree of loudness. Such a tone would waver in intensity but not in pitch, like a *tremolo* in organ music. A frequency-modulated tone, however, would not vary in amplitude or loudness but would wave up and down regularly in pitch like a *trill* in music.

Frequency-modulated radio broadcasts have been placed in a rather narrow band at about 3 meters wavelength and 88 to 108 megacycles in frequency. Receiving sets designed for the reception of these waves have been quite widely used in homes, and the freedom from static interference and the high fidelity of tone resulting with frequency-modulation transmission and reception provide the finest possible radio entertainment.

Since static disturbances are electromagnetic impulses in a hodgepodge of wavelengths and frequencies, it is difficult to sort them out of any broadcast band but much less is apparent with frequency-modulated radio. Static occurs whenever a bolt of lightning or some other similar disturbance sets up a short train of powerful waves radiating in all directions.

Television Transmission

The principal difference between the transmission of pictures by radio and the transmission of sound by radio lies in the method of picking up the energy which is to be converted into electromagnetic waves. The waves themselves are the same in each case except that, in television, shorter wavelengths and higher frequencies are used in order to avoid conflict and interference from static as well as from other signals.

The FCC has assigned specific bands or channels, 6 megacycles in width, in the short-wave section of the radio region of the electromagnetic spectrum for the broadcasting of television programs. The *video* (picture) signal is amplitude-modulated, and the audio (sound) signal frequency-modulated. The two are not broadcast at precisely the same wavelength, even though our receivers present them as a complete simultaneous program.

The following tabulation gives the present television channel frequencies and wavelengths:

Channel number	Channel frequency width, megacycles	Video carrier frequency, megacycles	Audio carrier frequency, megacycles	Average wavelength, meters
2	54–60	55.25	59.75	5.3
3	60–66	61.25	65.75	4.8
4	66–72	67.25	71.75	4.3
5	76–82	77.25	81.75	3.8
6	82–88	83.25	87.75	3.5
7	174–180	175.25	179.75	1.7
8	180–186	181.25	185.75	1.64
9	186–192	187.25	191.75	1.59
10	192–198	193.25	197.75	1.54
11	198–204	199.25	203.75	1.49
12	204–210	205.25	209.75	1.45
13	210–216	211.25	215.75	1.41

An additional band of much higher frequency has also been established by the FCC to provide for ultrahigh-frequency television transmission. These frequencies range from 470 to above 800 megacycles. The wavelengths, therefore, will be something less than 1 meter in length.

It has been explained how, in converting sound waves into amplitude- or frequency-modulated electromagnetic waves, a microphone causes fluctuations of the current in its circuit in accordance with the sound waves producing vibrations of its

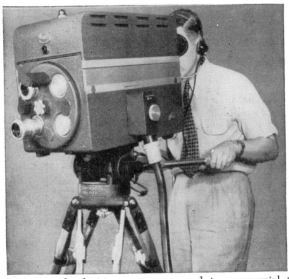

FIG. 10-6. A typical television camera as used in commercial television broadcasting. (*Courtesy of Allen B. Dumont Laboratories, Inc.*)

diaphragm. In television, the fluctuations are caused by the variations in light intensity over the surface of a scene to be televised within the range of "vision" of the television camera's lens.

There are two types of electron tubes in the cameras which are commonly used to convert the gradations of light into fluctuations of electric current. One of these is called an *iconoscope,* and it is used primarily in camera pickup of motion pictures and similar programs. The other is called the *image orthicon* tube.

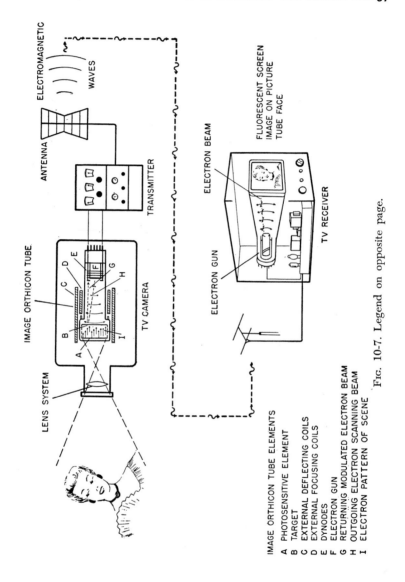

IMAGE ORTHICON TUBE ELEMENTS

A   PHOTOSENSITIVE ELEMENT
B   TARGET
C   EXTERNAL DEFLECTING COILS
D   EXTERNAL FOCUSING COILS
E   DYNODES
F   ELECTRON GUN
G   RETURNING MODULATED ELECTRON BEAM
H   OUTGOING ELECTRON SCANNING BEAM
I   ELECTRON PATTERN OF SCENE

Fig. 10-7. Legend on opposite page.

It is used in the camera pickup of studio productions or "live" programs, as well as for outdoor work.

The operation and construction of these tubes will be covered more fully in Chapter 15, but at this point we can think of them as devices which break the scene into horizontal lines of light and dark, one after the other from top to bottom until eventually the whole scene is scanned. The process is similar to reading this page. Instead of grasping the page as a whole, the eye travels along each line, carrying each word to the brain until eventually the whole page is read and its meaning impressed upon the brain. The individual words or lines mean but little until enough of them have been read to start the formation of a mental picture. So in television, a thin beam of electrons sweeps

---

FIG. 10-7. Schematic diagram of television transmission and reception with specific details of operation of image orthicon tube. Light from the scene being televised is focused by the camera lens to a photosensitive surface called a photocathode (A). Electrons (I) are emitted on the back side of this element, in a pattern consistent with the scene falling on the front. These electrons are influenced to flow in parallel paths toward a target by an electromagnetic field and are accelerated on their short journey by positive charges.

Upon impact with the target (B), a secondary emission of electrons takes place on its surface, so that a pattern of positive charges is produced thereon which coincides with the scene pattern of light. As shown in the diagram, the back surface of the target is scanned by a very slow electron beam (H) from a gun in the neck of the tube. Upon reaching the target surface, electrons in the beam are attracted to the target in amounts depending upon the positive charge present at that point.

The beam is then directed back toward the base of the tube, *minus* those electrons which have been lost (G). Thus, it can be seen that as the beam sweeps over the surface from side to side and from top to bottom, it returns in strength according to the pattern of positive charges which in turn coincides with the scene upon which the camera is focused. This returning beam, modulated in accordance with the scene, is brought to a series of elements called *dynodes* (E) which, in effect, multiply the strength of the returning modulated beam signal so that it can be carried out into the video transmitter and thence to the antenna. At the receiving end, the process is reversed except that an electron beam, modulated in accord with the signal from the transmitter, traces the picture on the fluorescent-screen face of the picture tube.

rapidly back and forth 525 times across an image on the screen of the camera tube, just as the reader's eyes sweep each successive line of printed page. In order to avoid a disturbing flicker at the receiving end, the whole scene must be swept in this manner 30 times in each second. Current from these tubes, which pulsates in accordance with the gradations of the scene lines, is converted into electromagnetic waves and broadcast in the same manner as the sound which accompanies and is synchronized with the scene.

The principles of color-television transmission and reception will be covered later in this chapter. Developments now in progress may eventually lead to television pictures in colored three-dimensional depth, projected upon a screen of good size in the average home. It probably will be called *stereo* television.

Television Reception

Television reception is basically the reverse process of transmission, that is, the transformation of electromagnetic waves of the broadcast wavelength back into those of light wavelength which can be seen. The receiver is similar in many respects to our ordinary radio except that the video oscillations, instead of being sent to headphones or to a speaker for transformation into sound waves, are sent to a cathode-ray tube for transformation into light. The details of cathode-ray tubes will be presented in Chapter 15, but we can discuss their function in a general way here.

A cathode-ray tube consists primarily of an electron gun which emits a thin needle-like stream of electrons, a system of either electrostatic plates or electromagnetic coils which deflect this stream of electrons up and down or sideways, depending upon how the control is operated, and a screen of fluorescent powder coated over the flat end of the tube. When and wherever the electron stream strikes the fluorescent screen, a tiny bright spot is created upon it. The brightness of this spot depends upon the strength of the stream, that is, on the number of electrons in it.

If the stream is swept almost instantly across the screen, the

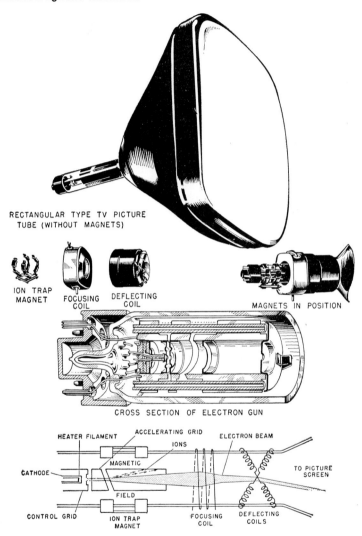

RECTANGULAR TYPE TV PICTURE
TUBE (WITHOUT MAGNETS)

ION TRAP
MAGNET
FOCUSING
COIL
DEFLECTING
COIL
MAGNETS IN POSITION

CROSS SECTION OF ELECTRON GUN

HEATER FILAMENT   ACCELERATING GRID   ELECTRON BEAM
                                     IONS
CATHODE   TO PICTURE
                                                                           SCREEN
              MAGNETIC
                  FIELD
CONTROL GRID   ION TRAP   FOCUSING   DEFLECTING
                 MAGNET   COIL   COILS

DIAGRAM OF ELECTROMAGNETIC FOCUSING & DEFLECTING SYSTEMS

FIG. 10-8. The electron gun of a typical cathode-ray tube used in television reception, showing the method of controlling the electron beam electro-magnetically.

eye sees its path, not as a series of light dots, but as a bright line. If during its progress across the screen the number of electrons in the stream decreases, the line will be brighter at the starting end than at its finish. If its strength fluctuates during the sweep, the line will have gradations of light and dark in accordance with the electron stream-strength fluctuations—the more electrons, the brighter the path they sweep.

The stream from the electron gun in a cathode-ray tube does just this, and it also sweeps 525 lines, one just below the other, across the fluorescent screen from top to bottom, completely covering the screen with light and dark areas. Furthermore, it makes the complete coverage thirty times each second, tracing somewhere in the order of a quarter of a million inches of light per second on a 20-inch television screen. It is the light and dark portions of these lines which make up the television picture on the end of a cathode-ray tube.

In the previous section on television transmission, it was explained quite briefly how the camera tubes do the same thing to the subject or scene being televised and how the current from them fluctuates in accordance with the light and dark areas of the scene as its own electron stream sweeps or scans the scene line by line. It was also pointed out that this fluctuating current is converted into amplitude-modulated electromagnetic waves and broadcast in the same manner as ordinary radio waves.

Television therefore is, in a sense, a means of converting the electromagnetic radiations of light into much longer wavelengths which can be broadcast and then of changing them back into light again so that they can be seen. Of course, the sound-transmission waves which are frequency-modulated are synchronized with the video transmission to complete the intelligence of the broadcast.

Color Television

It was explained in Chapter 6, in the discussion on color, that white light is composed of red, green, and blue light in approximately equal parts. When one of these is missing, the result is a combination of the remaining two. For example, if green is absent, the light is a purple color, or if red is missing, the result is a greenish blue. Also, if two of the colors are not present, the light is of the remaining pure hue.

Thus all colors (of light) regardless of their richness, shade, or tint can be broken down into certain amounts of each of the three primary colors. The fundamental principle of color television, therefore, is to separate out the amounts of the three primaries in a scene, broadcast each as a separate and distinct signal, and blend them together again at the television receiver. In this way, with the amounts of each determining the strength of their respective color signal, a reasonably true color picture can be obtained with all the hues and tints of the original scene.

There are several ways of accomplishing this. The two most important ones are called the *dot sequential system* and the *frame sequential system*. Their basic difference lies in the method of extracting each of the three primaries from the scene for separate transmission, as well as in the method of visually blending them back together again on the receiver screen.

In the dot sequential system, the color camera contains three pickup tubes—one for each of the three primary colors, red, green, and blue. Accurately arranged in front of these tubes is a system of mirrors one of which is called a *dichroic* mirror and has the property of sorting and reflecting each of the three primaries in a different direction. This provides a means of extracting one color from a blend and directing it to one specific tube, so that we have in the camera a tube responding to red only, one to green only, and one to blue only.

The operation of each color tube is similar to that of a black-and-white tube, except that it breaks up into lines or scans only that portion of the scene which contains the color upon which it is acting. For example, if an ocean scene is being televised and the water is blue-green in color, part of the ocean's light is directed to the blue tube and part to the green tube. If a red sail is in the scene also, it goes to the red tube only, and if it is the only red

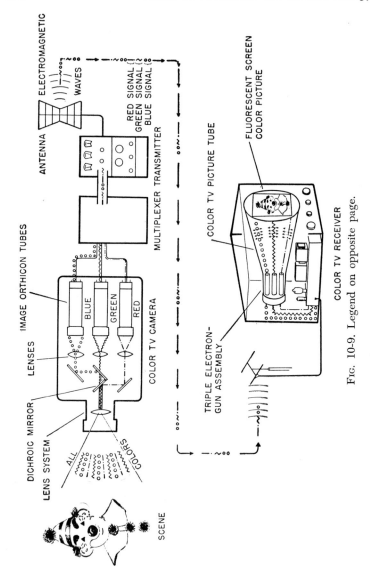

FIG. 10-9. Legend on opposite page.

in the scene, that is all the red tube receives. Thus, each tube is the source of a signal identified with only one of the three primary colors. The strength of the signal is governed by the strength or amount of the color in the scene blend. For example, if the ocean color is more green than blue, the green tube receives more green light, as reflected from the scene, so that the signal coming from it will be stronger than the one from the blue tube.

The current from each tube fluctuates in accordance with the variations of the specific hue it receives from the scene (deep red, pink, etc.). It is carried to electronic devices called *samplers* and *adders* and then to a standard television transmitter. This broadcasts the three signals simultaneously on the regular black-and-white channel assigned to the station or on any other higher frequency channel permitted by the FCC.

The reception and reproduction of a color scene are, in a sense, the reverse process of camera pickup and transmission. The simultaneous color signals are received in the usual way and pass through a sampler on their way to the color-picture tube.

The color-picture tube utilizes three electron guns instead of one as with a black-and-white tube—one gun for each of the three primary color signals. Its picture face or screen is made up of some 600,000 dots of fluorescent phosphors. A third of these dots produce red, a third blue, and a third green, and they

FIG. 10-9. Simplified schematic diagram of one system of color-television transmission and reception. A fundamental part of this system is the sorting out of the three primary colors of light as it radiates from a scene. This separation is accomplished with a dichroic mirror, which has the ability to transmit certain colors only and reflect others only. If, for example, the clown's nose, hair, and eyebrows are the only red, his buttons the only blue, and the stripes on his cap the only green in the scene (all else being white), only his nose, hair, and eyebrows would be reflected by the first dichroic mirror—the other colors passing through. On the other hand, the blue buttons would be reflected as shown, and the green stripes on his hat would pass through all mirrors. In this manner, a scene can be split into its color components and each component sent out as a signal to be re-blended again at the receiving screen.

are so evenly intermingled that they cannot be easily distinguished one from the other except under a magnifying glass.

The electron gun receiving the red signal sweeps its beam so as to excite only the red phosphor dots, the green gun only the green dots, and the blue gun only the blue dots. In this way the three simultaneous color signals can be made to reproduce the colored scene with considerable accuracy under favorable conditions and with properly operating equipment. In the marine scene with the red sail, if the green and blue electron guns were to be blanked out, we should see only the red sail on our color screen. The rest of the picture would be black. On the other hand, if the red gun only were not operating, the place where the sail should be would likewise appear as a black area on the screen.

The frame sequential system uses only one camera pickup tube. In front of the lens which focuses light to this tube, a disk made up of segments of the three primary colors rotates at a constant fixed speed. The segments are filters designed to transmit only red, green, and blue light.

Thus, with the camera shooting the same marine scene described above, only the red of the sail reaches the pickup tube as the red segment passes in front of the lens. Next, the green segment passes the lens, and only the green light from the water passes to the tube. This is followed by the blue, so that we have the scene split into its three primaries in the correct amount. Each color reaches the pickup tube in sequence, and as the tube scans each color sequence, its fluctuating current goes to the transmitter, where the three signals are broadcast in the same sequence.

At the receiver, the three signals arrive in the same order and pass through the set to a cathode-ray or picture tube similar to those used in standard black-and-white television. In front of this tube face, however, a disk of three primary-color segments revolves at the same precise rate as the one in front of the camera lens at the televised scene. The receiver disk rotation is synchronized with the one at the camera by a special signal pulse transmitted at intervals for that specific purpose. This means that at the instant the red segment is passing the lens at the camera, the red segment of the receiver disk is also passing before the screen of the picture tube and the red portion of the scene only is coming through at that instant.

The disks revolve quite rapidly, and as we watch the screen of the receiver with the disk turning in front of it, we do not recognize the sequence of colors but, rather, see the whole scene in color as it appears to the camera.

11

Ultrahigh Frequencies and Microwaves

It was mentioned in Chapter 10, Short-wave Radio, that, as the wavelengths of electromagnetic radiations become shorter and the frequencies higher, their characteristics and behavior change somewhat. As we proceed beyond the short-wave region into wavelengths still shorter (less than a meter), we find the waves abandoning many characteristics of the longer ones. As a matter of fact, a moment's reflection and a glance at the frontispiece will reveal that we are approaching the infrared or radiant-heat region and that such waves might be expected to behave something like radiant heat and even visible light. This is just about what they do in the upper limits of the microwave region thus far explored; that is, radio waves of these extreme high frequencies and short wavelengths can be focused more readily into a beam much like a searchlight.

In the consideration of microwaves, we must also shift the ideas of electric-current flow which were described in Part I. At low frequencies electric current flows *through* a conductor, but at the high-frequency alternation of microwaves the current flow becomes more dense in the surface of the conductor, actually penetrating it only very little. Thus, the resistance of a solid conductor to electron flow becomes greater as frequencies become higher.

Peculiar as it may seem, pipes are used instead of solid conductors to conduct the energy of these extremely high-frequency currents. They are not considered as electron current carriers as is a solid conductor but rather as a means of propagating the wave energy attending such electron flow from one point to another. Such pipes are called *wave guides* and may be round, square, or rectangular in cross-sectional shape. Wave guides carry microwave currents just as a speaking tube carries sound waves, keeping them within boundaries and allowing them to come out at the listening end, diminished slightly by losses which radiate away from the tube along its length. A few readers may have observed the way in which light flux passes through a fused quartz or Lucite tube—traveling around bends and out the end with but little loss through the sides. This analogy of wave-guide behavior is perhaps more physically accurate than the speaking-tube description.

The microwave region involves wavelengths of only a few centimenters, and physical dimensions of the wave guides become the essential factor in their function. The manner in which the radiations travel within their boundary limits is determined largely by their cross-sectional size and shape. The distance across either a round or square wave guide should be slightly more than one-half the wavelength of the radiating energy to be guided through it. For example, when conducting 7,500-megacycle current from one location to another within apparatus, the wave guide should be a little over 2 centimeters (about ¾ inch) across, since the wavelength of electromagnetic radiation at this frequency is 0.04 meter or 4 centimeters (see Chapter 4, Resonance). Or, at frequencies in the order of 3,000 megacycles and wavelengths of 10 centimeters, the wave guide width or diameter would necessarily be a little over one-half this length or about 2½ to 3 inches.

While wave guides could be used for longer wavelengths of radio, the size required to make them effective precludes their use. A wave guide to carry the television Channel 2 energy, for instance, would look like a big air-conditioning duct over 9 feet square.

Wave guides should not be considered as conductors in the

sense that they are connected to a source of energy such as an a-c generator. They are just what their name indicates. They guide electromagnetic radiation of microwave proportions from one point to another, the waves radiating perhaps from a small

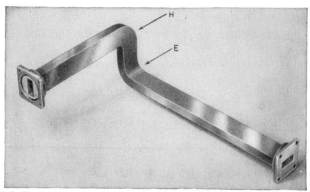

Fig. 11-1. Typical section of a rectangular wave guide with a choke flange at the left end and a cover flange at the right. This particular type is approximately ½ by 1 inch in cross section, and may be of any length as required. It is used with X-band radar equipment. In a rectangular guide, bends made one way are called *E-plane* bends; the others are *H-plane* bends, as indicated. Wave guides are usually made of copper, but aluminum is sometimes used, and occasionally silver for specific purposes. (*Courtesy of L. H. Terpening Company, New York, N.Y.*)

rod-like antenna placed at one opening of the guide, so that they can propagate along its length to the other end, where further control and use may await them.

Radar

Since microwaves exhibit certain properties usually identified with optics and acoustics such as reflection from surfaces (light reflection or sound echo), it is reasonable to expect that these characteristics can be used to advantage in communications work.

The first large-scale practical application of microwaves unfolded for the Second World War and is called *radar,* which means radio detection and ranging. After the war it was applied to commercial aircraft and boats as well as to other branches of commerce and industry.

Specifically, electromagnetic radiation in the microwave region can be sent out and controlled in direction like a searchlight beam, and when striking an object, it is reflected back in a way similar to that in which light would be reflected back. The important difference, however, is that the microwaves making up the ranging beams penetrate fog and haze whereas light is dispersed and absorbed by such atmospheric conditions.

The range of power used for radar work is tremendous. The electron tubes which produce these very high-frequency waves are capable of generating extremely powerful radiation. This energy is sent out in a beam, and upon striking an object a minute quantity is reflected back. The equipment which detects the reflected energy is extremely sensitive to the minute quantities which return to it. Some concept of the range of radiant-energy power involved in radar may be obtained from the following analogy:

If it were possible to scoop up all the sand on a typical seashore, throw it at a plane somewhere out of sight behind the clouds a hundred miles away, and have one grain bounce back to tell exactly where the plane was located, we should have a picture of the relative energies involved.

Since the speed of electromagnetic radiation of all wavelengths and frequencies is the same (186,000 miles per second), the location of the object can be accurately computed from the time involved for a pulse or packet of microwaves to travel to the object and return. Of course, such a time interval is extremely short and is measured in millionths of a second (microseconds).

In the discussion of sound waves in Chapter 5, it was pointed out that they travel at an approximate rate of 1,088 feet every second. If a cliff producing an echo is about 1,000 feet away and a rifle is fired, the crack of the rifle travels to the cliff in a little less than a second and returns to the observer in the same time—a total of nearly 2 seconds before the echo is heard.

Now if a powerful spotlight is quickly flashed to the cliff, it appears as though we see the reflection of it on the cliff at precisely the same instant it is turned on. It is not quite the same instant, however. Since light travels at 186,000 miles every second, a little arithmetic shows that it required approximately a millionth of a second for the light to reach the cliff and the same time for it to come back to our eyes. Thus, we did not see the reflection on the cliff at the same precise instant the spotlight was flicked on but about two-millionths of a second (2 microseconds) later.

All electromagnetic radiation—light, radio waves, microwaves, infrared, ultraviolet, etc.—travels at the same rate, so that when a radar pulse is beamed out and its "echo" or reflection is detected, let us say, exactly 100 microseconds later, it is established that the object reflecting this pulse is 53,750 feet or over 10 miles away.

There is no practical limit (except target size) to the distance radar can be effective providing there is a straight line between the antenna and the object at which the beam is directed. In 1946 U.S. Army engineers (Signal Corps) directed the first radar pulse at the moon, which is 238,000 miles away. The "echo" returned and was detected right on schedule—a little over 2½ seconds later!

The moon experiment was more than a curious and interesting bit of effort. It proved that objects high above the earth's atmosphere and beyond the influence of gravity can be located. These might be natural meteorites suspended in space hundreds of miles up or man-made objects sent up by rockets and controlled by radar.

At the earth's surface, the effective distance of radar is established primarily by the height of the antenna and/or the target (as well as the latter's size, shape, and structure), since a radar beam travels tangent to the earth's curvature rather than parallel to or following it. Of course, the power of the transmitter

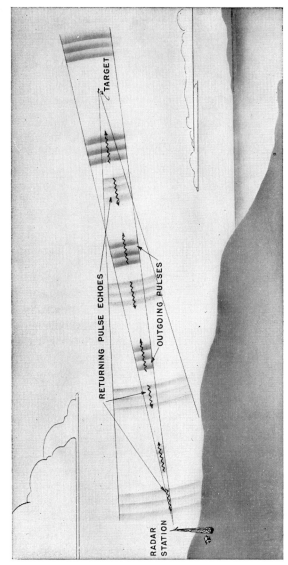

FIG. 11-2. Diagram showing the basic principle of radar operation. Microwave pulses leaving an antenna will be echoed from an airplane 100 miles away and arrive back at the antenna about a thousandth of a second later. Such a beam of microwaves can be swung around in a complete circle as well as upward in any solid inverted conical pattern desired, and thus explore almost completely the skies above and around the radar station for a distance of 200 miles or more.

as well as the sensitivity of the receiver also determine the
maximum effective distance. One boat can "see" another by radar
about 25 miles away across the water before the earth's curvature
interferes. (Radar does not penetrate water.) If the antenna is
low as on a submarine at the surface, the distance is less, but
high above the deck of a large vessel the distance would be
greater.

Under certain atmospheric conditions where moisture content
of the air is quite high near the surface of the water but
diminishes rapidly as the altitude increases, the higher frequency radar signals have a tendency to refract toward the
earth, thus extending effective distances well beyond the normal
horizon.

Aircraft can be detected and located from the ground or a
boat at much greater distances. Radar will find an airplane which
is 4 miles up about 200 miles away. To avoid such detection in
wartime, bombing runs are sometimes made over water and
land at altitudes of only a hundred feet or less depending upon
the terrain and other conditions.

Radar and Aviation

Radar has its greatest value, perhaps, when used in aircraft.
As a location finder, it provides a map of the ground beneath
obscured by haze and fog, showing contours of coast line, lakes,
islands, cities, mountains, and other information in considerable
detail up to a distance of a hundred miles or so, depending upon
the plane's altitude. The antenna may be located differently on
different types of planes, but it is always placed where it will
have an unobstructed sweep of the ground below and the
terrain ahead.

Military, commercial, and private aviation is largely dependent
upon short-wave radio and radar for successful operation. Commercial aviation in particular would be seriously handicapped
without it. Scheduled flights which are routine today would have
to be canceled, and the existing safety records could not have

been accomplished without the advantages of blind landing systems, radio beams, *ground-controlled approach* (GCA), radio and *radar altimeters,* air-traffic-control systems, and several other applications of short-wave and microwave radio.

The air over this country is a network of radio beacons and

FIG. 11-3. The instrument-landing system (ILS) for guiding aircraft onto airport runways under conditions of visual obscurity. An accurate line of flight is established where the vertical-localizer beam intercepts the sloping glide-path beam. Instruments on the plane's instrument panel indicate whether the plane is to the left, right, or on the localizer beam, and also whether the plane is above, below, or on the glide-path beam. Thus, by watching his instruments, the pilot can bring his ship into a safe landing without seeing the runway until his wheels practically touch the ground. Outer and inner markers are placed at points *A* and *B,* respectively. *C* is the approach monitor or tower. *D* is the localizer beam transmitter. *E* is the location of a precision-beam radar antenna, and *F* is the glide-path transmitter. (*Courtesy of United Airlines.*)

beams, and trained aircraft navigators and pilots rarely have difficulty in knowing exactly where they are; how high they are; precisely what the traffic pattern is ahead, behind, above, and below them; and what obstructions, if any, exist on their way to the next landing.

At the airport, the control tower can "see" by radar precisely where each plane is within a radius of several miles and can direct each one in successive order into the glide path, or down to within a few feet at the runway and even until the wheels touch the ground, in the thickest of fogs and the blackest of nights. All this can be done without the pilot's being able to see the runway lights or anything else outside the cockpit until his ship has practically landed.

When a plane is "talked down" in this manner, it is called an *instrument landing,* and while such landings are not without some hazard and require quick, accurate thinking by the pilot, they would be impossible without short-wave radio and radar. Thus, aircraft may use, when necessary, a "pathway" of microwaves sloping straight down to the runway when conditions completely obscure visual means of orientation.

Marine Radar

The use of radar as a navigation aid for ships is, in general principle, similar to its use in aircraft. It does not involve such distances, of course, because it is used much closer to the earth's surface across water. However, it is equally important for a ship's captain to know the exact location of other ships when entering a crowded harbor in a fog and at night or the presence of an iceberg drifting across his course at sea. Maximum radar range is about 50 miles at the surface for large boats with high antenna mountings, but since the speed of boats is relatively slow, long-distance operation is not so important as minimum range. If a vessel is entering a harbor under conditions described just above, a couple of hundred feet is critical to the helmsman, so that his radar information must be accurate within that distance. Actually, radar equipment can be designed to operate satisfactorily for a distance as short as a hundred feet, but it is not often required to do so.

More important in marine navigation is radio direction finding and long-range navigation. The latter is referred to as a *loran* and will be discussed a little later in this chapter.

Radar Antennas

As with many other things, radar equipment is designed and adjusted to suit a specific task. Such differences in design include not only the transmitter and receiver circuits and tubes but the equally important antenna.

The best way to visualize radar is to compare it with light. Just as some reflectors of light produce narrow beams and are called spotlights while others produce wider beams and are called floodlights, so radar antennas may be designed to produce a narrow or wide beam of microwaves. Also, just as we would use a spotlight for some applications and a floodlight for others, so narrow-beam antennas are best suited to certain types of radar work and wide-beam antennas to others.

When radar is used to scan the skies for airplanes, the antenna may rotate 360 degrees around its mast, tower, or base. Or if only a certain section of the horizon is important, the antenna equipment can be made to sweep back and forth within that sector. Furthermore, at each rotation or sweep across the arc it raises its beam a few degrees to scan the next higher portion of sky. The antenna motion may be timed to make one complete rotation or sector sweep each second or it may be slower, depending upon conditions. In any event, the entire area under surveillance will be scanned within a few seconds, and if a plane is in that area, the microwave "echo" comes back and its position is indicated on the viewing screen.

When a wide beam is used, complete coverage is accomplished more quickly but the precise location of an object cannot be determined, since if it is located anywhere within the effective width of the beam (except at the extreme beam edges), the "echo" appears on the viewing screen at the same location. At 100 miles from the antenna, a beam of microwaves 15 degrees wide is covering nearly 500 square miles—a "spot" about 25 miles in diameter— so that a single plane is placed only as to general location, and a group of them cannot be distinguished as to number.

A 2-degree beam at 100 miles, however, covers a "spot" of only about 28 square miles and 3 miles in diameter, and a plane can be located much more accurately, or the details of a flight formation determined with more precision.

Radar antennas can be designed to produce about any desirable beam pattern. Some will form a fan-shaped beam which

FIG. 11-4. A 15-foot marine radar antenna with rotating drive mechanism in the box below. This particular type sends out a beam of microwave pulses 10,000 megacycles in frequency and 3 centimeters (about 1¼ inches) in wavelength. The wave guide, which turns back on itself to spray microwaves from the open horn-shaped end, can be seen in front at the focal point of the reflecting antenna. The same antenna also intercepts the returning echo and focuses it back into the wave guide, which directs it to the radar receiver. (*Courtesy of Sperry Gyroscope Company.*)

is wide horizontally and narrow vertically, or the antenna can, in effect, be turned 90 degrees to produce thin horizontal dimensions, but wide from the ground upward.

The same antenna is generally used to catch the "echo" returning from the target. The design of antennas takes this into account as well as the required characteristics as a reflector of microwaves. The latter radiate toward the reflector from the open end of a waveguide located at the focal point of the antenna. The reverse process takes place when the echo signal returns; that is, the antenna intercepts a minute portion of the radiating microwaves of energy reflected from the target and focuses it back into the same wave guide which, a microsecond or two before, sent the original pulse out to the target. Just how the outgoing signal is separated from the incoming one and confliction is avoided will be explained in a moment.

Radar Frequencies and Wavelengths

Radar work extends between the approximate limits of 225 to 33,000 megacycles or in wavelength from about $1\frac{1}{2}$ meters to less than a centimeter. This region is divided into several bands which are designated by letters. The P band embraces wavelengths of around 1 meter, the L band from about 80 to 20 centimeters, the S band from 20 to $5\frac{1}{2}$ centimeters, the X band from $5\frac{1}{2}$ to about $2\frac{1}{2}$ centimeters, and the K band from $2\frac{1}{2}$ centimeters to a fraction of 1.

Radar Transmission

Radar signals are sent out in pulses or packets of microwave radiant energy. The duration of these pulses is dependent upon the type of radar work to be done. Where short distances and, therefore, short echo times are involved, the *pulse duration* or length must be short. If a pulse lasts for 1 microsecond, the packet or train of waves radiating out in the beam from the antenna is nearly 1,000 feet long, so that unless the target is more than 500 feet away, the first part of the train is echoed back to the antenna before the last part has left. Obviously, such a situation would result in interference and conflict with consequent inaccurate work. Therefore, for close ranging, pulses as short as $\frac{1}{10}$ microsecond may be used, thus making radio detection and ranging possible up to within about 100 feet with reasonable accuracy.

As distances increase, longer pulses are used, and in aviation work, a 1-microsecond pulse is common practice. In the moon experiment mentioned earlier in this chapter, a pulse duration of 500,000 microseconds ($\frac{1}{2}$ second) was used, and since it required $2\frac{1}{2}$ seconds for the signal to return, the pulse had ample time clear of the antenna before its echo put in an appearance on the receiver screen.

In addition to pulse duration, the time interval between each successive pulse is an important consideration. Here again the *pulse rate* or repetition frequency is determined by the nature of the detecting and ranging task at hand. As a general rule, a pulse is not sent out until the echo from the preceding one is back. Otherwise the distant echo of the first pulse might be misinterpreted as a close-range echo of the second one. Such an error is not too common, however, since the strength of the echo and other factors in the transmitter and receiver operation will help establish the identity of an echo. Pulses are timed from about 1,000 every second to as low as 10 per second depending upon circumstances of operation. Usual practice for most radar work is around 50 pulses per second, which allows plenty of time between pulses for an echo to return from a target over 100 miles away.

The electron tube which generates the high-power pulses in a radar transmitter is called a *magnetron* or, more precisely, a *resonant-cavity magnetron*. There are several types of magnetrons, the most common of which will be described in some detail in Chapter 15. Basically, the magnetron is a tube or device which is capable of producing very large quantities of power (hundreds of thousands of watts) for short periods of time (pulses) at extremely high frequencies (several thousand megacycles).

It does this by whirling electrons around in a spiral by a powerful magnetic field. As they pass the cavities which are bored to a very critical size in a copper block, a *resonant frequency* is set up which is carried by wave guides to the antenna. The frequency is established by the size of the cavities—the smaller the cavity, the higher the frequency of microwaves radiating from the antenna.

Pulse duration and rate are controlled by the more or less conventional or standard types of electron (radio) tubes in circuits designed for that purpose.

The pulses from the magnetron are propagated through a wave guide which shoots them out against the concave form of the reflector which "beams" them out as previously described. This reflector, however, is generally called the antenna, since it also collects and focuses the returning echo pulses back down the same waveguide to the receiving equipment.

Radar Reception

When the same antenna and wave guide are used to receive returning radar pulse echoes, there must be some method of directing them into the receiver instead of back into the transmitting equipment where they originated.

The electronic device which does this is called a *TR box* or *switch*. These letters stand for "transmit-receive," and the device does just what its name indicates. It guides pulses from the magnetron out to the antenna but guides the returning echoes into the receiver.

A mechanical switch would not function under the rapid pulse rate and short-time duration conditions, so gas-filled electron tubes are used which ionize instantly when the pulse strikes them. While the tube in the TR switch is thus ionized, the pulse passes through the wave guide to the antenna with no energy reaching the receiver directly. (Ionization of gases is covered more completely in Chapter 14.)

At the end of the pulse, the tube de-ionizes instantly, permitting no passage of energy, so that the returning echo is guided directly to the receiver from the same antenna that sent out the pulse a few microseconds before.

Radar receivers are, in some respects, similar to conventional radio sets. In other respects, however, they are vastly different.

These differences are due to the fact that a returning radar signal is of very short duration and extremely high in frequency. In addition the power of the echo is only an infinitesimal trace of the original pulse—perhaps only two- or three-trillionths of a watt (two- or three-millionths of a microwatt).

Before such minute signals can be detected, they must be amplified a few million times, then rectified from the extremely

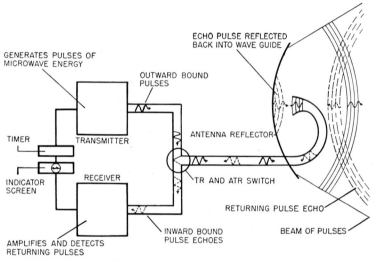

FIG. 11-5. Diagram of basic operating principles of radar transmission and reception, and the function of a transmit-receive switch, which guides the outgoing pulses from the receiver and the incoming pulses from the transmitter.

high-frequency alternating pulse to a single direct pulse. While there are other factors employed in the circuit which make it possible to detect this pulse, we must pass by them here without further explanation, since we are concerned only with a fundamental outline of the principles involved rather than a discussion of the circuit details.

After detection, the single pulse is again amplified and sent to a cathode-ray tube similar to that used in television.

In Chapter 10, Television, the fundamental principles of cathode-ray-tube operation were discussed. It was pointed out how a beam of electrons from the electron gun is swept across a fluorescent screen, creating a picture made up of lines which vary in their brightness—the brightness at any point depending upon the strength or number of electrons in the beam as it passes at that particular instant. So, on a radar screen, a picture

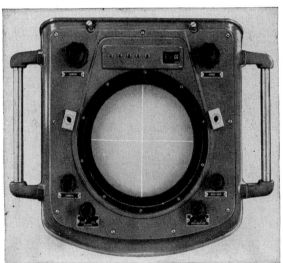

FIG. 11-6. The radar receiver and screen which operates in conjunction with the antenna shown in Fig. 11-4. The screen size is 12½ inches in diameter. The usual position of viewing is to look down upon the screen. (*Courtesy of Sperry Gyroscope Company.*)

or map is "painted" by an electron beam sweeping the fluorescent face of a cathode-ray tube. This time, however, the beam intensity is varied by the strength or presence of a returning echo.

There are several types of radar screen pictures. The one just mentioned is called PPI for *plan-position indicator*. It will be described more completely in a moment.

The simplest and most basic type of radar picture is called a *range indicator,* which in the true sense is not a picture at all but a horizontal sweep line with vertical columns called *pips* appearing at intervals across the face of the tube. These pips tell where the target is located.

Using round figures, let us assume that the beam sweeps across the face of the tube from left to right in a thousandth of a second or 1,000 microseconds and that the effective screen is 10 inches in diameter. It requires 100 microseconds, therefore, for the beam to trace a length of 1 inch on its way across. Since it takes a little over 10 microseconds for a pulse to go out 1 mile and echo back, it is clear that every inch of the line will represent almost 10 miles of distance and the complete line across the screen about 100 miles. This is called the *time base,* and on most radar equipment it can be lengthened, shortened, or otherwise adjusted with accuracy to suit the conditions of work at hand.

The time base starts its sweep at the left at the same instant a pulse leaves the antenna and sweeps across once for each successive pulse. At 500 pulses per second, the line, of course, appears continuous and solid. The pulse is indicated at the beginning of the sweep by a vertical pip which, if the pulse duration is 1 microsecond, would be $\frac{1}{10}$ inch wide.

Now let us assume that the pulse finds a target somewhere out in the path of the beam and an echo comes back, is collected by the antenna, is guided through the TR box, is amplified a few million times, and eventually reaches the cathode-ray tube. It is now a signal strong enough to cause a vertical deflection of the electrons streaming from the electron gun on their way across the screen in the process of forming the 1,000-microsecond time base. This vertical deflection will cause a second pip. Let us say that it appears just halfway across the screen—5 inches from the start. Since it requires 100 microseconds for the time base to advance 1 inch, the echo pip occurred 500 microseconds from the start. This means that the target causing the echo is 250 microseconds or nearly 50 miles away.

In the above example, we have used round figures in the interest of simplicity for mental calculation. Actually, under those conditions the target would be 46½ miles away, plus about 60 feet. Radar can be operated as a range indicator with precision that is amazing, and its value for large gunfire control can well be imagined.

In plan-position indicating, the cathode-ray tube and circuit are quite different. Here, the time base starts at the center of the

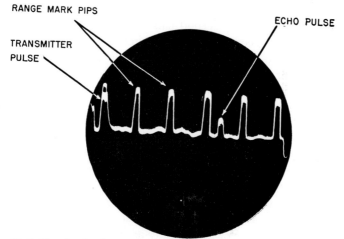

Fig. 11-7. Sketch of radar range-indicator screen, showing the range marks produced electronically by regularly and accurately timed pulses to represent equal-distance intervals from the antenna. If these marks are established for 20-mile intervals, on a 100-mile time base, the transmitter pulse is echoed back from an object about 68 miles away. Certain characteristics of the echo pip, such as its height, width, fluctuation, and rate of motion along the time base, are indications of the nature of the target.

screen and sweeps outward to the edge like the radius of a circle. Each successive sweep occurs slightly more to the right of the previous one, going around the circle like the second hand on a stop watch instead of tracing the same path over and over again as with the range indicator described just above.

This time-base rotation is synchronized with the antenna rotation. When the latter is pointing its beam to the north, the time base sweeps straight upward as a clock hand points to twelve. When the antenna has reached a due east position, the sweep is toward the 3 on a clock face, and so on, around the screen as the antenna completes its scan around the horizon.

It was pointed out in the discussion of antennas that their rotating speed can be fast enough to cover the 360 degrees in 1 second or may be much slower. In any event, the rotation of the time base corresponds to that of the antenna, so unlike the above-mentioned sweep second hand of a stop watch, the coverage of the circle is considerably less than 60 seconds.

As with the range indicator, the time base can be adjusted in length to suit conditions, so that the radius of the area it is sweeping may be anywhere from 10 to 100 miles or more.

The basic principle of pulses and echoes is the same for PPI as for range indicating, except that the echo appears as a bright spot on the time base rather than as a pip. Thus, when used in an airplane to scan the ground below, those things which reflect the pulses, such as land, islands, boats, or other aircraft, will be indicated on the radar screen as bright areas.

Now let us put the above information together. First, we have pulses of microwaves radiating in a beam out from the antenna at a rapid rate. Many of these pulses are echoed back to produce bright spots in a radial line on the viewing screen. Second, we have the beam swinging around to complete a circle once in perhaps every 3 or 4 seconds, so that the bright spots on the screen correspond to objects which are reflecting the pulses back from whatever direction the beam is pointing. Now if the bright spots on the screen will hold or retain their light after the beam has passed that position and hold it until the beam gets back around there again a few seconds later, we shall establish a pattern or map of the area below in light.

This is just what happens on a PPI screen. As the plane moves on, it is always at the center of the screen, and as the area below changes in coast-line contour, as lakes, rivers, boats, and other objects come within range of the radar beam, all such information is faithfully shown on the screen.

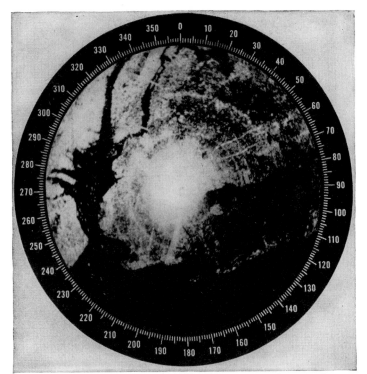

Fig. 11-8. New York City may look like this on an air-borne radar scope, even though the plane were several thousand feet up, above an overcast, flying approximately north. At the upper left, Manhattan Island is clearly outlined, and such details as the East River bridges and Central Park are recognized. At the left of Manhattan are the Hudson River and the New Jersey shore line. Below this are the upper end of Staten Island, the Narrows, and New York harbor. Directly beneath the plane we see Brooklyn, with its shore line, and at the bottom, Coney Island. At the top right is the Borough of Queens. (*Courtesy of Sperry Gyroscope Company.*)

With maps of the area to assist him, a navigator can follow his progress over the country and recognize cities, boats, and landmarks on the PPI screen even though he is thousands of feet up above the clouds at night.

There are uses for radar other than those we have discussed.

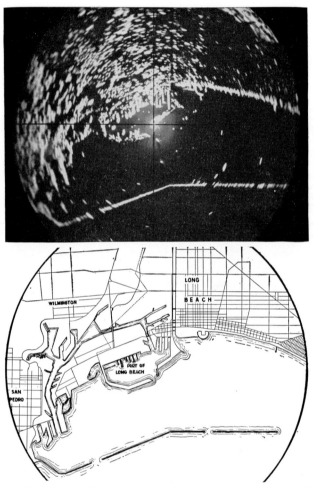

FIG. 11-9. Comparison of a radar-scope photo (above) with a map (below) of the port of Long Beach, California. This is a harbor-supervision radar installation operated by the harbor authorities of that port. It is used to survey harbor traffic, to direct pilot boats to incoming ships during poor visibility, and to advise pilots aboard vessels of their location in the harbor area for purposes of guiding them safely to anchoring or docking position. (*Courtesy of Sperry Gyroscope Company.*)

In application they are somewhat different, but in principle the behavior of microwave pulses is utilized and interpreted in much the same way.

Loran

From the standpoint of its position in the radio region of the electromagnetic spectrum, loran may not belong in a chapter discussing microwaves. Loran, which means long-range navigation, utilizes much lower frequencies (between 1.5 and 2 megacycles) and longer wavelengths than radar, but since pulses or short trains of waves are used, and since the application of loran is for purposes similar to those of radar, we can include a brief discussion of it at this point.

Loran uses the longer wavelengths because they tend to follow the curvature of the earth, thus increasing the effective range to several hundred miles over the ocean.

While the travel time of pulses is used, as in radar, there is no echo involved. Loran transmitters are located at points 200 or 300 miles apart along the coast line. These transmitters operate in pairs, each pair broadcasting pulses at the same instant at a predetermined rate of 20 or 30 per second. With the transmitters an exact known distance apart and forming two points of a triangle, a boat or plane anywhere except in a straight line with them will form the third point of the triangle.

Since the location of the two loran stations and the number of microseconds required for the signals of each to reach the ship are known and are indicated on its loran receiver screen, it is a relatively easy matter to determine the ship's exact location by a process of triangulation. In other words, with two points and three legs of a triangle known, the third point can be readily established.

If simultaneous pulses from each station arrive at the receiver at the same instant, the receiver must be equidistant from each transmitter. If, however, the signal from station 1 arrives, let us say, in 300 microseconds and the signal from 2 in only 250, the

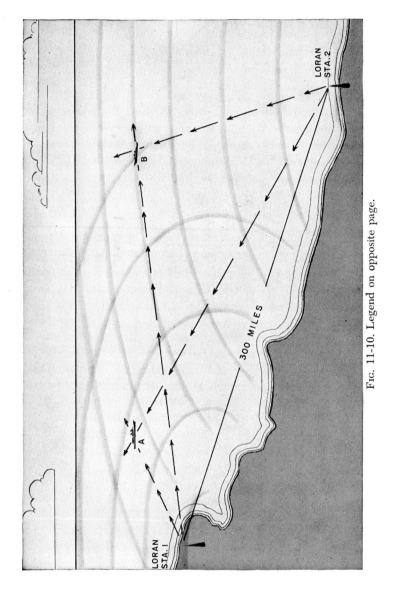

Fig. 11-10. Legend on opposite page.

receiver will be about 56 miles from station 1 and 46½ miles from 2. More precisely, the ship will be 9.315 miles nearer station 2, since, as mentioned in the discussion of radar, electromagnetic waves travel 0.1863 mile (983.66 feet) in 1 microsecond.

There are many more factors involved in loran operation than we shall be able to discuss here. However, the fundamental principle should be clear. The exact distance from two transmitters of known location is established by the time required for their pulses to reach a receiver. Pulses are indicated on a cathode-ray tube screen, much the same as in a radar range indicator described a few pages back.

Communication Beam Relay

Voice communication such as telephone conversation, television programs, and other intelligence may be carried from the originating point to other transmitters by wires (*coaxial cable*) or by *beaming* the signal in relays from one point to another with microwave beams.

A coaxial cable is a wire or conductor for carrying high-frequency currents. In order to prevent the energy from radiating away from the wire in electromagnetic waves, the conductor is run in the center of a metal tube which keeps the energy tc the conductor. While there are many types and designs of coaxial cables for specific uses, some with several conductors and square or channel-shaped tubes or shields, all serve the same funda-

---

FIG. 11-10. Simplified diagram and example of loran operation. The loran screen on ship *B* indicates that the signal from station 2 arrived in 825 microseconds, and from station 1 in 1,640 microseconds. Since the known distance between the loran stations is 300 miles, and since the pulses travel 1 mile in 6.18 microseconds, it can be established that ship *B* is 133 miles from station 2 and about 265½ miles from station 1, a fixed point at sea. Similarly, ship *A* receives signals from station 1 in 475 microseconds and from station 2 in 1,790 microseconds which fixes it approximately 290 miles from station 2, and 77 miles from station 1.

Fig. 11-11. One of a chain of 107 Bell System microwave beam relay towers, which beam telephone and television signals both ways between New York and San Francisco. The distance between towers varies somewhat with the terrain, but the average spacing is about 30 miles between towers. One antenna on each tower is a receiver and the other a transmitter, thus permitting two-way communication. Signals received by one tower are amplified and beamed out of its partner on the other tower to the next station 30 miles farther along the route. Frequencies of from 3,700 to 4,200 megacycles are used. (*Courtesy of Bell Telephone Laboratories.*)

mental purpose—to transmit high-frequency energy from one point to another with as little loss as possible.

When terrain conditions, distance, the nature of the signals to be transmitted, and other factors are such that coaxial-cable use is quite costly with relatively high losses, the transmission of such signals can be accomplished with better economy and results by beaming the signals from one antenna (reflector) to the next in relays until the transmission distance is completed.

Such relay systems have certain characteristics of radar in that similar antennas are used to focus the microwaves in beams like a searchlight and aim them at a receiving antenna several miles away. The distance between relay stations is dependent primarily upon the height of the respective antennas, since, it will be recalled, short waves travel in straight lines tangent to the earth's surface. Thus, two antenna towers atop high hills or mountains may be many miles apart and yet free of intervening obstructions.

Intermediate relay stations receive signals from the broadcasting station with one antenna and rebeam them to the next station with another, after sufficient amplification at the intermediate transmitter.

Such systems of relay provide a highly satisfactory and practical means of distributing television programs, telephone conversations, and other types of communication over wide areas, with relative freedom from static and other interference.

One of the frequency ranges used is between 5,925 and 7,425 megacycles. This is, in effect, a broad communications highway, which can be divided into many narrow bands or channels (10 megacycles) for simultaneous two-way communications work. Such microwave beams may be frequency-modulated or pulse-modulated depending upon the type of service desired.

Guided Missiles and Radio Control

For security reasons either in or out of wartime, the subject of *guided missiles* can be covered only in a general way. It is a subject which has received extremely extensive and intensive treatment during the past few years.

Having read thus far in this chapter, the reader should begin to recognize that the microwave region of the electromagnetic spectrum and the nature of such radiation permit a degree of control not possible with the better known, longer wavelengths and lower frequencies of conventional radio communication, even though the latter travel at the same speed as the microwaves.

A guided missile is just what its name indicates. It may be a projectile, rocket or some other peacetime or wartime object in flight from one to many miles above the earth. It contains a receiver for specific signals from the ground or air and sometimes a transmitter to send intelligence back to the earth control or other locations.

Signals from the ground or some other control point, upon being received by the missile, may be so translated magnetically, optically, or mechanically within the mechanism of the missile as to increase or decrease its speed, change its direction of flight, detonate and destroy it, or otherwise change its existing course of action. High above the earth beyond gravitational influences, an object sent up by rocket might conceivably float about in space until such time as it was called upon to behave in accordance with microwave ground control.

One example of missile control which has received some degree of publicity is the *proximity fuse,* sometimes referred to as the VT (variable-time) fuse. Briefly, it consists of a small transmitter and receiver of microwaves in the lower megacycle frequency range.

This transmitting and receiving equipment is placed in the nose of certain types of antiaircraft and other shells. When the shell is fired from a gun, the transmitter starts sending out pulses which, when the shell approaches or reaches the proximity of the target, reflect back to the receiver from the target and detonate the shell.

Since such a shell does not have to score a direct hit to deto-

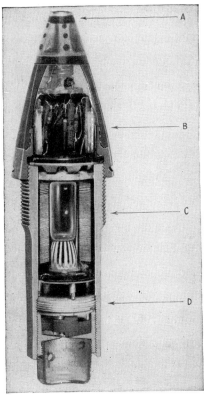

FIG. 11-12. Cutaway view of one type of proximity fuse, sometimes referred to as the VT (variable-time) fuse which detonates shells by radio. At the top (A) is shown a plastic nose in which an antenna of precise design is located. Beneath this (B) is a bundle of small tubes, resistors, condensers, and other equipment which comprise the radio transmitter and receiver. Farther down in the assembly (C) is the power supply consisting of a bottle of electrolyte, which breaks when the shell is fired, so that the liquid flows between the plates surrounding it, thus forming a "battery" source of power. At the bottom (D) are safety devices and a self-destruction switch which operates in the event the shell is not detonated by radio in the manner intended. The entire assembly as shown above is screwed into the nose of antiaircraft and other types of shells. It starts functioning when the shell is fired, with the chain of events indicated above taking place in a fraction of a second. (*Photo by Life photographer George Skadding, Time, Inc.*)

nate, and since, when designed to do so, it can cause as much damage if it explodes somewhere near the target, the result of its use can well be imagined. In effect, the proximity fuse increases the size of the target many times.

There are many more uses of microwaves than we have discussed in this chapter, but the fundamental principles of their application are about the same regardless of the nature of the devices or their specific use.

12

Now that we have covered the complete range of radio waves to the point where they begin to show some of the characteristics of infrared radiation, let us jump back over the electromagnetic spectrum to the other side of visible light and ultraviolet.

X Rays

Overlapped by short-wavelength ultraviolet radiation at one end and long-wavelength gamma radiation at the other, we find a region called *X rays* or *Roentgen rays.*

The term X ray is familiar to the civilized world, and there are few of us, in this country at least, who have not been subjected to these radiations by the dentist when he wants to study the roots of our teeth or by the surgeon, who finds it essential to know more about broken bones and organic disorders within our bodies.

The discovery and recognition of X rays as electromagnetic waves shorter in length than ultraviolet make a rather interesting story. In 1895, a scientist named W. K. Roentgen, while working on a high-voltage vacuum tube, noticed that some photographic plates enclosed in a box nearby frequently became cloudy and unfit for use even though they were never exposed to light. In searching for a reason, he soon discovered that this clouding occurred whenever a discharge took place in the tube. The correct conclusion was that some sort of extremely penetrating radiation emanated from the tube during its discharge. This radiation, being unknown at the time, he called X radiation or X rays.

Since that time, science has discovered that, when electrons are released from a hot metallic solid such as an incandescent filament, streak through a vacuum at terrific speeds, and strike the atoms of another metallic solid, the splash of energy released by the collision radiates away in electromagnetic waves. These waves may be as long as 600 or 800 angstroms, so that they may be considered as either X rays or ultraviolet at such wavelengths,

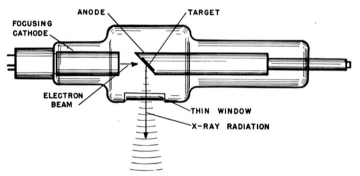

Fig. 12-1. Conventional X-ray-tube design of the type used for general dental and medical work.

or they may be as short as one- or two-hundredths of an angstrom. They vibrate at frequencies ranging from 2,000 or 3,000 trillion times a second to over 100,000 quadrillion times per second.

In general, the higher the voltage or pressure forcing the electrons out of one solid (the cathode) and on their journey to strike the other solid (the anode), the faster they will travel, the faster will be the vibrations of released energy resulting from the collision, the shorter will be its wavelengths, and the deeper the radiation will penetrate a solid. Extremely long-wavelength X rays will not pass through even thin glass (as was pointed out in the discussion of short-wave ultraviolet), whereas the shortest ones which are produced by pressures of several million volts will penetrate many inches of metal.

Since X rays, like visible light, infrared, and ultraviolet, are electromagnetic radiations but of much shorter wavelengths, it might be expected that they will have the reflection and refraction characteristics of those radiations in the longer wavelength regions. However, since their wavelengths are of the order of size of atoms, it is difficult to obtain anything other than a scattering and dispersion of rays, as well as absorption.

Certain crystals having a precise spacing of atoms in their lattice structure will break X rays into their component wavelengths similar to the way a prism breaks up light into colors. Only at extremely glancing angles, however, does regular reflection occur. One crystal which may be used in studying X-ray frequencies is ordinary rock salt (sodium chloride), since it has the necessary atom-arrangement characteristics.

Because of the atomic dimensions of X rays, they are used commercially to explore crystal structures. Million-volt X rays are applied quite extensively in industry where metal hardening is accomplished with high heat and a consequent change in the crystalline structure of the metal. X-ray analyses of this sort are responsible for much more efficient production of much higher quality metals.

While the infrared and ultraviolet regions are split up into portions referred to as *near* and *far*, depending upon their distance from the visible-light band, X rays are designated as *hard* and *soft*. Hard X rays are those resulting from voltages upward of 100,000 volts, whereas the soft ones originate with much lower voltages with, of course, much longer wavelengths and less penetrating power.

In ordinary medical work, X rays are made to pass through the body and strike a photographic plate where the amount of radiation penetrating is recorded similar to the way a camera will record the visible light passing through a translucent solid. Bones or foreign objects which may have become lodged within the body do not permit so much transmission as skin or flesh, so that they show up on the photographic plate as *shadows*. Thus, broken bones, bullets, swallowed buttons, pins, and similar objects can be readily located. Changes in tissue structure, such as might result from infection or malignant or tumorous growths, are also easily detectable on X-ray plates, so that the physician and surgeon find it possible to work much more accurately with an X-ray "blueprint" of their task.

Such shadow pictures are also used in many industries to locate defects in products made of wood, rubber, plastics, leather, and even metal. Different types of X-ray tubes and the manner in which they operate will be covered in Chapter 15.

Radium Therapy

The electromagnetic spectrum shows a wide overlap of X rays with a region of radiations called *gamma rays*. This indicates that the radiations within this overlap can be called either X rays or gamma rays and that they are identical in character, regardless of their name or of how they are produced.

Gamma rays are those which radiate from radioactive elements or substances such as radium or uranium. While the names of Pierre Curie and his wife Marie are associated with the discovery of radium, the radioactivity of uranium was noted shortly after Roentgen's discovery of X rays by a French scientist named Becquerel. Like Roentgen, Becquerel used photographic plates and found that uranium emitted radiations which fogged them. The Curies, in an effort to find more potent radiations than those resulting from uranium, experimented with pitchblende, the substance from which uranium is obtained, and did obtain radiations several times as strong. Further analytical work with pitchblende resulted in the discovery of a new element which they called *radium,* in which the radioactivity was several million times stronger than in uranium.

Radium is extremely rare, a great many tons of rich pitchblende ore being required to obtain one ounce of radium worth many thousands of dollars. Its radioactive property is the result of the instability of its atoms. All atoms, it will be recalled, are made up of a nucleus around which electrons swarm in definite energy levels, but radium atoms, as those of other radioactive elements, tend to change their own structure with explosive

FIG. 12-2. Equipment used in radium therapy. The tiny needles containing 10 milligrams of radium sulphate are stored in the solid lead block which provides 2½ inches of lead for protection in every direction. The storage cabinet weighs 180 pounds, but can be supplied in greater thickness when higher concentrations of radium are to be stored. The needles can be seen in the open drawer. The protection block in the right foreground consists of heavy lead shielding at the front and base for the protection of the abdomen and lower extremities of workers handling radium needles and tubes. The thick lead glass offers partial protection. Beneath it, in the forceps, is a tube containing 10 milligrams of radium sulphate. (*Courtesy of Radium Chemical Company, Inc., New York, N.Y.*)

force. There is a tremendous amount of energy (potential) within radium atoms, so that when the change takes place, the energy is released partly as electromagnetic radiation of extremely short wavelength and high frequency. The amount of energy thus released in the complete change of one gram of radium is approximately equal to the energy supplied in the burning of a ton of coal.

This energy is not released, of course, by all the atoms at once. They undergo their change at random, but there are so many billions of them in a visible amount of radium that released energy is radiated at a rate which can be considered constant.

For medical purposes radium is usually in the compound radium bromide of which about half is radium. Minute quantities of this compound are placed in tiny metal tubes no larger than a small sewing needle and inserted into tumor and cancer tissues, where the radiation destroys the tissues. Other methods may be used, but basically the treatment is to so apply the radiation that the diseased tissue will be killed without destroying too much of the surrounding healthy tissue. Obviously, the problems are usually extremely difficult, and the success of such treatments requires the skill and technique of a specialist. As has been explained, radium emanations are very penetrating, and their precise control deep within the body is not always possible. When stored, the minute radium pellets are placed in jackets of steel or lead and kept in boxes of lead of considerable thickness, so that no damage will be done to persons circulating in the vicinity of the storage vaults.

Since X rays of short wavelengths and gamma radiations from radium are one and the same, X rays replace radium in certain types of medical treatment. Such X rays, if they are to be of the same wavelength as gamma rays, must be produced by a million volts and more.

High-voltage X-ray technique has developed rapidly during the past few years. Since the equipment required is less difficult to handle (though larger) and the treatments less delicate, the cost involved may be appreciably less than with radium. For that reason, high-voltage X-ray equipment is found in many of the finest hospitals. The fact that such extremely high voltages are used does not indicate that there is danger of the patient's being electrocuted. Where such treatments are given, the electrical apparatus and X-ray tube may be quite remote from the patient, such as in a room on the floor above with the radiations passing through special devices in the floor to the patient, who reclines comfortably in pleasant surroundings in the room below.

Radioactivity

While there are about 40 elements occurring in nature, such as uranium, thorium, and radium, which are radioactive in varying degrees, other elements can be made artificially radioactive by means which we shall consider shortly. All radioactivity is a temporary process. That is, the activity decreases with time. This rate of radioactive decay is called *half life* and is a measure of time representing the seconds, minutes, hours, days, or years required for a radioactive element to reach one-half its maximum state of activity.

Some require many years to disentegrate completely, whereas others will last only a fraction of a second. Uranium, for example, has a calculated half life of about 5 billion years. During its transition from uranium 1 (U238) to its final inactive state which is lead, it passes through a number of intermediate stages, one of which is radium, having a half life of 1,600 to 1,700 years.

At the start, when the parent element such as uranium begins its decay, the process may follow one of three courses during which different radioactive materials will develop. Uranium 1 (U238), for example, will follow a course producing thorium, protactinium, uranium 2 (U234), thorium 230, radium in several successive forms, polonium 214, thallium, radioactive lead, bismuth, polonium 210, and finally stable lead. Some of these elements such as radium are many times more active than the parent uranium. This is called a *radioactive* series, and the one just mentioned the *uranium series*. Other successions resulting from radioactive decay are called the *thorium series* and the *actinium series*. During these, other elements are produced, some of which branch again, thus forming a sort of "subseries" of disintegration products.

It should be mentioned before leaving this phase of the subject that the term *half life* is not an indication of one-half the time required for a radioactive element to reach stability. If, for example, an element is 50 per cent as active in 10 days as it was when created, it will decrease in activity one-half of that amount in the next 10 days, one-half more in the following 10, and so on. Thus, while it has lost 87.5 per cent of its maximum activity in 30 days, it has lost one-half of each remaining amount every 10 days, so its half life is established at 10 days. This rate of relative decay prevails for all radioactive materials.

To state it another way, the half life of any quantity of radioactive material is when one-half of its atoms have undergone their next step in the disintegration process.

Radiation from Radioactive Materials

An element is radioactive because its atoms release their energy at a constant rate as outlined above. This energy release takes three forms. First, alpha particles fly out of the nucleus; second, gamma rays radiate away; and third, beta particles are ejected. A description of these three is found in Chapter 1. Such unstable atoms do not become inactive all at once but, as we have just seen, over a period of time.

Artificial Radioactivity

Normally stable elements such as iron, copper, aluminum, carbon, sodium, and many others can be made radioactive by bombarding them with fast-moving, high-energy subatomic particles such as alpha particles. When a stable atom of one of these elements is hit by such a "bullet," it may break into two other atoms and the particle or particles comprising the "bullet" may join one or the other of the two newly formed atoms.

As an example of this, let us consider what happens when an alpha particle (2 protons and 2 neutrons) smashes into the nucleus of a boron atom (5 protons and 5 neutrons) and cracks it apart. At the moment of impact we have a total of all particles in the combined two masses, that is, 7 protons and 7 neutrons. First and instantly, one of the neutrons is ejected along with radiant energy, which leaves a nucleus of 7 protons and 6 neutrons. This is an unstable or radioactive form of nitrogen which decays in about 10 minutes, ejecting a positive beta particle (positron) in the process.

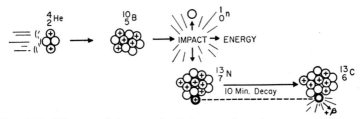

Fig. 12-3. When an alpha particle (helium nucleus, 2 neutrons and 2 protons, expressed $_2^4$He) smashes into a boron atom (5 neutrons and 5 protons, $_5^{10}$B), a neutron $\left(_0^1 n\right)$ leaves the combined masses so that radioactive isotope of nitrogen having 6 neutrons and 7 protons remains $\left(_7^{13}N\right)$. (Nitrogen normally has 7 neutrons and 7 protons and is expressed $_7^{14}N$). This unstable form of nitrogen ejects a positive charge, which can be called either a positron, a positive electron, or a positive beta particle—all meaning the same and expressed $+\beta$. This charge appears to have been released by a proton which becomes a neutron in the process. Thus we find the combined masses to consist now of 7 neutrons and 6 protons—a stable carbon atom $\left(_6^{13}C\right)$ which exists normally in about one part per hundred of natural carbon $\left(_6^{12}C\right)$.

At this point it must be explained that it is possible for a neutron to convert to a proton when a *negative* beta particle (electron) is ejected, and a proton can change to a neutron with the release of a positive beta particle (positron). The latter is what happens with the radioactive nitrogen we have obtained in the above reaction. With the positron ejection, one of the protons converts to a neutron so we have remaining from the process a stable carbon with 6 protons and 7 neutrons in its nucleus. Thus we have made artificially the element carbon and in the transition a short-lived radioactive form of nitrogen.

To illustrate further this most important and basic part of nucleonics, let us shoot a neutron at the nucleus of an aluminum atom. This nucleus normally has 13 protons and 14 neutrons. With the impact of the neutron bullet, the total number of particles split up into 2 nuclei, one of which contains 2 protons and 2 neutrons (an alpha particle or helium nucleus) and the other with 11 protrons and 13 neutrons. The latter is an unstable radioactive form of sodium, because in its stable form it contains only

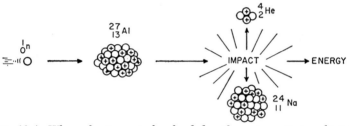

Fig. 12-4. When aluminum is bombarded with neutrons it is split into helium and sodium. The latter is unstable, however, since it contains an extra neutron, making its mass 24 instead of the normal 23. It is sodium nevertheless, since it has the correct number of protons (atomic number), 11.

12 neutrons. This bombardment of aluminum by neutrons has produced, therefore, a *radioactive sodium isotope* (see Chapter 1).

Radioactive isotopes of sodium, carbon, sulphur, iron, iodine, cobalt, gold, phosphorus, and other elements are used to considerable extent as *tracers* and are of extreme importance in biological and medical researches.

A description of how these subatomic particles are produced, accelerated, and "fired" at their targets by cyclotrons and other "atom smashers" is given in Chapter 15. The nuclear reactor or uranium pile process will be covered shortly in this chapter.

Measurement of Radioactivity

It has been pointed out that there are three types of emanations from radioactive elements: alpha particles, beta particles (positrons and electrons), and gamma radiation or radiant energy. All these cause ionization of gases to varying degrees, and it is on this principle that most radiation counters or measuring devices are made. Such instruments are called *Geiger-Müller counters*. There are other types called *scintillization counters* and *crystal counters,* and all these are discussed in more detail in Chapter 15.

Nuclear Fission

In the discussion a moment ago of atom cracking to form radio-isotopes and transmute one element into another, no account was taken of the velocity of the bullet. When specific results are desired, that is, certain end products are sought, the speed of the atom-splitting particle is critical. In other words, a slow neutron, called a *thermal neutron,* will cause reactions that a fast one will not. A fast neutron is one traveling at a velocity in the order of 12,000 miles per second, whereas a slow or thermal neutron moves at only 1.5 miles per second.

When a neutron traveling either fast or slow strikes an isotope of uranium having an atomic weight of 235 (U235), the uranium isotope is shattered into a barium and a krypton nucleus, as well as several smaller fragments, including neutrons, the total weight of which is a little less than the weight of the original uranium isotope. This indicates that some of the weight or mass has been converted into energy in the process, and the reaction is called *nuclear fission.*

Transuranium Elements

Uranium as found in nature consists of 140 atoms whose nuclei contain 92 protons and 146 neutrons (U238) and 1 atom of 92 protons and only 143 neutrons (U235). In other words, the ratio of U238 to U235 is 140 to 1 in natural uranium.

While the U235 atom is more easily split than the heavier one (U238) by either thermal or fast neutrons, the U238 will, when a thermal neutron of the proper velocity approaches, cap-

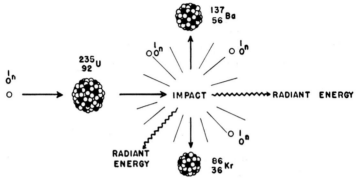

Fig. 12-5. A diagram of nuclear fission and conversion of mass into energy. A neutron $\left(^{1}_{0}\text{n}\right)$ collides with the readily fissionable uranium isotope nucleus $\left(^{235}_{92}\text{U}\right)$. The impact splits the uranium atom into several pieces. These may be a barium isotope $\left(^{137}_{56}\text{Ba}\right)$, krypton isotope $\left(^{86}_{36}\text{Kr}\right)$, and a number of neutrons, plus some radiant energy as indicated above, or there may be isotopes of other elements created. These pieces are referred to as *fission products*. The total number of *charges* (protons) in the fission products equals the number in the original nucleus. In the above instance, this would be

$$56 \text{ (barium)} + 36 \text{ (krypton)} = 92 \text{ (uranium)}$$

However, it will be noted that a loss in *mass* occurs because 137 (the protons and neutrons in the barium nucleus) plus 86 (the protons and neutrons in the krypton nucleus) and plus a few single neutrons (3 shown above) is *less* than the original mass of 235. The collision, therefore, converts some of the mass into radiant energy.

ture the neutron into its nucleus without splitting, thereby forming a uranium isotope U239. This isotope (half life 23 minutes) promptly emits a negative beta particle (electron) to form the first *transuranium element*. It is number 93 and is called *neptunium*. It has a half life of a little over 55 hours.

Neptunium, being unstable, decays with the emission of another negative beta particle (electron) (and also a neutrino emission) and becomes element 94, called *plutonium* with a *half life* of 24,000 years.

When U238 is bombarded with very fast alpha particles, the process ultimately results in the creation of element 95 called *americium*. Its half life is 500 years.

Americium has the property of being able to capture a neutron readily, resulting in an 18-hour radioisotope of the element which decays into another new element 96 called *curium* having a half life of about 5 months.

Berkelium, so named because of its discovery at the giant University of California cyclotrons (see Chapter 15), is produced by the bombardment of americium with high-energy alpha particles. It becomes element 97 with a half life of about $4\frac{1}{2}$ hours.

Another element, number 98, also produced in a similar way at California from curium, is called *californium*. It has a relatively short half life of approximately 45 minutes.

Chain Reaction

If, when the nucleus of an element such as uranium is split or fissioned by a neutron and releases other neutrons in the process, it follows that these neutrons also should cause fission of other nuclei. Then, each in turn ejects more neutrons, so that in time the whole mass will break down or explode if the reaction happens fast enough, with the release of an enormous amount of energy.

This is exactly what would happen with uranium if it were not for the fact that U238 captures many of the neutrons and, therefore, is not in itself too readily fissionable. U235, on the other hand, is more readily fissionable, but since it exists in only 1 part per 140 in natural uranium, it is not too plentiful and the task of separating enough of it for practical use as a fissionable material is a prodigious one.

This task was undertaken by American scientists and engineers, however, and the successful completion of it, along with the production of plutonium, is a remarkable example of coordinated thinking, skill, and effort. Plutonium, it has been explained, is derived from the nuclear reaction of U238 when the latter captures a slow neutron. It also is a readily fissionable material.

U235 is separated from U238 by a process called *gaseous diffusion*. At Oak Ridge, Tennessee, and other locations, large plants for this process are in operation. The process is a most involved one. A uranium compound must first be vaporized, so that the lighter molecules containing the U235 atom can be made to

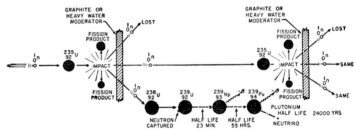

Fig. 12-6. Controlled chain reaction and the production of the transuranium elements neptunium $\left(^{237}_{93}\text{Np}\right)$ and plutonium $\left(^{239}_{94}\text{Pu}\right)$. This reaction takes place in uranium piles or reactors to create plutonium, a readily fissionable atom nucleus.

separate themselves from the rest of the gas which is heavier, since it contains the U238 atoms. The actual separating is done by passing the mixture through a barrier containing a series of microscopic holes. The lighter (U235) molecules get through faster than the others, thus resulting in a partial separation. At the Oak Ridge operation, thousands of separation stages have been used.

Plutonium is created in devices called *nuclear reactors* or *uranium piles*. These are charged with uranium "bricks" of a specific size which are stacked alternately with graphite "bricks." The graphite is called a *moderator* and is necessary to slow down the neutrons released by the uranium so that a chain reaction can be sustained. In order to keep the reaction under control and the process from running away with itself to become a molten mass, rods of special metal (cadmium, boron-steel, or others) are inserted into the pile at certain locations. These absorb neutrons and keep the reaction in "balance." If too many neutrons are being produced as indicated by a rapid rise in temperature, the rods are thrust deeper into the pile. If too few threaten to stop the chain reaction, the rods are pulled out to set more neutrons free. In the large reactors at Hanford, Washington, and elsewhere, this rod control of neutron flux is automatic, with adequate precautions to ensure proper control and safety.

Nuclear reactors were designed to produce plutonium, but they can be and are being used extensively to produce both stable and radioactive isotopes of normally stable elements. These have been shipped in large quantities to medical and research centers all over the world.

The production of plutonium in a uranium-graphite pile follows the procedure outlined in the discussion of transuranium elements a few pages back. The reaction starts when a neutron is introduced to a U238 atom. If, instead of letting it go by, the atom captures it and becomes U239, the latter transmutes to neptunium within a short time. This, in turn, decays in a few hours to plutonium, which is radioactive but does not decay for thousands of years.

This in itself is not chain reaction. But it should be remembered that there are also occasional U235 atoms in the uranium which do not capture a neutron but split when one strikes them and, as a result of the collision, release, let us say, three more neutrons. Of these three, one will be lost, the second will be captured by U238 and form more plutonium, and the third will split another U235 to release three more neutrons again. This is a chain reaction which can be controlled in a reactor as long as the neutrons are slowed down by the graphite and the metallic rods are there to absorb any neutrons produced in excess of those just necessary to keep the chain going.

If either plutonium or "pure" U235 is used instead of uranium (which is 140 parts U238 and 1 part U235) for a chain reaction with no control, an atomic explosion of tremendous proportions results.

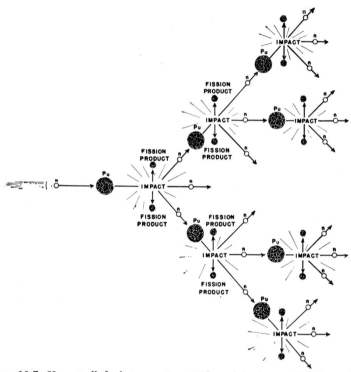

FIG. 12-7. Uncontrolled chain reaction. Either plutonium or U235 can be used, since both are readily fissioned by neutron collision. In the atomic bomb, this reaction, affecting the countless billions of atoms in the sizable quantity of these elements, takes place in less than a millionth of a second, with the release of enormous amounts of radiant energy in the infrared, visible-light, ultraviolet, X- and gamma-ray regions.

As might be expected there are many problems attending the design and operation of nuclear reactors. One, of course, is the production of a tremendous amount of heat. Reactors are maintained at a relatively constant temperature by circulating water through cooling coils. A second problem involves the extremely dangerous radiations produced by the reaction. Very thick concrete shielding walls are constructed around a reactor which are equal in effect to 2 or 3 feet of solid steel. A constant vigil is maintained over those working in its vicinity to be sure that such radiations are not escaping in serious quantity.

Heavy Water

There are other types of reactors than the one just described. One uses *heavy water* as a moderator or neutron absorber. An ordinary water molecule is composed of one oxygen atom and

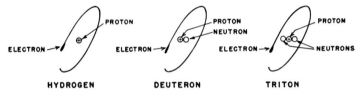

HYDROGEN   DEUTERON   TRITON

FIG. 12-8. The normal hydrogen atom (left) and its two isotopes. The molecules of ordinary water are clusters of one oxygen and two hydrogen atoms. Heavy-water molecules (deuterium) contain one oxygen atom and hydrogen isotopes whose chief nuclei are deuterons, and "triple" heavy water (tritium) consists of one oxygen atom and hydrogen isotopes whose nuclei are tritons. In each case, the atomic *number* or *charge* is the same as with normal hydrogen, but the atomic weight varies.

two hydrogen atoms. A hydrogen atom normally consists of a one-proton nucleus and one electron. However, for about every 5,000 of these there is one which is the same in all characteristics as the normal atom except that its nucleus consists of a proton and a neutron. It is called a *deuteron.*

These deuterons are somewhat less "active" than normal hydrogen atoms in that they have less self-vibration, so that a water molecule containing them is not so easily broken up into its individual atoms of oxygen and deuterons as ordinary water. As a result of this difference in characteristics it is possible to separate the 1 molecule in 5,000 from the rest by electrolysis. This means that, by passing electric current through ordinary water and collecting the oxygen and hydrogen gases released by the

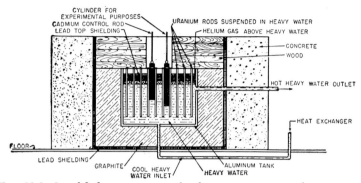

FIG. 12-9. Simplified cross section of a heavy-water reactor for sustaining a controlled chain reaction and producing plutonium from uranium. In this type of "pile," heavy water is used instead of graphite and acts as a cooling agent as well as the moderator to slow down fast neutrons which are liberated with fission. Graphite surrounding the aluminum tank reflects escaping neutrons back into the process.

There may be a hundred or more uranium rods suspended in the tank. When they have become adequately rich in plutonium, they are removed and the plutonium is separated from the remaining uranium by chemical methods. In the center are other rods which can be raised or lowered into the reaction. One, at least, is a cadmium control rod which is lowered to absorb neutrons and retard the action, or raised to speed it up. These operate automatically in accordance with the temperature being generated within the tank. Other rods or containers in the center are for the insertion of certain materials into the reaction for experimental purposes.

The heavy water is circulated through a heat exchanger to maintain a constant proper temperature. If the water is allowed to become very hot (by adjustment of the control rods), it can be used to generate steam for steam turbines and the production of electric power. In the latter case, a steam-generating plant of more or less conventional design could be used at the right where a heat exchanger is indicated.

process, the hydrogen gas has fewer deuterons in it than the water had. In other words, the remaining water is richer in deuterons than originally. By repeating or *cascading* this process many times, a product is obtained in which all or nearly all the molecules contain deuterons instead of normal hydrogen atoms. This product is called heavy water or *deuterium.*

Most of the weight in a water molecule is in the oxygen atom, so that even though deuterons are twice as heavy as normal hydrogen atoms, deuterium is actually only about 10 per cent more dense than ordinary water. It freezes and boils at slightly higher temperatures and is expressed chemically as D_2O instead of H_2O.

Heavy water is used in certain types of nuclear reactors as a moderator to slow down the neutrons which have been released in the chain reaction. There are many possible combinations for reactors using different moderators to produce various neutron energies, fuels (uranium) of different degrees of richness, and several methods of cooling and fuel mixing. Designs are determined primarily by the end-use of the products to be created.

The Atom Bomb

To affect an atomic explosion it is necessary to set up conditions whereby the chain reaction in a fissionable material will take place instantly. We have discussed above how two such fissionable materials, U235 and plutonium, are produced in quantity through a controlled chain reaction, but we have yet to consider how to obtain the instantaneous fission.

First, unless enough of the material is used, there will be no explosion. To cause fission, a neutron must hit a nucleus, which, as compared with the whole atom, is a target the size of a pinhead in an auditorium, and the neutron itself is even smaller. Thus we see that a neutron may go through millions of atoms before making a hit. Being an uncharged particle it is not influenced in its flight by the forces and charges which influence other particles.

It can be seen, then, that, if a quantity of uranium is too small, many of the neutrons produced will pass on out of the material without any collision and, as a result, no chain reaction will occur. On the other hand, there is a threshold or quantity large enough (with enough atoms) to provide a sufficient number of targets so that enough hits will be made to create a chain reaction. This quantity of fissionable material is called the *critical mass.*

A critical mass cannot be compactly assembled before the explosion is desired. If it were, the explosion would occur prematurely. The mass, then, must be maintained apart in at least two parts until the instant the explosion is to take place.

The structure of an atomic weapon of this sort is, of course, secret, but it is generally accepted that the parts of the critical mass must be brought together very rapidly—possibly as rifle bullets would collide—within the bomb at the moment an explosion is desired.

The result of an atomic explosion is well known. In less than a microsecond a small amount of matter is converted into a giant, hellish, seething ball of raw energy. Temperatures approaching and possibly exceeding 20 million degrees Fahrenheit are created with consequent enormous expansion of air and gases in the vicinity. An intense shock (or sound) wave such as would be produced by approximately 20,000 tons of TNT rolls outward from the center at about 750 miles an hour, crushing practically everything within a 2-mile radius. The flash of energy radiates light, infrared, ultraviolet, and X radiation in enormous quantities, sufficient to set fires and cause lethal burns over a mile away. Gamma radiation is released in the flash which should be equal in radioactive potency to 65 million tons of radium for a period of 1 second. These radiations and the released neutrons may be deadly at the moment up to a mile or more, and while the artificial radioactivity induced in objects and materials is relatively short lived, it is still a major hazard.

Yet less than 1 per cent of the total possible energy was released in the first few atom bombs. If all the energy could be released from 1 pound of U235, it would equal the energy of nearly 12 billion kilowatt-hours of electricity.

The Hydrogen Bomb

The sun has maintained its temperature for perhaps 2 billion years as a result of a building-up rather than a breaking-down process such as we have just discussed with uranium fission.

The build-up from a light element to a heavier one is a synthesis whereby ordinary hydrogen atoms of one proton each get together with neutrons to form helium, which has two protons and two neutrons in its atom (see Chapter 1).

This process is the principle of what has been called an "H" or hydrogen bomb. In order to accomplish it, use is made of another isotope of hydrogen, the nucleus of which contains *two* neutrons in addition to the one proton. It is called *triton*. Triple-heavy water whose molecules are thus composed is called *tritium*. Such molecules or atoms are not found in nature but can be produced by cyclotron bombardment (see Chapter 15) of frozen deuterium oxide (D_2O or double-heavy water) with deuterons.

Helium atoms can be built up from the tritium and deuterium atoms if the latter can be brought together. Since both have strong forces repelling each other, the atoms must be brought to collision at tremendous velocities. This can be accomplished at a temperature of several millions of degrees when the thermal speeds of the two will be sufficient.

As we have seen, the temperature at the center of a uranium explosion will be in the order of some 20 million degrees, so that in such an explosion we have the means of "triggering" the hydrogen to helium reaction.

At the instant of impact and transmutation of the hydrogen isotopes deuterium and tritium to helium, an inconceivable explosion of energy takes place. In such a bomb the uranium-fission explosion serves only to ignite the far greater one which has been called the H bomb.

Atomic Energy for Other Purposes—Radioisotopes

It has been mentioned that the nuclear reactors in operation in various parts of the country are producing radioactive isotopes for uses in the fields of biology, horticulture, and medicine. This use of atomic energy alone would justify the vast amount of time and money involved in the design and development of uranium pile reactors, and their contribution to medical research has been most extensive.

Radioisotopes are used as *tracers;* that is, when such atoms are injected into the blood stream, digestive tracts, or nervous system, their course through the body can be followed with sensitive instruments which detect the radiation they emit.

For example, if we inject a small amount of radioactive sodium into one arm, we find that it passes through the heart and lungs and will be located in the other arm only a few seconds later. It is also found that it diffuses into the tissues rapidly. Seventy-five seconds after the arm injection, the radiosodium can be detected in perspiration on the other arm.

Such researches tell us a great deal about how all our organs function and how disease and growths either flourish or can be conquered. Radioactive iodine and/or phosphorus, for instance, will help locate and diagnose tumors, particularly in the brain, without exploratory surgery. There are many other applications such as these, and more are developing each year.

In horticulture, radiocarbon is used in researches to learn more about photosynthesis (Chapter 8) and how plants thrive with sunlight. By exposing them to carbon dioxide in which some carbon atoms have been "tagged" radioactively, the progress of these atoms into the leaves and through the plant structure can be followed.

Radiocarbon also serves as an indicator of past events on this earth. Although it is found only in one part per trillion in the earth's atmosphere, it is enough to be detected. Plants depend upon carbon dioxide, which they "breathe," and the gas always contains this minute quantity of radiocarbon which has been freshly made by *cosmic radiation* from outer space.

Radiocarbon has a half life of 5,568 years, so that by measuring its activity in petrified wood or plant fossils, it can be determined with reasonable accuracy just about when the plant or tree lived and absorbed the "fresh" carbon isotope. Thus radiocarbon tells us when glaciers swept over the land and killed trees, when floods or other natural phenomena occurred at certain places, and even what land contour and topography looked like many thousands of years ago.

Power from Controlled Nuclear Reactors

It has been known and stated for many years that "there is enough energy in a drop of water to drive an ocean liner across the Atlantic." Only since July 16, 1945, however, when the first atomic bomb exploded on a New Mexico desert, has science been able to release such atomic energy all at once.

But the vital factor in the use of atomic energy for generating electric power is *not* to release it all at once. In the discussion of nuclear reactors, it was pointed out that, with controlled chain-reaction fission, great quantities of heat were generated. Since heat is the energy used in the production of steam for steam turbines and engines, it follows that nuclear reactors can be designed, using uranium fission as a means of heating water for the steam, to turn generators.

Primarily, the problems are economic ones. Coal, oil, and gas as used in producing steam are inexpensive as compared with uranium fission for the same purpose *where space, weight, and rate of consumption of the fuels are not important factors.* In an ocean liner, however, all three are major problems. The speed, cargo space, and voyage schedules of a vessel are all dependent upon the amount and weight of fuel she must carry. If, therefore, an engine utilizing a "nuclear fuel" is used in a ship at a great saving in space and weight, the economic structure of water transportation changes, providing such engine costs are comparable to other types.

There are a great many aspects to the application of nuclear energy for generating power. They involve not only economics and engineering, but the relative abundance of nuclear fuel in the earth's surface and where it is located, as well as the probable decline in other fuel costs as nuclear power comes over the horizon as a competitor.

In speculation, it is interesting and challenging to remember that nature gives us free, billions of kilowatts of energy every hour in the sunlight that floods the earth—and we have never tapped this source commercially.

Cosmic Radiation

Over 40 years ago, physicists concluded that some sort of radiation must exist in the atmosphere because under all circumstances air is found to be slightly ionized (a few of its atoms are found to be minus an electron and, therefore, positively charged). Furthermore, a comparatively simple device, called an *electroscope,* indicated the penetration of the unknown radiations at a depth of 30 feet or more in lake water as well as underground in mines and caves. The fact that these radiations were consistently much stronger at high altitudes than at the earth's surface led to the further conclusion that such radiations did not originate on this earth but rather somewhere out in the interstellar space.

It is now known that cosmic rays, when they enter the earth's atmosphere (primary cosmic rays), are very high-velocity atomic nuclei. As they rain down toward the earth, they collide with various atoms comprising the atmosphere, giving rise to showers of other particles (secondary cosmic rays) and gamma radiation.

The origin of cosmic rays has not been definitely established. The fact that they do not reach the earth with significantly greater strength during daylight hours eliminates the sun as a major source. Also, since their intensity does not diminish during the day or increase at night, they cannot be associated wholly with any particular group of stars such as the Milky Way. It is known that most of the particles are positively charged, since they are observed to travel mostly from west to east, a direction consistent with the influence of the earth's magnetic field.

Some of the particles are heavy atoms completely stripped of electrons—in other words, heavy atomic nuclei. Although hydrogen is much more abundant than other nuclei in cosmic showers,

Fig. 12-10. Cosmic-ray research is carried on at high altitudes through the use of special balloons with gondolas containing instruments such as a cloud chamber, camera, etc. This photograph shows an uninflated balloon beginning its ascent with cosmic-ray instruments. When the balloon reaches its ceiling altitude of many thousands of feet, it will become entirely filled by the bubble of gas at the top and may be as much as 100 feet in diameter. (*Courtesy of General Mills Laboratories, Minneapolis, Minn.*)

such heavier ones as iron, carbon, and silicon are present in quantities ranging from 1 to one-tenth of 1 per cent.

Theories as to the origin of cosmic radiation vary somewhat. One suggests that these particles have been wandering around in space since the creation of the universe and cease their travels only when they fall within the sphere of influence of a much larger body such as a star or planet. Another proposes that they

are constantly being born somewhere out in space, perhaps with
the creation of matter from energy.

FIG. 12-11. The track of a heavy cosmic particle photographed in a cloud
chamber suspended from an ascending balloon. The instruments at the bottom indicate an altitude of 3,250 feet, a temperature of 70° Fahrenheit,
and the time as approximately 8:25. The track, as shown, results from the
passage of a relatively heavy cosmic particle, probably a carbon nucleus,
since it has penetrated four ¼-inch lead plates. (*Courtesy of Edward P.
Ney, University of Minnesota, Minneapolis, Minn.*)

Cosmic radiation research is one of the most fascinating and
compelling branches of science and one from which we may
eventually learn something of the fundamental existence of all
things.

Part Four: Electron Tubes and
Sources of Radiant Energy

13

Electron Emission

At the very beginning of Part One it was pointed out that all materials contain electrons, some of which are not securely bound in atoms but can more or less move or vibrate rapidly from one atom to another within the substance. These are called *free* electrons. In solids they do not usually possess sufficient speed to overcome molecular or atomic forces and are confined to the limits of the material. In liquids, free electrons are not restrained quite so much as in solids, and in gases there is little or no restraint at all.

Heat is a convenient form of energy which can be used to speed up the activity of electrons, atoms, or molecules to such an extent that they will actually leave the substance of which they have been a part. When a kettle of water is heated sufficiently, for example, the molecules of water will leave the surface in the form of vapor or steam. We call this *evaporation*. If a solid, such as a metallic filament in an incandescent lamp, is heated sufficiently, the electrons become very active and acquire enough speed to overcome a so-called *surface barrier* and escape from the solid wire entirely. This is called *thermionic emission*. It differs from water evaporation in that electrons escape instead of molecules (see Chapter 1) and the electrons are negatively charged whereas the water molecules are uncharged.

In 1883, when he was thirty-six years old, Thomas A. Edison made the first experimental verification of electron emission, but it was several years later that his observations were satisfactorily explained. He sealed a short length of wire through the glass

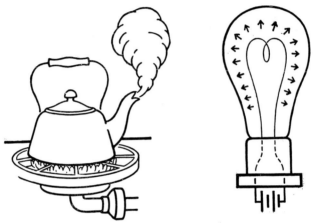

Fig. 13-1. Water evaporation (left) is similar to electron emission. The evaporation of electrons from a solid body, such as the filament in the lamp (right), is thermionic emission.

bulb of one of his incandescent lamps, above the filament, and connected a battery and meter to it. He noted that, when this wire was connected to the positive terminal of the battery, an electric current flowed through it, even though it was not in contact with the filament of the lamp. The wire, being positive, attracted the negatively charged electrons. This is known as the *Edison effect* and is the basic principle of all electron tubes today. The elements in electron tubes which correspond to Edison's filament may be filaments also, or they may be in the form of a ribbon, bar, cylinder, or block of metal. They are called *cathodes* and emit electrons when heated. The elements corresponding to the short length of wire in Edison's device may be wires, plates, cylinders, or other metallic forms and are called *anodes*.

Studies in thermionic emission show that the amount of electron flow from cathode to anode depends upon the temperature and nature of the cathode and upon the amount of positive voltage applied to the anode.

As indicated above, there are many ways of designing cathodes and anodes. One type of cathode which is quite satisfactory in certain tubes utilizes a small metallic cylinder to which heat is applied indirectly by means of a heater element or filament inside the cylinder and insulated from it.

The emission of electrons from cathodes can be greatly increased by coating them with certain materials such as the oxides of strontium, barium, and calcium. Another material used in some types of vacuum tubes utilizes thorium dissolved with

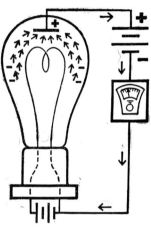

Fig. 13-2. The basic principle of all electron tubes today is the so-called *Edison effect* illustrated above. Edison experimented with this in 1883.

a small amount of carbon in a tungsten filament. This is called *thoriated tungsten* and has excellent electron-emission characteristics until such time as heat has reduced the metallic thorium content at the surface of the wire to an extent that the electron emission drops to the poorer characteristics of the tungsten. When this occurs, the cathode is said to be *deactivated*.

The distribution of electrons around a hot wire or cathode is called the *space charge* of electrons, and it varies with the temperature to which the cathode is subjected. This variance occurs in the quantity of electrons around the cathode and in the speed at which they travel. When the cathode is cold, the space charge is nil or practically so, but as the temperature is increased, more and more electrons leave it with increasing velocities, so that the space charge extends farther and farther away.

If the positive voltage on the anode or plate is kept constant, the flow of electrons to it will increase only up to a certain cathode temperature. Beyond that point the electron flow will remain constant even though more electrons are being driven from the cathode. This is due to the fact that in the immediate vicinity of the cathode the density of the negative electrons becomes greater than the positive plate or anode. The consequent cloud of free electrons formed around the cathode hinders the passage of newly emitted electrons to the anode, so that they return to the cathode. Thus, this cloud or space charge will limit the flow of electrons or *plate current.*

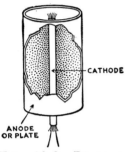

Fig. 13-3. Diagram showing the space-charge effect. The electrons are emitted from a sleeve surrounding a folded heater wire through which current is passed. The heat thus created drives electrons out of the sleeve which is called the cathode.

Electronics

The experiments of Edison resulted in the electrons being put to work and provided the foundation for the vast industry and science today called *electronics.* The American Standards Association defines electronics as " . . . *the branch of science and technology which relates to the conduction of electricity through gases or in vacuo.*" The word, then, is properly applied to a device or tube which is deliberately designed to make use of electron emission rather than one, such as an incandescent lamp, in which the electronic characteristics are more or less incidental. Within this category would come radio tubes of all types, fluorescent lamps, and a great many other vacuum or gaseous-discharge tubes which are used in the various fields of communications, medicine, surgery, transportation, entertainment, and general industry.

The Diode Tube

The simplest vacuum tube contains only a cathode and anode and is called a *diode.* The electrodes are placed in a glass tube or bulb from which as much of the air as possible is exhausted, and the necessary lead wires are brought out through airtight

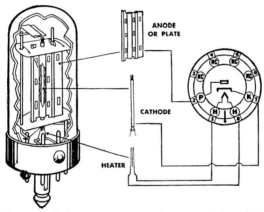

Fig. 13-4. Diagram of the construction and wiring of the diode tube. The base plan at the right indicates those pins having no connection (*NC*), those connected to the heater (*H*), and the connection to the plate and cathode (*P* and *K*, respectively).

seals. The high vacuum is desirable so that the electrons can move from the cathode over to the plate or anode without too many collisions with molecules of air, although gas-filled diodes are made and widely used today. The principle of the diode is identical with that in Edison's experiment.

One of the most important uses of diode tubes is to change alternating current to a pulsating direct current. Current thus changed is called *rectified,* and the tubes which do it, *rectifiers.*

Since electrons are negative charges, they fly to the plate only when the plate is positive. When it becomes negative, it repels the electrons back to the cathode from which they were emitted. Therefore, when alternating current is applied to the plate, it

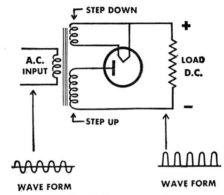

Fig. 13-5. The half-wave rectifier circuit.

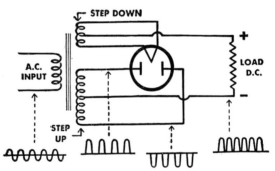

Fig. 13-6. The full-wave rectifier circuit.

(the plate) becomes alternately positive and negative so that plate current (electron flow) flows only during that half of the time when the plate is positive and only in one direction.

A diode tube operating in this manner cuts off the negative halves of the a-c cycles and is called a *half-wave rectifier.* To avoid the loss of half of each cycle, two diodes may be used and so connected that the anodes or plate of one will be alternately positive while the other is negative. This arrangement can also be incorporated in one tube, the voltage on one anode being positive while the other is negative, with the conditions reversing every half cycle. In this way both halves of the alternating cycle are ultilized, and the tube is called a *full-wave rectifier*. Groups of several diodes are used to rectify the current from three or more phase supplies.

Radio Detectors

It has been explained how radio waves radiate away from the antenna of a radio transmitter and set up an oscillatory current in the receiving antenna and how the receiver itself must be tuned to the frequency of these waves. It was also indicated that means must be provided for separating the modulating wave from the carrier before the headphones or loud-speaker can be made to produce sound waves.

This separating can be accomplished with a crystal detector or a vacuum-tube detector such as a diode. In either case, the detector acts as a rectifier or valve by allowing current to flow in only one direction through it, thereby changing the high-frequency alternating oscillations (radio frequency) to slow-frequency pulsations (audio frequency), which are then made to produce sound waves in the headphones or loud-speaker. Such *demodulation* or sorting out of the audio frequencies from the carrier- or radio-frequency waves (see Chapter 10) is necessary because the diaphragms of headphones and speakers will not vibrate at such high frequencies. Even if they did, the sound waves produced would be far above the upper limit of audibility, so that no purpose would be served.

Certain crystals such as galena, silicon, germanium, and carborundum have the property of unsymmetrical conductivity and allow current to pass through in one direction much more readily than in the other, thus rectifying the current. Crystal rectifiers will be discussed more fully later on.

The Triode Tube

In the diode tube there is no way to control the electron flow (plate current) except to change the plate voltage or cathode temperature. In 1906 Dr. Lee De Forest introduced a third element into the diode tube, making it into what is called a *triode*. This third element is a *grid* and consists, as a rule, of a

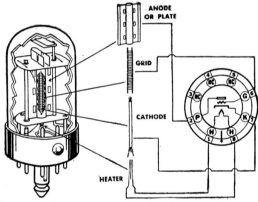

Fig. 13-7. Diagram of the construction of a typical triode tube, with wiring connections to the base.

spiral mesh of wire inserted between the cathode and the plate in such a way that the cathode is completely surrounded by it. The grid acts as a control of the electron flow from the cathode to the plate, since the electrons must pass through it on their way over.

The amount of electron current flowing in a triode depends upon the voltage applied to the grid. If it is made negative with respect to the cathode, the electrons will be repelled (being negative charges), and if positive, the electron flow may be even greater than if the grid were absent. Thus, by varying the voltage from a negative to a positive value on the grid, it can be made to act as a valve to regulate the flow of electrons from the cathode to the plate.

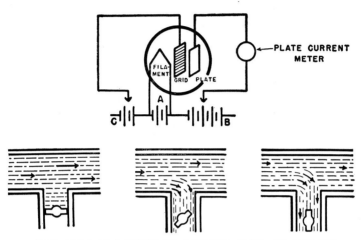

GRID ACTS AS A VALVE TO CONTROL FLOW OF CURRENT
FIG. 13-8. Basic hookup of triode tubes.

Amplifiers

As has been explained, the plate current (electron flow) is affected by either a change in the plate voltage or a change in the grid voltage. The latter, however, has a much greater effect than a plate-voltage change; that is, a slight change of grid voltage can vary the electron flow as much as a large change in the plate voltage. The ratio between the two values required to maintain a constant plate current or electron flow is the *amplification factor* of the tube.

It can be seen by a study of Fig. 13-9 that large variations in plate current resulting from grid-voltage changes will induce voltage variations in the inductance L through which the plate current flows. These induced voltages will be greatly magnified or amplified reproductions of a radio signal voltage when it is applied to the grid. Several such triodes acting as amplifiers and properly connected can increase the strength of a radio signal by thousands of times.

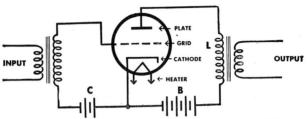

FIG. 13-9. Hookup of a triode tube used as an amplifier.

Oscillators

In the section covering the production of radio waves in Chapter 10, it was mentioned that oscillating carrier waves may be produced by a certain type of vacuum tube called an *oscillator*. Triodes are used for this purpose when connected as shown in Fig. 13-10.

If the inductance *L* is so connected that part of the energy resulting from the plate current is fed back to the grid circuit, the circuit will produce oscillating currents of constant frequency and amplitude. In such a circuit the tube operates as a rapidly acting valve which transfers energy to the grid circuit at the precise moment to sustain oscillations—much the same as a rubber ball can be kept bouncing by striking it downward at the top of each bounce.

Oscillators of this type are widely used for both radio and wire communication circuits to provide the carrier waves. There are several types of circuits employing various methods of producing oscillations.

In high-frequency and ultrahigh-frequency work, quartz crystals are used in conjunction with oscillators to provide extremely precise control of frequency. The crystals are cut from the mother crystal in wafer and other forms with a very high degree of accuracy, and the angle of cut with respect to various axes of the mother crystal determines their piezoelectric characteristics. The method of cutting such crystal plates with re-

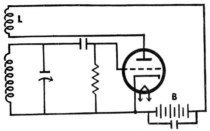

Fig. 13-10. Wiring diagram of a triode used as an oscillator.

spect to the various axes of the mother crystal and an explanation of piezoelectricity were given in the discussion of Ultrasonics in Chapter 9.

Tetrodes, Pentodes, and Beam-power Tubes

The grid and plate of a triode operate in a manner similar to a condenser having capacitance (see Chapter 4, Capacitance and Resonance). Energy can be fed back from plate to grid through this capacitance, so that triodes used as amplifiers frequently begin to oscillate. In order to avoid this, a second grid, called a *screen grid,* is placed between the first (control grid) and the plate and is usually operated at a lower positive voltage than the plate. Such a four-element tube is called a *tetrode.*

When electrons strike the plate of a tube, they cause other electrons to be knocked off the plate, much the same as a stone raises dust when thrown against the dry ground. This release of other electrons is called *secondary emission* and in a triode causes no trouble because the newly released electrons fly right back to the positive plate from which they were knocked. In a tetrode, however, many of them may be drawn to the screen grid under certain conditions when the screen-grid voltage is relatively high instead of returning to the plate. This results in

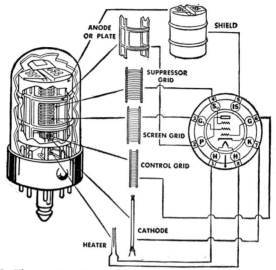

FIG. 13-11. The construction and basic wiring of a typical pentode tube.

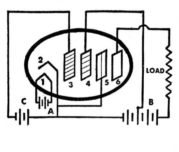

1 — HEATER   4 — SCREEN GRID
2 — CATHODE   5 — SUPPRESSOR
3 — CONTROL GRID   GRID
                    6 — PLATE

FIG. 13-12. The basic hookup of a pentode circuit.

a counter flow of electrons which can be eliminated by adding a third grid called a *suppressor grid*. This third one is placed between the plate and the screen grid and is connected to the cathode and thus, by virtue of its negative potential, forces the secondary electrons back to the plate. A five-element tube such as this contains a cathode, a control grid, a screen grid, a suppressor grid, and a plate and is called a *pentode*.

When pentodes are used for higher power output, unsatisfactory operation results from the fact that the wire suppressor

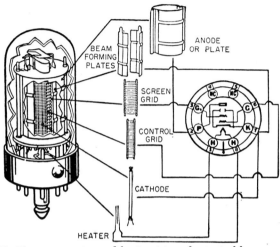

FIG. 13-13. The construction and basic wiring of a typical beam-power tube.

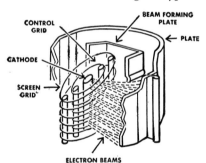

FIG. 13-14. Cutaway view of beam-power-tube operation.

grid introduces distortion and nonuniform suppressor action. This is overcome by the use of beam-forming plates instead of a suppressor grid. These plates concentrate the electrons in a beam during their passage between the screen grid and the plate, and the suppressor action is obtained from the space charge which occurs with the concentration of electrons. Large tubes of this type are used in radio transmitting circuits, whereas smaller ones function as amplifiers (audio and radio frequency) in receivers.

There are other methods of radio-tube construction employing

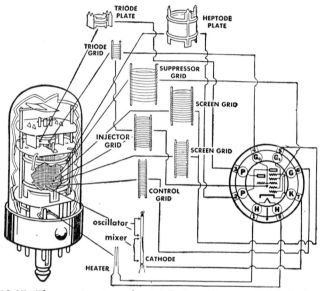

Fɪɢ. 13-15. The construction of a triode-heptode converter and the connections of the base pins.

more devices than those just discussed. The pentagrid converter, for example, utilizes five grids in addition to its cathode and plate. In other types, the functions of two separate tubes have been combined in one, such as the previously described full-wave rectifier. Fundamentally, these other types are similar to the more common ones covered in this chapter.

14

Incandescent Light Bulbs

If we are to adhere to the definition of "electronics" given in the previous chapter, an incandescent light bulb cannot be considered as an electron tube. Although electrons are released from the tungsten filament as a result of its becoming white-hot, such thermionic emission is incidental and serves no purpose in the production of light.

Incandescent bulbs, however, are the most widely used producers of radiant energy in the visible-light region of the electromagnetic spectrum, and as such, some space should be devoted to them in a book of this type.

Ever since 1878, when Swan demonstrated his first crude incandescent lamp, and about a year later, when Edison passed an electric current through lengths of carbonized bamboo, horsehair, and filaments of metal sealed in evacuated glass bottles and finally produced light for 45 hours, the development of light bulbs has been rapid. The filaments have undergone changes in material as well as in shape. The early carbon filaments were replaced by tantalum and other metals for a short time until finally, when a method of drawing tungsten into fine wire was established, that metal was, and still is, used. The effectiveness of tungsten as a filament lies basically in its high melting point. It is capable of becoming extremely hot without melting, thus producing a comparative abundance of light.

The shape of the filament has also changed from the original single loop of carbon wire 8 to 10 inches long to a coiled coil of wire about the same length when straightened out, but only little more than $\frac{1}{2}$ inch long in its coiled-coil form. The primary reason for concentrating the filament in this manner is to keep its heat from being carried away (by gas) as rapidly as with a straight wire, thus providing more heat on the filament with a consequent increase in light ouput.

Other changes involved the gases used to surround the filament. The first light bulbs were evacuated as completely as possible at the time, and the use of vacuum lamps became widespread. In fact, many of the smaller types of incandescent bulbs today are evacuated. When it was discovered that an inert gas such as nitrogen would retard the evaporation of the filament, resulting in less pronounced bulb blackening and higher efficiency, the gas-filled lamp appeared. Nitrogen was used exclusively for a while until argon proved to be more effective, being heavier and acting somewhat like a blanket around the filament in keeping the evaporation rate at a minimum. There are other advantages to the use of gas in light bulbs, and at present argon mixed with nitrogen, in varying proportions depeding upon wattage, is used in all gas-filled incandescent light sources.

During these 60 years or more of development, the efficiency of incandescent lamps has in some instances increased in the order of 1,000 per cent. One-hundred-watt lamps, which in the early days had efficiencies of 2 or 3 lumens per watt, are now rated at 16.2 lumens per watt (see Chapter 6, Measurement of Light).

It appears that future increases in incandescent-light-source efficiencies will be small, since each increase in the operating temperature of the filament brings it nearer to its melting point. The lighting industry has developed other methods of producing light, however, which even at the outset showed efficiencies more than double those of filament lamps. These sources involve the entirely different principles of gaseous discharge and fluorescence and will be discussed shortly.

Incandescent light bulbs have certain physical, electrical, and economical advantages which make them preferable to linear and other types of light sources for a great many applications. They are concentrated sources, and except for highly specialized

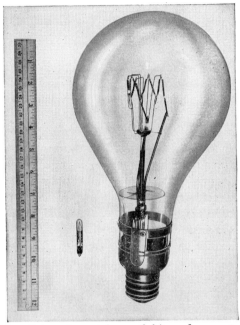

Fig. 14-1. A small incandescent lamp (left) used as a circuit signal for telephone switchboards. These lamps range in size from 4 volts, 0.170 ampere to 60 volts, 0.045 ampere. A standard 2-kilowatt PS52 incandescent lamp (right) such as is used in certain types of floodlighting and high-bay illumination. There are still smaller incandescent lamps, such as the "grain-of-wheat" light used in medical work, and larger ones up to 50,000 watts.

gaseous-discharge tubes, their use in conjunction with specular, spherical, or parabolic reflectors and lenses is essential. Wherever light projection, as in spot and floodlighting either inside or outside, is used, or where beams of light are necessary to fulfill the requirements of a lighting installation, incandescent light bulbs are the most effective and practical sources.

There are thousands of different types and sizes commercially available. Many of them are being replaced by fluorescent lamps for general lighting, but uses of other newer types with built-in reflectors and lenses and shapes designed for a particular purpose are rapidly increasing.

Photoflash Lamps

No treatise on sources of radiant energy in the visible light region of the electromagnetic spectrum would be quite complete without a brief consideration of photoflash lamps. We have already seen how, in radar work, extremely powerful pulses of microwaves are produced by magnetrons in conjunction with other tubes in the circuits and how the short wave trains or pulses are sent out in a beam to reflect or echo back to the receiver.

In a similar manner, a photoflash lamp produces one powerful pulse of radiant energy which we call a flash of light. This, too, is sent out in a wide beam or flood of light for an instant and reflects back to the camera from the object to be photographed.

The duration of the pulse of light, however, is measured in *milliseconds* (thousandths of a second) instead of microseconds (millionths of a second) as with radar. Different types of lamps produce pulses of different time durations depending upon the type of camera used and the nature of the photographic work. Also, the characteristics of the flash are designed to be different in various lamps; that is, some will reach their maximum brilliancy in approximately 5 milliseconds with a total effective light duration of about 10, whereas others are made to reach their peak much slower and last nearly 100 milliseconds (1/10 second) to coincide better with the type and speed of the camera shutter.

All good photographic work requires the careful correlation of three factors: the amount of light affecting the film (actinic light), the camera characteristics (lens, shutter speeds, etc.), and the film (sensitivity). To meet the requirements of the last two factors, photoflash bulbs are made in three basic types. These types are different in the time required for the flash to reach its peak, and they are designated as fast (5 milliseconds), medium (20 milliseconds), and slow (30 milliseconds).

Amateurs with inexpensive cameras use a flash lamp with quite different characteristics from that used by professional

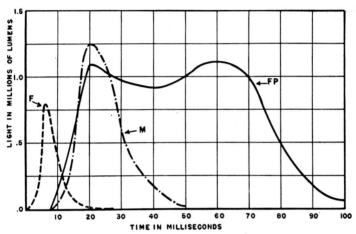

FIG. 14-2. Curves showing the performance of three different classes of photoflash lamps. The F (fast) curve indicates that the lamp reaches its peak brilliancy of 800,000 lumens about 1/200 second after it is triggered. The M (medium) curve shows the maximum brightness of a million and a quarter lumens occurring about 1/50 second after the start. The FP (focal-plane) type of lamp reaches its peak brilliancy in about 1/50 second and holds it for 1/20 second. The triggering mechanism is designed to open the camera shutter at the precise instant when the flash will be most effective.

studios, whose equipment operates with a much higher degree of precision. As a general rule, studio work demands a slower flash because the shutter speeds and lenses can be more carefully regulated to coincide with the flash time.

The brightest flash bulb (No. 3) produces between 4 and 5 million lumens (see Chapter 6, Measurement of Light) for a period of 10 milliseconds. It requires about 30 milliseconds to build up to this value and nearly 40 to fall back to zero again. Another type (No. 2A) builds up to a million lumens in about 20 milliseconds, holds this average brilliancy for approximately 50 milliseconds, and then dies out in about 30 milliseconds more. To build flash bulbs which will perform consistently within such critical limits of time and intensity demands extreme care in design and manufacture.

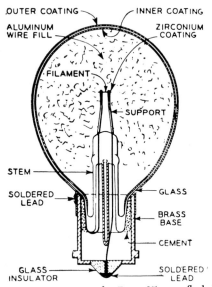

FIG. 14-3. Cross section of a Press 25 superflash bulb.

The flash itself is produced when a tangled web of pure aluminum wire ignites in a low-pressure atmosphere of oxygen. This, of course, is enclosed in the glass bulb which is protected from shattering at the moment of flash by an inner and outer coating or skin of transparent plastic.

The aluminum wire is ignited or "triggered" by a short length of filament wire which is coated with a zirconium compound. The latter starts to burn within 1 millisecond after current from a battery passes through it. A current of at least 1.5 amperes at 3 volts is necessary to assure firing of the lamp.

There are electronic methods of producing pulses of light for purposes other than photography. While they may also be used for certain types of photographic work, the simplicity, dependability, and low cost of photoflash bulbs makes their use more or less general throughout the photographic industry. The electronic flash tubes mentioned above will be described later.

Another type of photographic light source is called the *photoflood* lamp. It is an incandescent filament lamp designed for very high light output, at the sacrifice of lamp life. A photoflood lamp will produce nearly twice as much light as a standard light bulb of equal wattage, but since its filament burns at a much higher temperature than normal, the actinic value is much higher so that, from a photographic standpoint, it will be several times as effective as the standard lamp. The rated life of photoflood lamps is from 3 to 15 hours, depending upon the type. For photographic work, light output per watt is of greater importance than lamp life.

For infrared photographic work as mentioned in Chapter 7, photoflash lamps are coated with a red filter material which screens out most of the visible light and transmits most of the infrared radiation produced by the lamps.

Infrared Sources

The infrared region of the electromagnetic spectrum was covered in Chapter 7, and it was mentioned that sources of infrared for therapeutic purposes are quite widely used. There was also a brief description of those employed by industry for baking, drying, dehydrating, and similar purposes.

All infrared sources are fundamentally the same. They consist of either a carbon or tungsten filament in a gas-filled glass bulb. These filaments operate at a temperature to produce the maximum amount of infrared radiation, rather than visible light as in an incandescent light bulb. This means that the filament burns somewhat cooler than in a light bulb at the same wattage.

Some lamps have their own aluminum or gold reflectors coated on the glass bulb itself. Others have clear glass bulbs and are used in conjunction with external reflectors of gold, copper, or some surface which reflects infrared efficiently.

FIG. 14-4. The 375-watt R-40 infrared lamp, which has its own aluminum reflector flashed on the back of the bulb. Lamps such as these are used for the smaller applications or where a self-contained reflector is advantageous from a maintenance standpoint.

While the infrared cooking lamp mentioned in Chapter 7 operates on the same fundamental principle as other sources, it is considerably different in design. Seven levels of heat are possible through the use of two filaments which are operated separately or together at either 120 or 240 volts. The lamp is of Vycor glass, and a gold reflecting surface is coated on the inside back portion of the bulb. Two sizes have been developed for use in household cooking ranges.

In applications of infrared where visible light is objectionable, as in some photographic work, external filters are used to screen out the undesirable light without appreciably affecting the infrared radiation. Also, some types of therapeutic lamps employ a ruby glass bulb to reduce glare and brightness to a minimum.

Ionization of Gases

Normally, gas is a poor electrical conductor. There are, however, several methods by which it can be made conductive. The method with which we are primarily concerned in the production of light involves charged particles in the gas or *ionization* of the gas.

These electrified particles are called *ions* and were described in some detail in Chapter 1. They may consist of atoms (or molecules) of the gas from which one or more negative electrons have been removed, thus leaving the atoms positively charged and the negative electrons free to take up an orbit around some other neutral atom or to remain unattached. Atoms which have adopted an extra electron are negatively charged and called

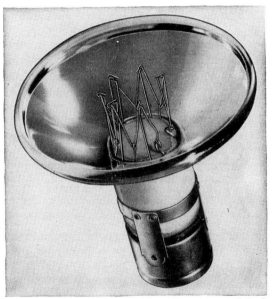

Fig. 14-5. Infrared cooking in household ranges is accomplished with high-wattage gold reflector lamps such as the one shown above. The glass bulb in this unit is made of Vycor, an extremely hard, heat-resistant glass manufactured specifically for the purpose.

negative ions. Those which have lost an electron are *positive* ions. The electron removal may be the result of one or more influences. Ultraviolet radiation, for example, will ionize air, as was pointed out in the discussion of the ionosphere or Kennelly-Heaviside layers, high above the earth's surface. X rays, gamma rays, and cosmic rays also cause the same effect.

Another method which is the basis of gaseous-discharge lamps may be called *ionization by collision*. Under all circumstances there are a few ions in a volume of gas, and when a high enough potential or voltage is applied across such a volume, these positive and negative ions will start to move toward the terminals of opposite polarity from themselves. In so doing they collide with neutral molecules of the gas, splitting them up into ions also, so that they in turn enter into the activity. Thus the gas becomes ionized within an instant, and an electric discharge or arc is formed.

A gaseous discharge of this nature enclosed in a glass tube has certain characteristics which appear in accordance with the

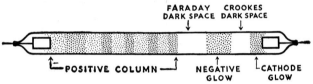

FARADAY   CROOKES
DARK SPACE DARK SPACE

POSITIVE COLUMN —   NEGATIVE   CATHODE
                     GLOW   GLOW

FIG. 14-6. Dark spaces and glow columns are found in low-pressure discharge lamps. These columns of luminous gas and dark spaces vary in accordance with the gas pressure.

pressure of the gas and with the voltage applied to the electrodes. The major characteristic is the production of visible light and ultraviolet radiation. Part of the electrical energy is absorbed when atoms or molecules are knocked apart to form ions, and part is absorbed in forming *excited atoms*. An excited atom is one in which an electron does not leave the atom but merely shifts its orbit or energy level for an instant. These excited atoms immediately release the energy they have absorbed as the electron returns to its normal energy level, so that the energy radiates as infrared, visible light, and ultraviolet.

The color, brilliancy, and distribution of this light along the length of the tube depend to a large extent upon the pressure of the gas being ionized as well as upon the voltage applied. At times there are two dark bands which appear to separate the continuous column of light. These are called the *Crookes* and the *Faraday dark spaces.* The first occurs quite near the cathode end of the tube and is separated from the second, which appears nearer the center, by a band of light called the *negative glow.* The Faraday dark space occurs between the negative glow and a wide band of light called the *positive column,* which itself may be striated. These dark spaces and bands of light change in size and intensity as the gas pressure, voltage, or both are varied, the dark spaces becoming more pronounced as the gas pressure is reduced. Thus we have a method of producing light without the extremely high temperatures required in an incandescent lamp.

Under the proper combination of conditions, these light and dark bands in a linear discharge tend to disappear, so that in light sources such as neon tubes and fluorescent lamps the distribution of light along the tube is relatively uniform.

Gaseous-discharge Light Sources

Perhaps the most elementary forms of gaseous-discharge light sources are those with which many high-school physics students are familiar. They are called *Geissler tubes* and are simply tubes with electrodes sealed in at each end. The glass tubing is bent in various shapes and filled with different gases at whatever low pressure will produce the most light when the proper voltage is applied. Geissler tubes were the forerunner of present-day gaseous-discharge-tube advertising signs, usually referred to as *neon* signs because neon gas is used to produce the attention-compelling orange-red glow within the tubes.

The history of the development of gaseous-discharge tubes for advertising display or for lighting is not the history of a single development by one individual, but rather the intermingling of numerous developments by several investigators. Several demonstration lighting installations of tubing were made at the beginning of the present century.

While neon gas has been widely used in display tubing, its

color obviously eliminates it as an acceptable light source for ordinary visual work. Certain other gases such as helium and carbon dioxide produce a much more nearly white light, but it was not until the vapors of such metals as sodium, cadmium, or mercury were introduced into the tubes that they became relatively successful sources of useful light.

The sodium-vapor lamp, which has been most successfully used for the illumination of the clover-leaf type of highway intersection, bridge and bridge-approach lighting, and similar applications, is a lamp utilizing neon gas and sodium vapor at very low pressure. When these lamps are first lighted, their color characteristics are the orange-red of ionized neon gas, but as the sodium becomes vaporized by the heat of discharge, the spectral quality of the light shifts to a golden-yellow color identified with sodium.

Light of this nature is monochromatic or nearly so; that is, it contains only one narrow band of yellow light from the visible spectrum with none of the other colors present. There seems to be a mistaken impression abroad that monochromatic light as produced by sodium-vapor lamps has great advantages over other sources in increasing the acuity of vision at night. While it does appear to aid the eyes in determining the character and shape of very small objects at low levels of illumination, the value of a sodium-vapor lamp as a source for highway lighting is not its monochromatic light, but rather its high efficiency (40 to 50 lumens per watt, depending upon size) as well as its low brightness resulting from the relatively large physical dimensions of the discharge.

Mercury-vapor lamps have found extensive use, primarily in industry. There are several types all basically the same with respect to the method of producing light, but different in gas pressure, physical size, shape, and operating characteristics. Their blue and blue-green color is easily recognized, and they are frequently used in conjunction with incandescent lamps to provide color correction in the illumination.

These sources utilize argon or a gas which ionizes readily and, of course, mercury vapor. Those operating at low and medium pressures and temperatures are less efficient than the high-pressure sources. The once well-known Cooper-Hewitt lamps were low-pressure tubular lamps and the first linear light sources to become acceptable to industry. They utilized a pool of mercury for a cathode and an iron anode. Such low-pressure mercury-vapor arc discharges produced considerable ultraviolet radiation, but the glass used for the tube was of a type opaque to ultraviolet wavelengths so that no serious amount of radiation passed through.

With an increase in the vapor pressures above a certain maximum, much of the radiant energy from the lamp is shifted from the shorter wavelengths to longer ones, so that high-pressure mercury-vapor lamps produce less ultraviolet and more visible light and are, therefore, more efficient as light sources. The efficiencies of high-pressure mercury-vapor lamps are about the same as those of sodium-vapor light sources, ranging from about 30 to 60 lumens per watt, depending upon the size and type, but their color characteristics make them much more suitable for industrial lighting applications.

One type of mercury-vapor source operates at very high vapor pressure with a consequent high temperature and efficiency (65 lumens per watt). This

Fig. 14-7. The 400-watt mercury-vapor lamp used for street lighting and industrial purposes.

source requires a quartz envelope to enclose the discharge as well as an outer bulb of hard glass so that cool water may be circulated around the inner quartz tube. Since the discharge itself is of small dimensions, the lamp is extremely brilliant. These sources are used primarily for special projection purposes.

A newer type of mercury-vapor lamp combines fluorescence from a phosphor coated on the inner surface, with light from the discharge to obtain high efficiency and a color which is more suitable by itself for industrial illumination.

The blue tubes used in advertising signs a few years ago employed mercury vapor also, and to obtain the green color, yellow-tinted glass tubing was used in conjunction with a mercury-vapor discharge. The combination of the blue discharge and yellow glass produced the green color. During the last few years, however, such advertising-tube colors result from a fluorescent coating on the inside of the tube rather than from the discharge itself.

Electric-sign tube operation is somewhat different from that of the discharge sources directly used for illumination. The vapor pressure is low; the cathodes are operated cool as compared with the temperature of the thermionic types used in radio tubes, fluorescent lamps, and the sodium- or mercury-vapor lamps just discussed; and higher voltage is required to operate them.

FIG. 14-8. The 400-watt fluorescent mercury-vapor lamp. This lamp utilizes the visible light of the discharge, *plus* the ultraviolet produced to excite a fluorescent coating on the inside of the bulb. Thus, we have a mixture of light at high efficiency with a much more favorable color quality than mercury-vapor light alone.

There are several other types of gaseous-discharge light sources. Most of them, however, are comparatively low in power and brilliancy and therefore they are used as indicators, night lights and for similar purposes rather than as a source of illumination for seeing tasks. These bulbs are usually referred to as *glow lamps*. The glow they produce results from ionized neon, argon, or krypton gases.

One type of glow lamp utilizes very short wavelengths of ultra-violet (Schumann region of ultraviolet) as produced by ionized neon to excite fluorescent phosphors coated on the inside of the bulb. Since these lamps do not depend upon mercury vapor for the production of ultraviolet, ambient temperatures are not a factor in their operation, and they can be successfully used out of doors in cold weather for decorative and similar purposes.

Another source which has limited application but which should be mentioned because of its unusual method of producing light is referred to as the *concentrated-arc lamp*. There are several sizes manufactured, and the light in each is emitted from a spot of incandescent liquid zirconium about the size of a pinhead or smaller. The brightness of this tiny spot is extremely high, and the lamps are well adapted to critical optical systems of reflectors and lenses where the efficiency and performance of the systems depend upon light sources of small physical pro-portions. Special circuits and equipment are needed to operate these lamps.

Fluorescent-light Sources

It has been explained how gases and vapors enclosed in an en-velope of glass are ionized when their molecules collide with electrons emitted from a cathode and how the ions thus formed move about and cause further collisions with other molecules of the vapor. It has also been explained how energy is released and radiated at various wavelengths in the visible-light and in-visible ultraviolet regions.

It will be recalled, further, that certain low-pressure mercury-vapor discharges are rich in ultraviolet radiation but relatively poor in visible-light radiation. Basically, the fluorescent lamp is a means of converting this invisible ultraviolet energy into visible light with a degree of efficiency hitherto not accomplished with any light sources generally applicable to commercial and industrial illumination.

The converting process is accomplished by certain chemical

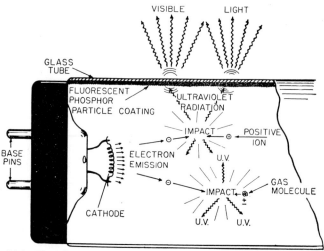

Fig. 14-9. The electronic principles involved in fluorescent-lamp operation. Electrons, being emitted from the cathode in large quantities, collide with ions and molecules in the mercury-argon gas and vapor within the tube. The impact of millions of these particles produces an abundance of radiant energy, a large part of which is ultraviolet at a wavelength of 2,537 angstroms. Such ultraviolet excites the phosphor coating on the inside of the glass tube. This excitation involves a momentary shift in the electron-energy levels of the atoms comprising the phosphor compounds, with a consequent release of radiant energy at wavelengths between 4,000 and 8,000 angstroms, which we see as visible light.

compounds such as zinc silicate, cadmium borate, and several others which are coated on the inside of the tube. These compounds are called *phosphors* and have the property of absorbing the radiant energy of ultraviolet wavelength and re-radiating it at longer wavelengths, which we can see as visible light. In other words, the compounds are *excited* to fluorescence by ultraviolet energy of the proper wavelength.

This exciting process of the phosphors is similar in one respect to the ionizing process of the gas. The ultraviolet energy disturbs the normal electron orbits of atoms making up the compound molecules so that the electrons, in returning from their temporary states of higher energy to their normal levels, release energy of a visible-light wavelength. In the case of the zinc silicate compound, the predominant wavelength of the released energy is in the order of 5,200 angstroms, so that we see the radiation as green light. Excited cadmium borate, on the other hand, radiates visible light at wavelengths in the region of 6,000 angstroms, and so the color we see is predominantly pink. Barium silicate, another compound, is excited to blue light of wavelengths around 4,500 angstroms. By careful blending of these compounds it is possible to provide almost any desired color with a high degree of efficiency, but certain colors have been established for standard fluorescent lamps. The green fluorescent lamp, while not applicable to general lighting because of its color, has the highest efficiency, over 70 lumens per watt.

At the present time, there are seven commercially available "white" fluorescent lamps. The visible color difference between these lamps is quite pronounced in some instances and rather subtle in others, and it is difficult to describe them adequately on paper without recourse to color-temperature designations. The latter procedure, as pointed out in Chapter 6, Color Temperature, would not be fundamentally correct, so the following descriptions may serve somewhat better:

Lamp color name	Approx. color temp.	Description
Daylight	6500°K	Blue white
Soft White	None*	Pink white
White	3500°K	White with slight yellow tint
Standard Cool White	4500°K	Snow white
Deluxe Cool White	None*	Snow white with red tint
Standard Warm White	3000°K	Incandescent white
Deluxe Warm White	None*	Incandescent white with red tint

* See explanation of Soft White below.

The fluorescent compounds coated on the inside of Daylight lamps have been deliberately blended to match *standard daylight* closely. This has been established and designated as a combination of sky conditions producing natural light of a color temperature of 6500° Kelvin.

The Soft White lamp, being a combination of colors from opposite ends of the visible spectrum, does not have a color-temperature approximation. The lamp was originally designed for certain display purposes where red was needed to avoid color distortion of red or pink merchandise. It is expected to be replaced eventually by the Deluxe Warm White.

The White lamp enjoys wide application at present and is a good compromise of all color characteristics. It may be replaced eventually by other colors as further appreciation of their use develops.

The Standard Cool White is most suitable in many offices and industrial uses where a psychologically cool lighting atmosphere is required. While this color of light does not distort the color appearance of surfaces, it does not seem to enhance or enliven any particular color.

The Standard Warm White lamp with its touch of yellow or incandescent light color is well adapted to home lighting and places where an approximate match with incandescent light is desired.

The Deluxe Cool and Warm lamps have characteristics similar to the Standard cool and warm colors just described, except that a red component is added to the phosphors to provide a "warmer" or slightly redder color in each case. The red component can be a calcium silicate compound or possibly some other ingredient to increase the amount of red radiation from a fluorescent lamp. The introduction of this red component reduces the total light output of the lamp somewhat, so that the Standard colors operate at higher efficiencies than the Deluxe colors.

While the fluorescent compounds used in fluorescent lamps become excited throughout a fairly wide range of ultraviolet wavelengths, different ones show their maximum or peak excitation at different wavelengths. In the spectrum of a mercury-vapor arc at a few microns pressure, there is a very pronounced line at 2,537 angstroms, at which wavelength 80 per cent or more of the ultraviolet energy is radiated. This wavelength is not the most potent exciter for all the phosphors used in fluorescent lamps, but it is the most potent one for the largest number of them, and it is not very far from the peak excitation region of the others.

In fluorescent-lamp manufacture there must be a very careful correlation between the excitation properties of the fluorescent chemicals and the pressure characteristics of the vapor discharge. Even a slight increase in pressure will shift some of the radiant energy to longer wavelengths which do not possess so much ability to excite the chemicals, resulting in a lower output of visible light.

In addition to accurate pressure control, extreme purity of the argon gas and mercury is essential along with the highest quality methods of exhausting, in order that swirling or "snaking" arcs may be avoided. Swirling arcs were sometimes found in early fluorescent lamps. They are caused by the presence of extremely minute quantities of a foreign gas such as carbon dioxide or of a vapor such as water, which either are not removed in the exhausting process or are present in the argon when it is placed in the lamp. Such impurities may also be driven from the cathode into the discharge under adverse starting conditions. The negative ions of a foreign gas or vapor of this nature seek the outer limits of the column of gas, where they form in rings or "doughnuts" around the inside of the tube. Convective gas currents within the tube cause them to rotate in an eccentric fashion, and the arc, constricted where it passes through the "holes," is forced to follow the motion of the doughnuts. With two or three of these rotating within a lamp, the discharge takes a spiral or swirling path along the tube.

Our primary interest in this discussion of fluorescent lamps lies in the basic electronic principles involved rather than in their characteristics and applications as light sources, particularly since the latter have been adequately covered in handbooks, manuals, and published bulletins. However, some of the physical elements of fluorescent lamps as well as certain essential features of their operating circuits may be included, since they are related to the electronic performance of the lamps.

Standard fluorescent-lamp cathodes are similar in basic purpose to those in a radio tube. They consist of a coiled-coil tungsten wire coated with a material which facilitates thermionic emission (see Chapter 13).

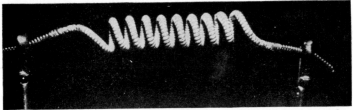

FIG. 14-10. The cathode of a standard preheat 40-watt fluorescent lamp. This is a coiled-coil tungsten filament which has been coated with the correct amount of barium, strontium, or calcium oxides to facilitate the release of electrons from the tungsten metal into the gas surrounding it. When this coating becomes worn away after several thousand hours of use, electron emission does not take place as readily, and the lamp does not start as quickly.

A very small quantity of extremely high-purity mercury is placed in the lamps in a free form during the exhausting process. This vaporizes when the lamp is turned on and, when ionized or excited, results in the production of ultraviolet radiation which is rich in the wavelengths necessary to excite the phosphors.

Fluorescent-lamp Circuits—Starting

There are a number of ways to start and operate fluorescent lamps. The major difference between them is the manner in which the initial ionization is started. Once started, the lamps operate basically the same. In the commonly used hot-cathode circuit, the cathodes are preheated for a moment to produce abundant electron emission and consequent ionization of gas at the ends of the lamp just prior to lamp starting.

In the instant-starting circuits, which include cold-cathode and Slimline lamp circuits, emission and consequent instant ionization result from the impression of high voltage across the lamp. Such open-circuit voltages will vary from 400 or 500 to 3,000 or more depending upon the lamp length and other characteristics.

The so-called *lag-lead* and similar circuits utilize, in effect, a combination of the above two types. In any event, the basic function of the circuit is to obtain adequate electron emission from the cathodes as rapidly as possible in order to produce ionization of the column of gas in the tube without undue rough treatment of the cathode.

It should be mentioned that, for optimum lamp performance, the lamps, and in particular the cathodes, should be designed for the circuit with which they will be called upon to operate.

Fluorescent-lamp Circuits—Operating

In the preheat or hot-cathode lamp circuit, the cathodes at each end of the lamp are in series with each other through either a manual starting switch or an automatic thermal (or magnetic) starter, as well as in series with a choke coil called a *ballast*. When the current is first turned on, it passes through a choke coil, one cathode filament, the closed starting switch, and the other cathode filament and thus completes the circuit. With current flowing through the cathode filaments, the cathodes become hot, and thermionic emission takes place, thereby ionizing a volume of gas at each end of the lamp. As long as current is permitted to flow through this series circuit, the filaments glow and gas will be ionized at each end, but a discharge through the column of mercury vapor along the length of the lamp will not take place.

At this point, if the switch or starter is opened, either manually or automatically, the continuous series circuit is broken and each cathode becomes a single terminal with the column of low-pressure mercury vapor separating it from the other cathode. In the discussion of inductance in Chapter 4 it was pointed out that a counter emf is generated by the magnetic field of an inductance coil through which alternating current is flowing and that this force resists the stopping of the current through the coil after it is once flowing. Thus, when the fluorescent-lamp starting circuit is broken, the tendency of the counter emf to maintain a flow of current in the ballast usually develops an instantaneous surge of high voltage (800 to 1,000 volts) which will more readily start current flowing or ionize the column of mercury vapor between

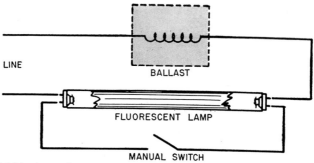

LINE

BALLAST

FLUORESCENT LAMP

MANUAL SWITCH

Fig. 14-11. A simple single-fluorescent-lamp circuit with a manual starting switch.

the cathodes and light the lamp. Once the discharge is formed, it tends to draw more and more current, so that the lamp would be destroyed immediately unless some means were taken to regulate the current. The ballast coil also serves in this capacity and maintains the proper operating characteristics of the lamp.

If we refer to the discussion of inductance and power factor in Chapter 4, it will be recalled that, when inductance is introduced into a circuit, the current peak occurs after the voltage peak and a *lagging* power factor exists. Therefore, in the simple fluorescent circuit just described, we find a lagging power factor of around 55 or 60 per cent. Since this results in a wasteful use of wiring capacity, and since one lamp operating alone produces an objectionable flicker with each alternation of the current flow, it has become general practice to correct both faults by using a two-lamp auxiliary.

In the two-lamp circuits, one lamp operates essentially as described above. The other lamp, however, utilizes a capacitor of proper characteristics in series with its ballast coil, so that its total reactance (Chapter 4) is capacitive rather than inductive as with the first lamp. Referring once more to the power-factor

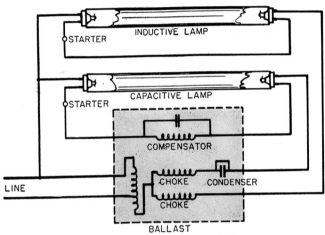

FIG. 14-12. Circuit of a two-lamp ballast with built-in starting compensator, for two 30-watt or two 40-watt lamps on 110- to 125-volt circuits.

diagrams in Chapter 4, we find an explanation of how, with capacitance in a circuit, the current peak will occur before (or ahead of) the voltage peak or lead it, which results in a *leading* power factor. Thus, with one lamp lagging and the other leading by about the same power-factor values, the two-lamp circuit produces a combined power factor of 95 per cent or better.

The smaller sizes of fluorescent lamps (15, 20, 25, 30, and 40 watts) frequently will not start readily when operated on the capacitor circuit because of excessive limiting of the starting current by the capacitor. To offset this, another small choke

268

Primer of Electronics and Radiant Energy

coil, called a *compensator*, is connected in series with the starter so that it functions only during the lamp-starting process.

The two-lamp circuit does not reduce the a-c flicker of individual lamps, but it does cause one to reach its higher brightness values while the other is in a state of low brightness, so that illumination resulting from a good blend of the two will show little or no annoying flicker.

It has already been briefly explained that the fundamental difference between most fluorescent-lamp circuits is in the method

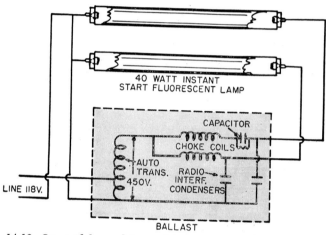

Fig. 14-13. One widely used type of instant-starting fluorescent-lamp circuit using the single-pin 40-watt lamps.

of starting and that the instant-start Slimline and cold-cathode circuits accomplish this with high voltage. This high voltage, however, does not persist after the lamp has lighted. The transformers used are so designed that with current flowing through the lamp (ionization) the voltage drops down to a level which is more than sufficient to maintain the discharge once it has started.

There is also a sequence starting circuit which utilizes a four-lamp ballast and is applicable in certain types of installations where either continuous rows of fixtures or adjacent pairs of fixtures, containing two 85- or 100-watt fluorescent lamps each, are used on a 265/460-volt three-phase four-wire distribution system of wiring. This circuit saves considerable copper and steel, not only in the ballasts but in the wiring system as well, and has been used to some extent in a few of the largest industrial plants.

For single-lamp operation, ballasts having a high power factor (90 per cent or more) are available. There is also a method of operating two 14-watt (15-inch) fluorescent lamps in series with a special incandescent lamp which serves as a resistance ballast on either a-c or d-c systems. The larger sizes of lamps may be used on d-c systems providing resistances having the proper values are used in series with single-lamp ballasts, but with such a combination the total auxiliary losses are considerably higher than with a-c operation, so that the over-all efficiency is reduced appreciably.

Stroboscopic Effects

Stroboscopic effects are caused when rotating machinery or moving parts are viewed under a single flickering lamp or under two or more which have not been corrected as described above. In extreme cases, when the rotation or vibratory motion of machinery coincides with the frequency of the flicker, the machinery may appear to be stationary or nearly so. At other times, it will appear to be going backward or forward at slower speeds than its actual motion.

Stroboscopic effects are sometimes deliberately created to aid in the study of high-speed rotating machinery. For such purposes, a special electron tube called a *strobotron* is used. This source will be discussed later.

Fluorescent-lamp Starters

As explained a few pages back, fluorescent lamps are started under one set of conditions and operated under another. In the preheat circuit, this change-over consists simply of breaking the circuit in which the two cathode filaments are in series with each other after they have become sufficiently heated to provide adequate thermionic emission. This circuit breaking can be done manually with a single-throw switch of any type (push button, twist, knife blade, etc.), or it can be accomplished automatically by a magnetic or thermal device which will remain closed long enough after the current is turned on to allow the necessary

FIG. 14-4. One type of glow starter used in conjunction with 30- and 40-watt fluorescent lamps. The bimetal strip and contact can be seen in the normally open position.

cathode preheating. Such a time-delay switch is called a *starter*, and although there are several possible types, we shall confine this discussion to the one which depends upon electron emission and ionized gas for its operation and therefore is, in a true sense, an electronic device.

Starters of this type are called *glow starters*. The operating parts, which are enclosed in a small, sealed bottle containing argon or neon gas at relatively low pressure, consist of a bimetal strip and a second contact element quite close to it. (A bimetal strip is made up of two pieces of metal having different expansion characteristics, so that when heat is applied to a ribbon or strip having one metal on one face and the other metal on the other face, the strip will bend or curl.) These contacts are normally apart or open; that is, when the starter is cold and not operating, the bimetal does not touch the other contact. All fluorescent starters are placed across (in parallel with) the lamp, so that when the current is first turned on, the line voltage is received across the starter. In the case of 40-watt lamps and 118-volt lines, a transformer is incorporated in the ballast which raises this to about 200 volts.

The voltage necessary to produce a discharge through the argon gas in the bottle is established between 130 and 160 volts (for 30- and 40-watt starters—less in smaller ones), so that the gas ionizes when the current is turned on and a glow discharge takes place. Heat generated by this discharge causes the bimetal strip to move over and make contact with the other element and thus light the two cathodes, which at this point are in series with each other through the contact just established in the starter.

At the instant of contact and as a result of it, the glow discharge stops, thus removing the heat from the bimetal, but there is enough heat lag in the elements to hold them in contact with each other for a sufficient length of time to assure proper cathode-preheating time. When cool, the bimetal moves away from the other element, thus breaking the contact and producing a high-voltage surge through the ballast coil which initiates the arc and starts the lamp. With the lamp lighted, the voltage across the starter is too low to produce a discharge through the gas in the starter bottle, and so the starter remains inactive with the lamp in operation.

Other types of thermal starters operate by means of a resistor, a high-resistance contact between carbon and nickel, or some method other than ionized gas, to supply heat and move the bimetal strip. Magnetic starters, which have been replaced almost entirely by the thermal and glow types, use electromagnetism to move and hold the contacts as required for lamp starting.

Electroluminescence

The phenomenon of visible-light production by electrolumines-cence has been known for many years, but only relatively re-cently has it been developed to the point of commercial application.

Electroluminescence involves neither incandescence nor ioni-

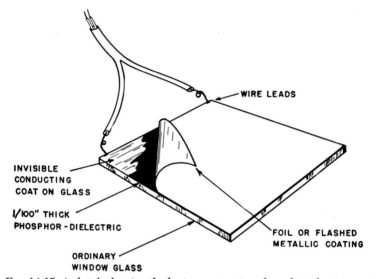

Fig. 14-15. A sketch showing the basic construction of an electroluminescent light source. The conducting coating on the glass and the flashed metallic coating function as the two plates of a condenser with a phosphor contain-ing a dielectric material sandwiched between the two plates. When an oscillating electric field is applied to the two plates, some of the energy loss in the dielectric is reradiated as visible light.

zation of gases. It does involve the excitation of fluorescent phos-phors in an electric field. Light sources of this type are, in effect, condensers (see Chapter 4) with an electrically conducting transparent glass panel as one plate, a metallic reflecting surface as the other plate, and the phosphor in dielectric suspension between the two.

While these sources are not so brilliant as incandescent or fluorescent lamps, the application of voltages and frequencies higher than those normally supplied by the power companies (120 volts, 60 cycles) result in considerably higher light output, although still well below light bulbs and fluorescent lamps. Even with the limitations of low brightness, electroluminescent panel sources have the advantages of simplicity, size (thinness), and, theoretically at least, extremely long life.

In short, the incandescent bulb is a concentrated *globular* source, the fluorescent lamp a *linear* source, and the electroluminescent panel an *area* source—each operating on different electrophysical principles.

Germicidal Tubes

Chapter 8 was devoted entirely to electromagnetic waves in the ultraviolet region, and some discussion was given the bactericidal band within it. Since the peak of the bactericidal effect occurs at wavelengths in the order of 2,537 angstroms, and since a mercury-vapor discharge at a few microns pressure produces an abundance of radiation at this wavelength, it is obvious that mercury-vapor sources will kill bacteria provided that the radiations can pass through the glass wall of the tube enclosing the discharge.

Germicidal or bactericidal tubes (or sterilizing lamps) are practically identical with fluorescent sources as far as their electrical and discharge characteristics are concerned. They may operate with either hot or cold cathodes, and the essential difference lies in the fact that ultraviolet-transmitting glass (or quartz) is used and, of course, no fluorescent powder is applied (except in special types).

With the hot-cathode types, standard fluorescent auxiliary equipment (ballasts) and starters are used, whereas the cold-cathode types require a transformer and operate at voltages ranging from about 300 volts for 10-inch tubes to 500 volts for 30-inch tubes. The hot-cathode types are manufactured in sizes corresponding to 15- and 30-inch T-8 fluorescent lamps, and other standard sizes are possible. There are also on the market several types of special bactericidal tubes having bent shapes and single-end special bases—some utilizing quartz for specific applications.

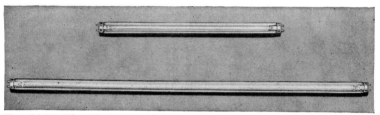

Fig. 14-16. The 15- (top) and 30-watt hot-cathode-type germicidal lamps. These sources produce radiation rich in bactericidal ultraviolet at 2,537 angstroms. They operate in conjunction with standard ballasts and starters for 15- and 30-watt fluorescent lamps.

Black-light Sources

To the average individual, the term *black light* seems to have an ominous and mysterious meaning. Two antithetical words such as these, bound together as a term or phrase, quite naturally cause some amount of subconscious questioning because the words do not seem to belong together. As a matter of fact, black light is neither black nor light but is invisible ultraviolet radiation in the wavelength region of 3,600 angstroms. The word *light* is used because the radiation is only just beyond visible violet light in the electromagnetic spectrum and also because it produces fluorescence of certain compounds or pigments which can be mixed with paints, dyes, lacquers, inks, and similar products to make them glow with light. The word *black* is associated with *light* because the glass envelope or filter surrounding the mercury-vapor discharge is black (or very deep red-purple in color) and, therefore, opaque to practically all visible light.

Black light is not new. It has been a theatrical stage-lighting trick for many years. Carbon-arc lamps, which are powerful sources of ultraviolet (of all wavelengths) as well as of visible light, are used with heavy red-purple glass filters to absorb all visible light but to permit the ultraviolet to pass through. Stage scenery and costumes are treated with fluorescent chemicals and glow beautifully and eerily in the nearly invisible "black" beams of the "light."

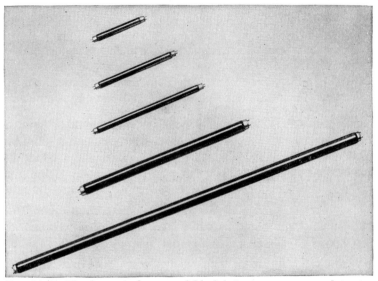

FIG. 14-17. The hot-cathode type of black-light sources, arranged in size from the 6-inch 4-watt T/6 (top) to the 36-inch 30-watt T/8 (bottom). These lamps use standard fluorescent-lamp starters and ballasts of comparable size for their operation. The glass tubing is essentially opaque to visible light but transmits the near ultraviolet (black light) in considerable quantity.

While black light is best known and recognized in theatrical work and signboard display advertising, there are several uses for it in industry and commerce. It is used as a means of illuminating instrument dials, particularly in wartime aircraft cockpits, where good visibility of the instrument panel is necessary but where even a low degree of general illumination or brightness can be a hindrance to the busy pilot and navigator.

In submarines, it has been a successful means of lighting dials and instruments where dark-adapted eyes are needed in scanning the night horizon through a periscope.

In these applications the numerals, symbols, and indicators on instrument dials are treated with the fluorescent material so that they become dimly visible in the presence of black light without producing an undue amount of distracting illumination to those who must watch the dials as well as the progress of the operation.

There are a few industrial operations utilizing black light. One of the most successful is a process whereby metal castings are dipped or otherwise coated with a fluorescent solution. Under ultraviolet, even minute surface cracks and flaws appear which otherwise might not be detected in the ordinary inspection process.

Sun Lamps

Over the past 20 years, there has been considerable development of lamps designed to produce a tanning effect on the skin. The physiological effects of ultraviolet were discussed to some extent in Chapter 8, where it was pointed out that artificial sunlight sources, when properly used, are a definite aid in maintaining certain health factors.

There are several types of sun lamps made, all of them based upon a high-pressure mercury-vapor arc discharge comparatively rich in wavelengths around 3,000 angstroms. The glass used in sun lamps is so formulated that the shorter, germicidal wavelengths of 2,537 angstroms, which are harmful to skin and eyes, are not transmitted and only those causing sun tanning are passed by the glass. Some lamps are tubular in shape like fluorescent lamps or may be looped, coiled, or otherwise bent in some form consistent with reflector design. Others utilize a small capsule-like tube, further enclosed in an outer bulb which has its own reflector. The former operate in conjunction with a transformer to provide the proper electrical characteristics, whereas the latter type use a tungsten filament as a resistance and are started by means of a thermally operated switch which is enclosed within the outer bulb, so that no auxiliary devices are used for use on standard 120-volt, 60-cycle house current.

FIG. 14-18. The 275-watt RS-type sun-lamp which produces infrared radiation as well as an abundance of sun-tanning ultraviolet. This lamp operates directly from 110- to 125-volt, 50- or 60-cycle a-c lines. It requires no auxiliary transformers or resistors, such elements being incorporated in the lamp construction.

Phosphors have been developed which, when excited by 2,537-angstrom ultraviolet, fluoresce and radiate considerable energy at about 3,000 angstroms as well as some visible light. Tubular sun lamps are also made which utilize this method of generating sun-tanning rays.

15

Strobotrons

The strobotron first became generally known in conjunction with the science of high-speed photography as developed by Dr. Harold E. Edgerton and his colleagues at the Massachusetts Institute of Technology. Nearly everyone has seen Edgerton's fascinating pictures of a splash of water, a football being kicked, a bullet piercing an incandescent lamp, hummingbirds in flight, and other examples of "stopping" high-speed motion with remarkable photographic detail.

The technique involves many things, not the least of which is a light source capable of extremely rapid and distinct flashes only a few microseconds in duration. Incandescent filaments, of course, do not cool sufficiently even at a 60-cycle frequency to show appreciable flickering, and although fluorescent lamps do flicker to some extent at 60 cycles, there is a *holdover* or *lag* in the fluorescent compounds which practically eliminates distinctive flicker at higher frequencies. Therefore, neither of these sources has been used specifically as a source of high-frequency flashing light.

A strobotron is a low-pressure discharge tube utilizing a cold cathode coated with cesium. In the smaller types, neon gas, which produces the characteristic orange-red light, is used. The larger tubes may be filled with argon, krypton, or a combination of these and other rare gases, and the light produced is usually a brilliant blue-white. The strobotron's primary function, as indi-

278

cated above, is to provide a source of extremely rapid and distinct flashes of light or, by virtue of the discharge, pulses of current.

The frequency of the flashes can be controlled either by rapid mechanical interruption of the circuit or by rapid capacitor discharges. In this way, several thousand separate and distinct flashes or pulses per minute can be obtained, or the frequency can be reduced to one per minute or less if desired.

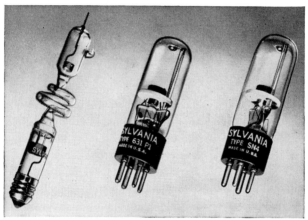

Fig. 15-1. Three types of strobotrons. At the left is the tube used in the Strobolux unit. In the center is the Strobotac tube, and at the right is a similar type used in industrial applications where lower frequency current pulses are desired.

In high-speed photography, the flashes of light act as a camera shutter would, so that it is possible to obtain an exposure of a fast-moving object of only a few millionths of a second in duration or a large number of exposures per second of the same object. Of course, special film and equipment are used, and when developed and printed, the photographs show the object as it was during the instant of time that the stroboscopic light fell upon it, or they may show the successive positions of the object at each flash of the strobotron.

For the study of rotating or vibrating machinery, the strobotron's flashes are synchronized with the rotation or vibration frequency so that the machine appears motionless. For example, if an electric fan is turning at the rate of 1,200 rpm and a strobo-

tron is made to flash 1,200 times per minute or in multiples of that figure, the flashes will occur when the fan blades are always in the same position. Thus, although the flashing frequency and fan rotation are too fast to be distinguished by the eye, we see the fan always in the same position by virtue of the stroboscopic light, so that it appears to be standing still. Airplane propellers are studied this way in order that stresses and strains, which appear only while they are turning at high speeds, can be determined and corrective measures taken in the propeller design. Strobo-scopic light is used in hundreds of industries for problems similar to the propeller applications. It has aided considerably in certain ballistics studies.

FIG. 15-2. The 200-million-lumen xenon-filled strobotron used in runway-approach lighting. The intense white light flash it produces lasts for only about 1 millisecond.

In the section devoted to ultrasonics in Chapter 10, mention was made of the strobotron as a means of controlling ultrasonic pulses for determining marine depths. In applications of this nature, the current of the strobotron's discharge is used rather than the visible light which results from it. Very short packets of ultrasonic waves are sent to the ocean bottom, where they are echoed back to a receiver. These packets or pulses must be of extremely short duration to be properly timed and individually distinguishable, and the strobotron functions as a *trigger* tube in this respect by controlling the frequency of the pulses as well as their time duration.

FIG. 15-3. Strobotac and Strobolux units for controlling the flash frequency of strobotrons. Neon gas is used in the Strobotac tube at the left so that its flash is red light. It triggers the Strobolux equipment at the right, which uses a tube containing xenon producing a brilliant blue-white light flash. (*Courtesy of General Radio Company.*)

FIG. 15-4. General view of the set-up for photographing projectiles in flight with stroboscopic light at the Jefferson Proving Grounds. The projectile is photographed in its flight through the box at the right. A switch for opening the camera shutter is hung on the stand in the center about 15 feet in front of the box. This switch is tripped by the pressure wave as the projectile passes by. A microphone inside the box picks up the sound waves as the projectile passes through and trips the microflash unit during the interval of 1/100 second that the shutter is open.

Perhaps the most spectacular strobotron application is in runway approach lighting for airports. For this purpose, the tube is coiled several times like a short spiral spring. It is filled with the rare *xenon* gas to produce an intense flash of white light lasting

FIG. 15-5. A 76-millimeter tracer with nosecap and windshield separated from the projectile, 75 feet from the muzzle. A tendency to yaw from the true line of flight under such a condition is quite apparent.

FIG. 15-6. Behavior of the windshield on a 76-millimeter projectile 100 feet from the muzzle.

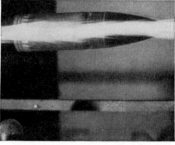

FIG. 15-7. A photograph of a 76-millimeter tracer in perfect flight. The light streak of the tracer appears to precede the projectile because the camera shutter does not close until after the projectile has passed, the actual exposure resulting from the microflash. Note the microphone at lower left to trip the microflash unit.

less than 1 millisecond. This flash, at its peak, measures over 200 million lumens.

The tube performance is designed to give maximum penetration of fog, haze, or overcast. The flash is so short that blinding glare is not experienced by the pilot under such conditions. In the complete approach-light units, a strobotron is combined with neon tubes which are operable as a steady light, either alone or with the strobotron flash. The neon's red glow serves as an identifying color for recognition by the pilot, who can ask for the flashes to be turned on or off as he wishes.

Fig. 15-8. The complete runway-approach unit, showing the strobotron assembly in the center and the neon tubes at each side.

Fig. 15-9. A complete strobotron approach-lighting installation.

The strobotron is placed in a reflector which produces a 60-degree beam. It is visible over 20 miles in daylight. In operation, a row of 40 or 50 units are used under the glide path to the runway. All units do not flash at once but are timed for rapid sequence, starting at the one farthest out, about a half mile from the end of the runway, and following up to the strip itself.

Photoelectric Tubes

Photoelectric tubes are converters of radiant energy into electric current. The radiant-energy wavelengths to which they are sensitive embrace the infrared, visible-light, and ultraviolet regions,

Fig. 15-10. Typical photoelectric-tube construction.

and the process of conversion bears some resemblance to the reverse of the process by which light is produced in a glow lamp.

A photoelectric tube may be either vacuum or low-pressure-gas filled and is comparatively simple in construction. It consists of a cathode which emits electrons when radiant energy impinges upon it. The cathode is usually in the form of a plate, curved so that the greatest amount of electron flow from it will reach the anode, which may be a small rod placed upright at about the focal point of the curve. There are other forms of cathode-anode mounting, but all function in about the same way—to convert radiant energy into electric current.

As explained in Chapter 1, radiant energy comes to us in waves of separate and distinct little quantity units called *photons*. There are definite relationships between the energies of these photons at various wavelengths and the number of electrons they cause the cathode to emit when they fall upon it. Since the shorter wavelengths have photons of more energy, ultraviolet is basically a better producer of photoelectric emission than visible light, and visible light is better than infrared.

The cathodes used in photoelectric tubes are coated with materials such as cesium and potassium which help electrons to be emitted more readily. The coating used depends upon the wavelength of energy to be converted into electron emission (current flow from the cathode to the anode), since the different materials have different characteristics with respect to the wavelength of energy falling upon them. Thus, photoelectric tubes are designed for a number of wavelength regions. Those most sensitive to visible light would not always be suitable for infrared or ultraviolet.

Photoelectric tubes or *electric eyes* as they are popularly called have hundreds of commercial and industrial uses. Since the door-opening application is familiar to a great many people, we can discuss it briefly. A thin beam of light is placed across the path of traffic to a door so that it strikes the cathode of a photoelectric tube (or a photocell) which is on the opposite side of the path from the light source. As long as this light beam remains uninterrupted, an electron current flows from the cathode to the anode in the tube. This current, when amplified, operates sensitive relays, contactors, and other mechanism and keeps the door closed. When the beam is interrupted by someone approaching the door, the current ceases to flow so the door is no longer held closed, and an air-pressure or mechanical device swings it open.

The same fundamental principle of either interrupting a beam of light or creating one, so that the electron flow from the cathode to the anode of a photoelectric tube is either stopped or created, is the basis for practically all electric-eye installations utilizing a tube to intercept the light. Another method involves a light-sensitive cell called a *photocell* or a *barrier layer* photoelectric cell. This photocell is not a tube but consists, rather, of a plate of some material such as copper oxide or selenium which has the property, when in conjunction with other elements making up the cell, of generating small currents when light falls upon it. The movement of electrons occurs when light strikes the sensitive surface. The rest of the circuit is somewhat similar to phototube circuits, consisting of amplification (when necessary) and a series of relays and contactors for controlling the installation.

The use of photoelectric tubes and cells for machinery control, lighting, sorting or inspecting operations, smoke control, and hundreds of other operations is rapidly increasing. Widely used instruments such as exposure meters and foot-candle or light meters employ selenium cells to intercept light and convert it into electric current so that readings may be made quickly and accurately.

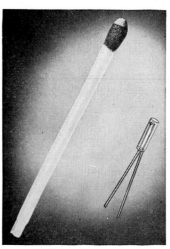

For automatic multiple counting, inspecting, and recording systems where very small space is essential, a tiny unit called a *germanium photodiode* is used. It is a point-contact device employing a sharply pointed tungsten whisker firmly seated against a small block of polished germanium. These components are embedded in plastic to assure rigidity and consistent operation.

Fig. 15-11. The germanium photodiode compared in size to an ordinary wooden match.

Germanium is photosensitive to wavelengths throughout the visible-light spectrum, the sensitivity being slight at the blue end but increasing toward the infrared. The peak response is in the infrared region at about 17,000 angstroms. Thus, when the germanium photodiode is exposed to such radiation, electrons flow from the germanium and the unit becomes a self-generating photocell of very small currents. There is sufficient energy generated, however, to operate small, highly sensitive relays, or it may be amplified for control purposes.

Germanium Crystal Diodes

The fundamental principles of diode-tube operation were explained in Chapter 13, where it was also pointed out that certain crystals, including germanium, have the property of unsymmetrical conductivity. That is, they will allow current to pass in one direction more readily than in the other.

Germanium crystal diodes are not tubes in the sense that they have a cathode and a plate in a vacuum or gas-filled envelope, with a space charge and electrons flowing across from one element to the other. They function similarly, however, in that a bar or block of germanium acts as a cathode with electrons flowing out of it at the point of contact with a tungsten whisker. Like diode-tube operation, the current will flow essentially only one way, so that in many circuits this device can be used instead of a tube.

Also, like diode tubes, they function basically as rectifiers. In television receivers they operate as high-efficiency video detectors, and in radio and

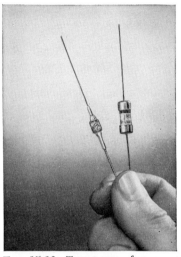

FIG. 15-12. Two types of germanium crystal diodes having the same function in electrical circuits. The one at the left is sealed in a tiny glass tube. The whisker can be seen extending down to contact a germanium slab imbedded at the bottom. At the right the same elements are enclosed in a ceramic tube with ferrule ends. The glass type, being permanently sealed against dust and moisture, is used where such conditions prevail, while the ceramic unit can be used under ordinary conditions and is somewhat lower in cost.

other electronic applications they are used as rectifiers, detectors, and modulators and for many other purposes where their compactness, light weight, ruggedness, and other factors are a decided advantage.

One type uses a hermetically sealed glass cartridge construction, whereas others are ceramic enclosed. When used in groups of two and four, they are called *duo-diodes* and *varistors,* respectively.

Germanium Crystal Triodes

Germanium triodes, which are often called *transistors,* are devices which can be made to function in a manner similar to certain types of vacuum tubes used as amplifiers and oscillators. They have the advantages of very small size, low power use, very long life, and ruggedness, which make them most valuable where these factors are important in circuit and equipment design.

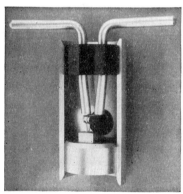

FIG. 15-13. Enlarged cutaway view of a point-contact type of transistor, showing two whiskers in contact with germanium slab. (*Courtesy of Bell Telephone Laboratories.*)

These devices are similar in construction to germanium diodes except that a second whisker is placed on the same face of the crystal near the first one and is referred to as the *emitter,* whereas the other is called the *collector.*

The germanium slab may be only about twenty-thousandths of an inch thick. Germanium is a semiconducting crystal, and there may be either more or less electrons in its structure than the exact number for perfect lattice arrangement. Where there are more electrons than needed in the structure, they can be caused to migrate in the crystal. But where there is a deficiency of them, vacancies or "holes" exist where the electrons normally would be. These "holes" exhibit properties of positive particles and will also migrate, something as an empty "bubble" might, toward a negative electrode called the *collector*.

Thus, we have in germanium crystals certain inherent unique characteristics which can be used to control currents by the proper application of positive and negative charges on the crystal surface. There is no thermionic requirement to start electrons (or the "holes") on the move within the crystal, so that practically no power is needed.

By applying the same basic principles to germanium triodes that are used with electron tubes, they can be used as amplifiers, as oscillators, and for similar purposes where higher frequencies (above 10 megacycles) are not involved.

The greatest interest in crystal triodes is for compact circuit devices such as hearing aids where physical size and other advantages becomes most pronounced.

FIG. 15-14. The spidery object at the right is another type of transistor called a *junction transistor*. In it, no whisker contacts are used. Instead, a thin wafer of electron-deficient germanium (called *p-type* for positive) is sandwiched between two slabs of electron-rich germanium (called *n-type* for negative), so that the particle movement takes place over the whole area of contact with a consequent increase in efficiency over the whisker type. At the left is a commercial electron tube of standard size, which does about the same job of amplification as the tiny transistor. (*Courtesy of Bell Telephone Laboratories.*)

Glow Modulator Tube

Originally, this tube was designed as the heart of equipment for receiving pictures transmitted by radio called *facsimile recording* (wirephotos). However, it has found many new uses in recent years. The outstanding feature of this tube is its ability to generate pulses of light at rates as high as 40,000 per second.

In facsimile recording, a photograph is taken by any camera in the usual way and a print made. This print is placed on a cylinder, much like an Ediphone record, and revolved at a moderate rate of speed. A needle-like beam of light is focused on the picture as it revolves. The tiny shaft of light acts about as the needle of an Ediphone record would; that is, it travels laterally along the cylindrical photo as it revolves until the whole picture has been covered. This pin point of light is reflected from the picture back to a photoelectric tube. The amount of light

Fig. 15-15. The glow modulator tube, showing the small opening in the top element through which a thin beam of light passes. The intensity of this beam pulsates in accordance with the signal from the transmitter and thus traces on sensitized paper a facsimile of the picture being scanned at the transmitter.

reflected is dependent upon the variations of black, white, or gray on the photograph. Thus the photoelectric tube generates its current in accordance with the variations of light striking it. This current passes into a radio transmitter and is broadcast, the photoelectric tubes taking the place of a microphone.

The next problem is to get the signal back into the form of a picture, and it is in this capacity that the glow modulator tube functions. Instead of earphones or a loud-speaker, the signal, after being amplified, goes to the tube, which is sensitive to very slight variations in the energy from the signal. Consequently, its light output responds instantly in accordance with these variations. The tube is opaque except for the end where the thin beam of high-intensity light is emitted. This beam of light, which is fluctuating with the radio signal, is high in actinic (photographic) value and is narrowed down to another needle-like shaft by lenses. This pin point of light is focused upon a cylinder like that of the transmitter, except that blank sensitized paper is used. As the cylinder revolves, the recorder tube faithfully records the photograph as it is being broadcast.

Thus, in facsimile recording we have, in effect, a slow type of television, since the picture is broken up into lines, scanned, and reproduced in a manner similar to the operation of a cathode-ray tube.

A tiny electron tube is used for regulating the voltage in the facsimile recorder. It is essential in this apparatus that the voltage from the amplifier does not fluctuate. If it does, the picture being transmitted or received by radio will be decidedly inaccurate as far as its density is concerned, since the light shaft from the glow modulator fluctuates as the picture reflects it at the transmitting end and does the recording in the same way on the receiving end, so that fluctuations of light due to unstable voltage cannot be tolerated.

The operating characteristics of this little tube are such that the voltage drop across it remains substantially constant, even though the supply voltage varies, because the drop is independent of the current passing through the tube.

In addition to facsimile recording, the glow modulator tube is used to scan pictures on the transmitting end of a system which makes a plastic plate or cut for printing pictures, directly from the signal at the receiving end. At the transmitter the glow modulator is a source of high-frequency alternating light which is modulated by the variations of light and dark areas of the picture being transmitted. This corresponds to the modulated carrier waves in radio, and it can be amplified and demodulated in the usual way.

The plastic plate itself is cut by a red-hot stylus which makes large or small dot impressions in the plate as determined by the received signal. Other uses for this tube include certain timing operations, seismograph recorders, photoelectric counters, and similar applications under development.

Cathode-ray Tubes

In Chapters 10 and 11, cathode-ray tubes were discussed to some extent in connection with television, radar, and loran screens. In addition, this tube as used in an *oscilloscope* has become the

Fig. 15-16. A 7-inch screen-cathode-ray oscilloscope of the type used in radio and television work as well as in industrial research laboratories.

most important tool in the study of electrical phenomena. Since space will not permit a complete description of oscilloscope operation, and since there are several excellent textbooks dealing with them almost exclusively, we can treat the subject here only in a very brief way.

An oscilloscope is an instrument which shows visually what is happening to an electric circuit or device. It paints a picture of electrical-energy behavior on the cathode-ray-tube screen.

We know, for example, that in an a-c circuit the current

Fig. 15-17. A cathode-ray tube, made by Sylvania Electric Products Inc. especially for these photographs, to show electrostatic deflection of the electron beam. The entire assembly in the neck of the tube is called the *mount*. The cylindrical element at the left is the electron gun and contains the cathode which liberates electrons and other elements which form them into a beam and accelerate them. This stream of electrons emerges from the small hole in the disk at the end of the gun. Next, beyond the gun, can be seen two sets of parallel plates which deflect the beam from side to side or up and down. The pair of plates nearest the disk are end-on to the line of vision in this photograph and the top plate is charged positively so that the beam is deflected upward as shown. (*Courtesy of Life magazine.*)

values rise and fall with each alternation of the generator (Chapter 3) and that oscillating currents of high frequency do the same thing. In the design of many types of electrical equipment it is essential to know whether such current values reach their peak quickly and fall off slowly or the reverse is true. An oscilloscope gives this information visually and in addition tells when changes take place in the wave form, if they do.

It has been explained how a thin needle-like stream of

electrons is shot from the *electron gun* in a cathode-ray tube
and how this stream is deflected either electromagnetically with
magnetic coils or electrostatically by two pairs of plates between
which it must pass. For the sake of simplicity let us consider

FIG. 15-18. With the tube rotated 90 degrees from the position in Fig.
15-17, to show better the function of the deflecting plates, the beam is
now seen to be deflected downward by a positive charge on the bottom
plate of the outer set. In Fig. 15-17 such deflection would be toward
the reader. (*Courtesy of Life magazine.*)

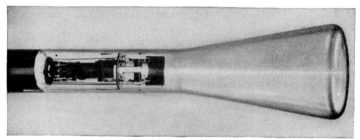

FIG. 15-19. With no charge on any of the four plates, the stream of electrons is not deflected in any direction, but passes straight on out from
the gun to the center of the tube face at the right. (*Courtesy of Life magazine.*)

only electrostatic deflection at the moment and call one pair of
plates upper and lower and the other left and right. Electrons,
being negative, are repelled from a plate having a negative
charge and attracted to one of positive charge.

If an alternating current is connected to the upper and lower deflecting plates, the plates will change their polarity with each alternation, reaching their maximum and minimum values in accordance with the characteristics of the generator. Since the electron stream is being deflected by each of the two plates in accordance with the alternating voltage impressed upon them,

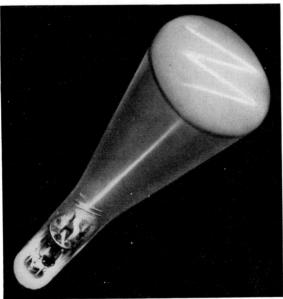

Fig. 15-20. When alternate charges are placed on both sets of plates to deflect the beam up and down and side to side at the same time, the beam traces a wave-like pattern which can be seen on the face of the tube coated with a fluorescent material (phosphor). When the frequency of the horizontal and vertical sweep of the beam is correctly adjusted, this wave form appears stationary on the screen. It is called a *sine wave*. (*Courtesy of Life magazine.*)

it can be seen that the stream will keep tracing a straight line, up and down, at the center of the fluorescent screen.

Now, if we deflect the stream from side to side by means of the left and right plates at the same time that it is moving up and down and do it once for every complete 360-degree rotation

of the generator, the straight vertical line we had before becomes
spread out into a wave extending from one side to the other
across the fluorescent screen. This wave will be a true indication
of the wave form provided by the generator.

The left-to-right sweep of the electron beam is obtained by
means of a tube in which the oscillations can be controlled and
held at a stable value. In other words, the left and right plates
are subjected to controlled oscillations so that the beam will
sweep across from left to right, jump back, and then retrace the
same path again when synchronized with the vertical deflection
of the beam. Each sweep takes places in the fraction of a second,
so that the pattern on the end of the cathode-ray tube appears
as a steady wave line.

While this explanation of cathode-ray oscilloscope operation
is considerably simplified and would be subject to much further
treatment before a complete picture of the instrument's functions
could be obtained, it may serve to provide a basic understanding
of how a large amount of the study of electric-current phenomena
is carried on.

Iconoscopes and Image Orthicon Tubes

An indication of the method by which visual images are converted into electrical impulses for television transmission was
given in Chapter 10. The iconoscope, one type of tube which
makes this conversion, is a complicated electron tube involving
not only precise control of electron movement in a thin beam
but also a photosensitive screen or plate 3 or 4 inches square,
called a *mosaic,* and several other elements as well.

The surface of the mosaic is made up of millions of tiny
photoemissive units, each of which is insulated from the other so
that each can acquire a charge independently of its neighbor.
Each minute unit consists of a silver globule treated with
cesium. When a scene or optical image is focused upon this
mosaic surface, each of the tiny units emits electrons in a
strength or quantity which varies with the intensity of light

striking it. Obviously, a focused image will vary appreciably in its pattern of light, so that there will be a wide range in the emission from different globules.

Since electrons are emitted, the units are left positively charged, and the screen becomes a pattern of positively charged units conforming to the optical image focused upon it.

In order to convert this electrical-charge picture into pulses

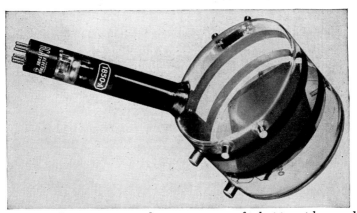

FIG. 15-21. The iconoscope used in certain types of television pickup work. The scene to be televised passes through the flat glass window after first passing through a lens system to reduce it to proper size. The scene thus imposed upon the mosaic plate, which can be seen within the tube, is scanned by an electron beam. The signal which results on the plate as the electron beam scans it passes from the tube through the two terminals shown on the underside. (*Courtesy of Radio Corporation of America.*)

which can be transmitted via electromagnetic waves, an electron beam completely sweeps the plate in successive lines and, in so doing, effects certain changes in the charge of each unit in the mosaic. These charge changes are then converted into signal pulses and broadcast so that the complete picture is almost instantly reduced to electromagnetic oscillations and, at the receiving end, just as rapidly traced back into the picture again on the fluorescent screen of a cathode-ray tube.

The *image orthicon* tube functions on much the same basic

principle, but there are several differences in its operation which make it superior to the iconoscope in many respects.

Low-velocity electrons are used in the scanning beam, which reduces certain problems attending the higher velocity beam as used in the iconoscope. These problems have to do with too much secondary electron emission on the mosaic plate.

The scanning beam of the image orthicon is essentially perpendicular to the mosaic plate instead of at an angle as with the iconoscope. This also results in better performance for many television operations. The tube is much more sensitive to light

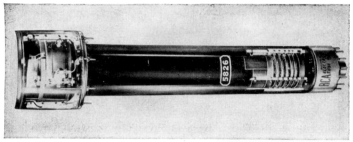

Fig. 15–22. The image orthicon tube used in television pickup work. There are several types, all of which are similar in design and function in much the same manner. (*Courtesy of Radio Corporation of America.*)

variations, so that less intense lighting is required in staging television productions.

There are other methods and tube types such as the image dissector tube for television camera work, but the two briefly described above have been adopted for the more or less standard transmitters.

Electron Image Tubes

In Chapter 7 it was mentioned that the electron image tube was used in conjunction with the conversion of infrared radiation into visible light and that it was incorporated in a rifle sight for nighttime use. Basically, it combines some of the principles of both the image orthicon and the cathode-ray tube, the pickup parts being sensitive to infrared which is then converted into visible light on a fluorescent screen and viewed through a lens eyepiece.

Electron Microscope

The electron microscope has become one of the most important contributions that the science of electronics has made to human welfare. With it we are able to study the mysteries of fundamental matter so small that the optical or light microscope fails to reveal them by a wide margin.

Visible light, as has been explained in detail, travels in waves of definite length. The waves of deep-yellow light, for example, may be 6,000 angstroms or a little more than a forty-thousandth of an inch from crest to crest. When objects or particles become small enough to have dimensions approaching the actual lengths of the waves of light, we reach the limit of light's ability to reveal them.

Electrons, on the other hand, together with a nucleus, make up the structure of an atom. Since atoms themselves are something less than a hundred-millionth of an inch in diameter, some idea can be obtained of the size of an electron, although its solid form, if any, is not established with any degree of certainty.

There is a similarity in the behavior of electrons and of light. The latter is refracted when it passes through a transparent medium such as water, air, or glass, and the optical microscope is a precise means of controlling this characteristic with glass lenses. Electron behavior, however, is controlled by means of electrostatic or electromagnetic fields, so that a beam consisting of countless billions of electrons may be deflected in a manner comparable to the refraction of light. The electron microscope is based upon this phenomenon. While it is a complex instrument, we can confine our brief discussion to the basic principles involved in its operation.

In the electron microscope a beam of electrons is provided

thermionically. This beam corresponds to the light beam of an optical microscope, but instead of glass lenses for refraction, electric or magnetic fields between plates are used to deflect or form the electron beam into a cone as desired. Thus an object to be observed is placed in the path of an electron beam prior to deflection. Electrons will pass through it in accordance with

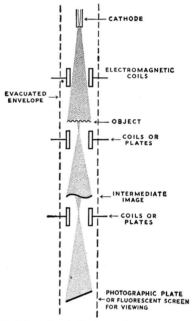

CATHODE

ELECTROMAGNETIC COILS

EVACUATED ENVELOPE

OBJECT

COILS OR PLATES

INTERMEDIATE IMAGE

COILS OR PLATES

PHOTOGRAPHIC PLATE OR FLUORESCENT SCREEN FOR VIEWING

Fig. 15-23. Principle of electron-microscope operation.

its thickness at the point of penetration, so that the portion of the beam which has done the penetrating becomes an electronic *likeness* of the particle. By diverging the beam with the deflecting plates, the likeness can be enlarged and directed so that the image will be reproduced on either a fluorescent screen or a photographic plate.

The resolving power of an electron microscope may be as much as a hundred times greater than that of a good optical microscope, which would mean nearly 200,000 diameters instead of the optical instrument's 1,500 or 2,000. The highest resolving powers of the electron microscope are the result of electron velocities, which are greater at high than at low resolving powers.

The electron microscope is being used in the study of many industrial materials, as well as in bacteriology and medicine. Its development and use are unfolding a great many aids to medical science in its battle against diseases and to physical science in its effort toward greater comfort and happiness for mankind.

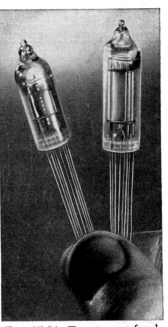

Basic Electron-tube Types

In Chapter 13, certain fundamental types of tubes were discussed. These were classified generally as diodes, triodes, tetrodes, and pentodes in accordance with the number of basic elements (cathode, grids, and plate) used in each. There are so many hundreds of different variations of these fundamental types manufactured today that no attempt can be made in this or any other book to cover all of them completely.

Fig. 15-24. Two types of subminiature tubes. These small tubes are made as oscillators, amplifiers, and rectifiers. There are many types available for purposes similar to those of more standard size.

The use of these tubes with their differences in design can be broken down into three general classes: rectifiers, oscillators, and amplifiers. How these tubes accomplish their work in each of the three categories was also covered in Chapter 13, but at this point it seems desirable to discuss them a little further as a group of tubes used to *control* the amount, speed, and direction of electron flow through them.

Rectifiers are almost always diodes and permit a one-way flow of current through them like a valve. In high-vacuum types this flow is regulated by either the filament (cathode) temperature or the voltage applied to the plate (anode). They may also be gas- or mercury-vapor-filled for specific operating purposes. The two principal uses of such diodes are to convert alternating current to direct current and to demodulate or detect radio signals.

Some types are called *kenotrons*. Another large type employs a pool of mercury, ionized mercury vapor, and an arc to accomplish rectification and is called an *ignitron*. It is usually water-cooled when designed to handle large loads.

Amplifiers may be triodes, tetrodes, or pentodes or in some types may utilize even more grid elements. As explained in Chapter 13, their function involves the application of a weak voltage or signal to the control grid for the purpose of controlling the flow of electrons from cathode to plate. The wave form of the latter will be an amplified replica of the signal wave form applied to the grid. Amplifiers designed for large amounts of power are usually externally cooled by radiator fins or by forced water circulation in jackets.

When it is desired to provide high power output, good power sensitivity (sensitive to low-voltage inputs), and high efficiency, special elements called beam-forming plates are incorporated in the amplifier tube design which confine the electron flow in a beam. Such tubes are called *beam-power amplifiers.*

Oscillators are basically triode amplifiers which, when properly connected in a circuit, result in part of the plate or output voltage being returned and applied to the grid or input circuit. This *feed-back* condition makes the tube self-exciting, so that it will generate rapidly oscillating (radio-frequency) currents.

When additional grids are used in a tube which serves purposes in addition to being an oscillator in special circuits, one of the grids serves as the oscillator plate. Oscillators are vacuum

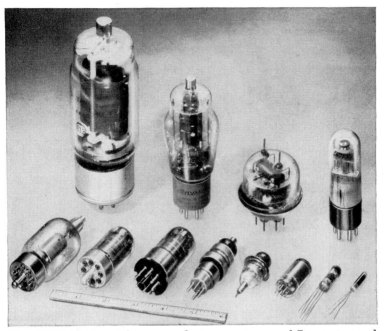

Fig. 15-25. Electron tubes are made in a great many different sizes and shapes with several types of bases. A few typical ones are shown in this illustration.

In the back row from left to right are: (1) a beam-power amplifier No. 813, used for radio transmission; (2) another type of transmitting beam-power amplifier No. 807; (3) a push-pull type of radio-frequency beam-power amplifier No. 832A; (4) an electron-ray tuning indicator tube No. 695.

In the foreground from left to right are: (1) a very-high-frequency transmitting air-cooled tetrode No. 3D24; (2) a radio-frequency amplifier No. 7A7 with lock-in base, widely used in standard radio receivers; (3) also a radio-frequency amplifier, but with an octal base; (4) a broad-band reflex klystron No. 6BL6, used as a cw (continuous wave) oscillator for frequencies of from 1,600 to 6,500 megacycles; (5) a planar triode No. 2C36, used as a pulse-modulated oscillator for frequencies up to 1,200 megacycles; (6) the standard miniature radio-frequency amplifier No. 6BA6, used in radio receivers; (7) a subminiature pentode No. 5840, designed as a radio-frequency amplifier for frequencies up to 400 megacycles; (8) a tiny subminiature diode No. 5647, used as detector or rectifier in applications where space is very limited.

tubes, and like amplifiers, those which handle large amounts of energy must be cooled by radiator fins or forced air or water circulation.

Thyratrons

A thyratron is a triode which is filled with a low-pressure gas such as argon, xenon, hydrogen, or mercury vapor. The presence of such a gas completely changes the tube's operating char-

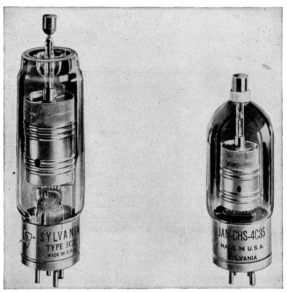

Fig. 15-26. Two common types of hydrogen thyratrons. These tubes serve as drivers for pulsing magnetrons and other oscillators and as high-speed switches. Being hydrogen-filled they de-ionize very rapidly. The one on the left handles higher currents than the other. They both can be made to produce pulses ranging from a fraction of 1 microsecond to several microseconds in duration.

acteristics as compared with a vacuum triode. The grid is used to start a flow of electrons from the cathode. When this flow is established and the gas ionized, the grid ceases to be an effective control of the current as in vacuum tubes. To stop the current flow the plate voltage must be reduced to practically zero.

Thus, a thyratron is a grid-controlled rectifier which will "fire" only when critical grid-voltage conditions are reached, and not before, and will "go out" or de-ionize when the plate-voltage value reaches zero. This characteristic makes the thyratron a device to "trigger" large pulses of energy at rapid rates. There are, of course, several other factors which influence its operation, but we can only indicate fundamentals here.

A *hydrogen thyratron* is a tube specifically designed for very high repetition frequencies, high peak currents, and high voltages. Hydrogen is used because of its extremely short de-ionization time—a requirement to obtain pulses of short duration and rapid frequency.

Magnetrons

While the principles involved in magnetron operation are somewhat complex, we can consider certain factors which are fundamental and which may help in an understanding of how the extremely high-power, high-frequency pulses used in radar are generated.

An electron in motion constitutes a moving electric charge, and as such a magnetic field will exist around its path just as a magnetic field exists around a current-carrying wire. When another, external magnetic field is introduced near that of the electron, the latter is influenced to the extent that the direction and/or speed of the electron may be changed, depending upon the relative directions of the lines of forces of each field.

Since an electron is a negative charge, it is also influenced by electric fields, being repelled from negative elements in a tube and attracted to positive ones (anodes).

Thus, we have two means of controlling electron flow. As indicated earlier, for example, some cathode-ray tubes use *magnetic deflection* for electron beam control, whereas others have *electrostatic* (electric-field) *deflection*. In a magnetron, *both* controlling factors are employed in one device.

A magnetron is a high-vacuum diode. Its anode may be a cylindrical copper block in which an even number of holes or cavities have been bored or cut in symmetrical circular arrangement. Or it may be a cylindrical system of fins forming a number of segments or chambers. The cathode extends axially down the center of the anode cylinder. The cavities of the anode, whether

FIG. 15-27. A typical magnetron shown without magnets and with the casing around the cavities. The cathode in this tube extends down the axis of the body at right angles to the black disk shown at the top. Magnets are applied so that the magnetic field is parallel to the cathode. In other words, one pole is placed on the top disk and the other on the underside.

in a copper block or formed by fins or vanes, are open toward the cathode by slots running parallel to the cathode.

As in all electron tubes employing thermionic emission, electrons are liberated from the cathode in a cloud when current is applied to the filament or heater coil. In a magnetron used to generate pulses of very great power, an enormous number of electrons are emitted from the cathode.

Immediately upon release, the electrons respond to the electrostatic influences of the anode and start toward it. But they are also influenced by the electromagnetic field of a powerful external magnet which is placed around (or built in) the tube in such a manner that the magnetic lines of force are parallel with the cathode.

Under these circumstances, the electrons will whirl around the cathode at high velocities, and as they whiz by the slots or gaps

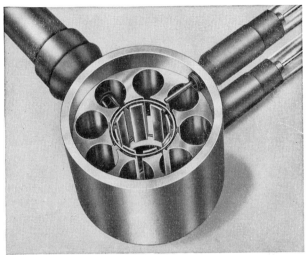

FIG. 15-28. The interior of a multiple-cavity magnetron, showing the arrangement of cavities drilled in a solid copper block. The cathode is not shown in the picture, but would extend from the rod protruding at the top right to a similar one at the bottom and would be parallel to the slot openings of the cavities along the axis of the cylinder. In the cavity at the top left is seen the loop from the center conductor of a coaxial line which collects the energy generated in the magnetron and transmits it to the outside.

leading to the cavities, they set up in the cavities high-frequency electromagnetic vibrations called *resonant frequencies*. The frequencies generated are determined primarily by the physical size and shape of the cavities.

All the cavities in a magnetron are in "tune" with each other and work together in building up the high-powered pulses for which the magnetron is designed. There are several methods of getting this microwave energy out of the tube and into a wave guide to the antenna. The simplest involves coupling the wave guide to one of the cavities which has another open slot at its back, opposite and parallel to the slot facing the cathode and

Fig. 15-29. A high-power X-band magnetron. At the left is shown a coupling for joining the wave guide to carry away the high-frequency electromagnetic radiation. The folded elements in the back and foreground are powerful permanent magnets which spin the electrons around the resonant cavities and thus set up resonant frequencies. Energy to the cathode is supplied through the seal at the top. Since magnetrons are highly evacuated, a method of sealing must be used which will maintain the high vacuum, but keep the high-frequency radiation from being lost through the sealing.

likewise parallel to the axis of the cavity. When a coaxial transmission line is to be coupled to a magnetron, a small loop from the center conductor of the line is inserted in one cavity in such a position than it "collects" the energy to be transmitted from the magnetron to the outside.

It should be recognized, of course, that there are a great many more factors involved in magnetron design and operation, and that certain liberties have been taken in the above explanation in an effort to present only a very basic idea of how a magnetron works.

TR and Anti-TR Boxes

One of the outstanding developments in the field of microwaves is the transmit-receive switch, commonly called the *TR tube*. The TR and its companion, the ATR (anti-TR) tube, are used principally as automatic electronic gates or switches in radar equipment. They perform three main functions:

1. They permit a radar system to use the same antenna for both the transmission and the reception of a pulsed signal.
2. They protect the ultrasensitive receiver from damage from the high instantaneous power of the transmitted signal.
3. They prevent dissipation of the weak reflected signal in the transmitter during reception time.

Microwave switching requires an element having an admittance which varies widely with the power incident upon it. The simplest kind of such an element is the spark gap. Use of the spark gap is made more effective when the gap is part of a resonant circuit, because in such a circuit the gap will fire much nearer the beginning of the pulse.

The most convenient resonant circuit at microwave frequencies is the cavity. TR tubes, therefore, are cavity resonators, tuned to the frequency transmitted and filled to a low pressure with gas. Their purpose is to direct the outgoing transmitter microwave energy pulse straight from magnetron to antenna and to direct the incoming target echo from antenna to receiver. The switching is accomplished automatically by the energy itself and is a result of the great difference in power level between the transmitter pulse and the target echo. The former easily strikes an arc in each tube, whereas the latter lacks by far sufficient power to cause any gaseous discharge. Consequently, when properly connected in microwave circuits, the tubes present either a short circuit or an open circuit to perform the desired switching functions.

When the magnetron oscillates during the transmitter pulse, the high-power microwave burst energizes the tubes and strikes extremely high-frequency arcs in them so that the transmitter pulse travels unimpeded from oscillator to antenna. At the same time, the receiver is shorted out so that very little energy reaches the crystal detector and burnout cannot occur in spite of the terrific power.

FIG. 15-30. A microwave gas switching tube called a *band-pass TR box*. It is d e s i g n e d for automatic switching service in 10,000-megacycle rectangular-wave-guide systems in radar equipment.

There is a fixed relationship between the wavelengths being used and the distance apart that the TR and ATR tubes are placed in the wave-guide circuit. Since we are dealing with pulses of very great power for transmission and extremely minute for reception, all factors in the system must be precisely matched for successful operation.

X-ray Tubes

As explained in Chapter 10, X rays are electromagnetic waves having wavelengths from a small fraction of an angstrom to 600 or 800 angstroms. They are generated when electrons traveling at high speeds through a vacuum tube collide with the solid metallic anode called the *target*.

X-ray tubes are high-vacuum diodes, and while there are many types, the fundamental electronic principle of each is the same. The various types differ in that some are made for low-power penetration and others for extremely deep penetration of metals and other solids. Since those designed for very deep penetration require millions of volts potential between cathode and anode to drive the electrons over at terrific speeds, considerable heat is generated. The conditions imposed by these high temperatures demand specific design and manufacturing techniques which become more and more critical as the requirements for deeper penetration increase. Thus the simplest, small, low-power X-ray tube will be identical in basic operating principle with a 20-million-volt tube, but the latter may be equipped with shielding devices, intricate adjusting and control mechanism, oil or water cooling for cathode assemblies, and similar apparatus for effective use.

The cathodes of X-ray tubes are usually tungsten filaments which release electrons thermionically. The design of the cathode structure is such that the stream of electrons is focused and

Fɪɢ. 15-31. A typical X-ray tube with copper anode and stationary target. The latter appears as the black square inserted at an angle on the end of the anode. This type of tube is used in conventional medical X-ray work. (*Courtesy of Machlett Laboratories, Inc.*)

directed toward the anode target—generally a block of tungsten, molybdenum, platinum, or copper embedded in a holder of some other metal.

This stream of electrons travels to the positively charged anode or target at speeds determined by the potential applied across the two elements. At comparatively low voltages and therefore slow speeds, the X rays produced by the collision at the target are of relatively long wavelength and low penetrating power. As the potential is increased, the speed of the electrons increases with consequent shorter wavelength X rays of greater penetrating power being produced.

For example, in an X-ray tube operating at a potential of 20,000 volts, the electrons will fly from the cathode to the target at a velocity of about 52,000 miles per second (somewhat less than one-third the speed of light) and produce X rays having a wavelength of about 0.6 angstrom with a frequency in the order of 10 trillion megacycles. Since the X rays are electromagnetic waves, they radiate away from the target at the 186,-000-mile-per-second speed of all such radiant energy. At 50,000 volts, however, the electron velocity will be over 82,000 miles per second and the X-ray wavelength 0.25 angstrom with a frequency somewhere around 20 trillion megacycles.

The largest tubes, which operate at 10 million volts and over, drive electrons onto the target at speeds approaching that of light (and all radiant energy). The resulting X radiation is high in the gamma-ray region of the spectrum with wavelengths as short as a thousandth of an angstrom and less and frequencies ranging between 1 and 10 quadrillion megacycles. Such radiation is used in industry to penetrate massive steel parts in order to reveal flaws and interior cracks in castings and in the field of medicine and surgery for radiation therapy.

When electrons strike the anode target, part of their energy is absorbed or lost in the target in the form of heat and part is converted into X rays. At high velocities the heat generated at the target is considerable, so various methods are used to conduct it away. In some tubes water is circulated through coils within the anode structure, and in others oil is used instead of water.

A most interesting development in this particular field is called the *Dynamax* tube. Its target is a pure tungsten disk which rotates at 3,300 rpm in one model and at slower speeds in others. The reason for rotating the disk target is to avoid a concentration of the electron stream at one spot on a target.

In the Dynamax tube the electron stream is directed at the beveled edge of the disk so that, in effect, the concentration of energy is distributed over a much wider area than if the target were stationary.

The anode, which is motor driven, is mounted on the same shaft as the rotor, and the stator windings are *outside* the glass

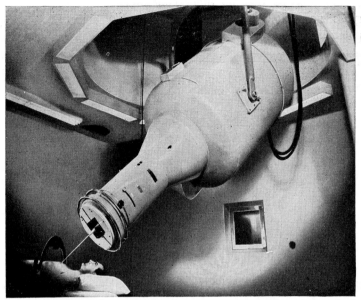

FIG. 15-32. Two-million-volt X-ray equipment as used in hospitals for radiation therapy. (*Courtesy of General Electric Company*).

FIG. 15-33. The Dynamax X-ray tube, showing the rotating tungsten-disk anode. (*Courtesy of Machlett Laboratories, Inc.*)

of the tube so that no inner contamination is possible from gases generated by the motor. Dynamax tubes operate at potentials of about 100,000 volts.

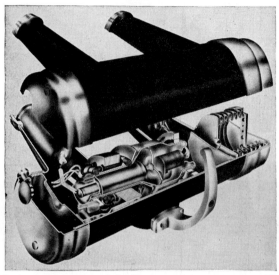

FIG. 15-34. A cutaway view of the Dynamax equipment assembly showing the motor windings outside the glass of the tube. This type of X-ray equipment was developed specifically to meet the need of diagnosticians requiring high-powered radiation for fine-focus X-ray film work. (*Courtesy of Machlett Laboratories, Inc.*)

Betatrons

The betatron is a 24-million-volt electron accelerator which produces X rays of extreme penetration for radiography work in industry, advanced physics research in laboratories, and X-ray therapy in hospitals.

One of the most difficult problems in X-ray therapy results from the fact that, in order to secure an effective dose deep in the tissue, the skin dose becomes excessive and burns may result. This can be overcome by crossfire techniques using several surface exposures with beams converging at the inner location where maximum treatment is required, but such methods are not always wholly satisfactory.

At 24 million volts, however, the penetration characteristics

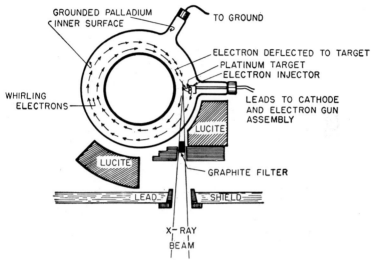

FIG. 15-35. Schematic diagram showing the operation of a betatron "doughnut" tube. Electrons are liberated thermionically from a cathode in the injector and shot into the tube at rapid intervals lasting about 4 microseconds. In the tube they are accelerated in a whirling path to a speed very nearly that of light (and other wavelengths of radiant energy). At the precise moment they are deflected by an electrical pulse to strike the target and produce X rays. These rays are kept within bounds by filters, lead shielding, and other means. The Lucite blocks act as barriers to reduce to a minimum the number of electrons and neutrons in the X-ray beam. The magnetic field in which the tube operates is perpendicular to the plane of the "doughnut" tube—that is, to the reader looking at this diagram, one pole of the magnet is toward him or above the page and the other under the page.

of the radiation are such that the effectiveness 2 inches under the skin is many times that at the surface. Thus, with the betatron's radiation, the skin becomes a much less critical limiting factor in the treatment of tumor growths.

At higher voltages (above 24 million volts) with consequent greater penetration, the exit dose becomes a serious consideration. In other words, while the radiation may enter the body and cause no surface burns at the point of entry (with proper handling by the radiologist), the skin area where the radiation emerges may be subject to damage. It seems, therefore, that for X-ray therapy, 24 million volts will be the optimum level.

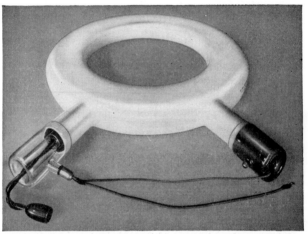

Fig. 15-36. The "doughnut" tube used in the 24-million-volt betatron. The electron injector or cathode as well as the target is in the "horn" at the left. The target is a small triangular piece of platinum mounted on top of the injector assembly. (*Courtesy of Machlett Laboratories, Inc.*)

The heart of the betatron is a "doughnut"-shaped tube of very modest size considering its electron-accelerating power. Like other X-ray tubes, it is a high-vacuum diode and operates in a powerful magnetic field similar to a magnetron. Electrons are emitted thermionically from a hot cathode and injected into the tube by an electron gun (see Chapter 10). Once in the doughnut," the influence of the external magnetic field accelerates them in a circular path around the tube at an average velocity of almost 180,000 miles per second—very nearly that of light.

It will be recalled that in a magnetron these whirling electrons excite resonant frequencies in the cavities, but in the betatron they are smashed against a platinum target, at the moment of greatest energy, after traveling almost 250 miles in 1/720 second.

Fig. 15-37. The 24-million-volt betatron. The "doughnut" tube can be seen in the center of the device, between the poles which produce a very powerful magnetic field. As positioned in this photograph, the stream of electrons would be emitted toward the reader's left, parallel to the floor. (*Courtesy of Allis-Chalmers Mfg. Co. and Picker X-Ray Corp.*)

At the instant of greatest energy, an electrical pulse deflects the whirling stream to the target, and the consequent collision results in a beam of extremely powerful X rays or beta particles (see Chapter 1).

The "doughnut" tube itself is about 18 inches in diameter and

made of a ceramic material rather than glass. The inner surface
has an electrically conducting coating of palladium which is
grounded. The field strength of the magnet alternates at 180
cycles, and the electrons are shot into the tube for a period of 4

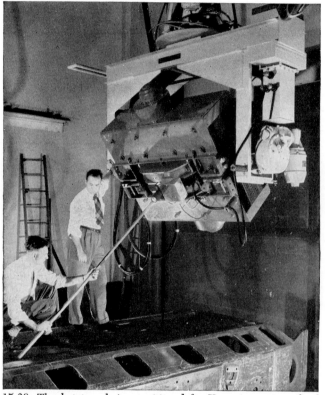

Fig. 15-38. The betatron being positioned for X-ray inspection of a heavy
steel casting used on army tanks. (*Courtesy of Allis-Chalmers Mfg. Co.*)

microseconds each time the field strength is on the increase.
Thus, the radiation is generated in short, rapid pulses.

While radiation therapy is widely used in treating cancer,
medical history shows many cases of radiologists who developed

cancer before the dangers of X rays and radium emanations were fully appreciated. Although no accurate record was ever kept of such accidental cancerous developments, the radiation doses were undoubtedly large and prolonged over years. The use and handling of X-ray equipment require expert knowledge and adequate protection from possible stray radiation.

Synchrotrons

A synchrotron is a device very similar to a betatron except that the electron velocities are accelerated by a different method involving a high-frequency resonant cavity which is part of the "doughnut" device. Electrons entering the cavity receive additional acceleration, so that they whirl around the tube many more times, thus developing very high electron energies.

In addition to electron acceleration, the synchrotron is used in the study of atomic nuclei as an accelerator of protons. Large machines of this type are many feet in diameter, occupying whole buildings two or three stories high.

Cyclotrons

Cyclotrons are devices by which nuclear particles and ions may be accelerated to high energies. Their basic operating principles are similar in many respects to betatrons and synchrotrons, although their structure and function are different.

Instead of a "doughnut" tube for particle acceleration, a hollow metal chamber consisting of two half cylinders called *dees* are used. Each is shaped like the letter D, and the flat sides face and are insulated from each other. This arrangement is maintained at a high vacuum when in operation, and like the other accelerators mentioned above, the chambers are placed between the poles of a large electromagnet.

The source of protons, deuterons, ions, and other particles to be accelerated is located at the center (as with the cathode in a magnetron). These particles are emitted and whirled around the dees in a spiral path at extremely high velocities. An oscillating electric field provides a potential difference between the two dees, so that each time a particle passes from one dee to the other it is urged to greater velocity. Within the dee, the magnetic field, which is perpendicular to the plane of particle motion, maintains the circular path of the particles, but in passing from one dee to the other they spiral outward.

Eventually, when the outer orbit is reached, they emerge through a thin aluminum window at the side and will collide with any material placed in their path. Such bombardment of

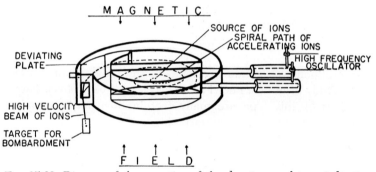

Fig. 15-39. Diagram of the operation of the *dees* in a cyclotron, indicating how ions are whirled around in a spiral path, accelerated, and ejected out of the device at the left to bombard a target placed there for investigation.

materials by fast-moving nuclear particles has been the foundation for building much of our present-day science of nuclear physics.

The method by which the various particles are ejected into the cyclotron for acceleration is somewhat complicated for a discussion here. The sources may be radioactive materials which are constantly releasing particles (Chapter 12), or in some instances ionized gases are used as a source of certain particles such as deuterons.

Cyclotrons and their higher energy brothers *synchrocyclotrons* are sometimes built to huge proportions. One at the University of

FIG. 15-40. The University of California giant 184-inch cyclotron. It fires deuterons of 200 million electron volts, alpha particles of 400 million electron volts, and protons of 350 million electron volts. It is the biggest of three cyclotrons constructed by cyclotron inventor Ernest O. Lawrence, Nobel prize-winning physicist and director of the University of California Radiation Laboratory. It is now being operated under the auspices of the Atomic Energy Commission.

The huge steel crosspiece (another is under the floor) and the two side pieces constitute the yoke of the 4,000-ton electromagnet. The huge bowl-shaped objects connected to the crosspieces are the coil casings of the electromagnet. Between these coil casings in the accelerating chamber. Also shown at the right foreground is vacuum equipment for pumping the air out of the accelerating chamber. This cyclotron was constructed from an original grant of the Rockefeller Foundation. (*Courtesy of University of California*)

California is referred to as the "racetrack" and utilizes a magnet weighing several thousand tons. This particular device is directly responsible for the discovery of many new important facts about atomic nuclei and the properties and behavior of nuclear particles.

Cloud Chambers

The cloud chamber is a device which has proved to be perhaps the most valuable tool of all to the nuclear physicist. It was developed in 1911 by C. T. R. Wilson for photographing the tracks that charged particles make as they pass through water vapor.

With a cloud chamber, the properties of various atomic particles can be observed, particle collisions witnessed, and the particles themselves identified by their behavior, particularly when a magnetic field is applied around the chamber to influence the direction of the particles as they pass through the chamber.

Fundamentally, the cloud chamber is relatively simple, but as designed and used for nuclear physics research, it becomes quite complex, since cameras, light sources, Geiger counters, particle sources, and other apparatus are incorporated to render its operation automatic.

Water vapor does not condense readily into visible droplets unless there is some sort of particle for it to condense or collect around. Raindrops, for example, usually form around a dust particle before they fall to the ground. Steam is invisible at the mouth of the teakettle spout, but when it has risen an inch or so into the air, it condenses around the minute dust particles which are always present, so that we see the millions of droplets and call it steam.

A cloud chamber operates on this principle. It consists of a cylinder and piston. In the area above the piston a gas is introduced which is saturated with water vapor. When the piston is rapidly pulled downward, the gas is suddenly expanded and cools, so that it becomes supersaturated. Under these conditions any particle in the gas or introduced into the chamber will serve as a center around which the vapor will instantly condense, gradually increase in size, and settle to the bottom of the chamber, which would be the top end of the withdrawn piston.

A source of atomic particles such as radioactive material, a cyclotron, or any other device which liberates and will direct such particles into the chamber at the proper time supplies the means for providing nuclei around which the water droplets will form. While the droplets may not collect around the particles themselves, the ions formed in the gas by the particle as it races through the chamber do serve as centers around which water vapor will condense.

FIG. 15-41. A large high-pressure cloud chamber located at the Brookhaven National Laboratories on Long Island, N.Y. It is designed for a pressure of 300 atmospheres. The chamber itself is 16 inches in diameter and 6 inches deep. The chamber yoke weighs 70 tons, and 10 tons of copper are used in the field coils. (*Courtesy of Brookhaven National Laboratories*)

Thus, we have a means of rendering visible the trail a particle takes through a cloud chamber. Even though the path is visible only for a second or less, it is ample time for photographing through a thick glass window in the side of the chamber.

In a magnetic field various particles are deflected differently in their flight depending upon their charge, speed, and mass. The track they leave will have characteristics which establish the identity of the particle causing it. A slow electron, for example,

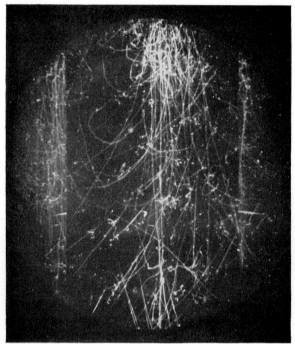

Fig. 15-42. What appears to be a child's scribbling actually is a photograph of a cloud chamber at Brookhaven National Laboratory, Upton, N.Y. The crooked lines are caused by a shower of electrons which are curved by the magnetic field of the cloud chamber. A cloud chamber is used to study nuclear events—that is, the disintegration of particles in the nucleus of an atom, or the interaction of such particles with other atoms. Although the particles themselves are much too small to see as they dart through an atmosphere supersaturated with alcohol or water vapor in the cloud chamber, they leave a trail of small droplets which can be photographed. These trails, which show up as streaks in a photo, add to knowledge of the structure and characteristics of nuclear particles. (*Courtesy of Brookhaven National Laboratory*)

leaves a thin, wobbly track of few droplets. Because of its small mass and relatively slow speed it is bumped around by the gas molecules, ionizing comparatively few of them. An alpha particle, on the other hand, is a heavy composite bundle of energy consisting of two protons and two neutrons (a helium nucleus—see Chapter 1). Consequently, its path is straight, thick, and heavily ionized. Since its mass is a great many times that of an electron, it tends to blast almost anything in its way without deviating from its course. Other particles such as protons and mesons show tracks

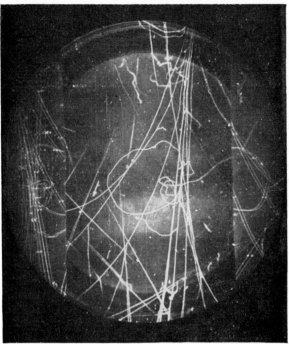

FIG. 15-43. A small electron shower produced in the Brookhaven National Laboratory cloud chamber. It shows both positrons and electrons of varying energies. The electrons curve to the left and the positrons to the right in accordance with the magnetic field influencing them. The greater the curvature the smaller the energy of the particle. (*Courtesy of Brookhaven National Laboratory*)

with characteristics indicative of their properties. Neutrons, carrying no charge, do not produce tracks themselves, but the result of their impact with other particles is usually evident.

When a collision of particles occurs in a cloud chamber, the resulting tracks show what happened as well as the nature of the particles colliding. If, for example, a heavy particle and a light one meet, the heavier, as would be expected, shows only a slight or possibly no deviation from its path whereas the light one may be bounced away at considerable angle depending upon how "squarely" they met.

In studying cosmic radiation, cloud-chamber observations have been the major source of information concerning its nature and the effect of cosmic showers in ionizing particles and passing through lead sheets without significant losses of energy. The existence of the more obscure particles has been determined in this way, and sometimes hundreds of photographs must be taken before the search for a suspected particle is rewarded with a picture of its track.

The Mass Spectrograph

Another instrument for determining the properties of particles is called the *mass spectrograph*. While there are several types, they are all based upon the fact that heavier ions are deflected less than lighter ones in an electric field and also that a magnetic field alters their paths in accordance with their speed.

A mass spectrograph separates a beam of particles of different velocity. The particles fly through a highly evacuated space and, under the influence of both electric and magnetic fields, will separate—the heavier ones passing out through one end of a slit, the lighter ones through the other end, and those of intermediate weight between the two extremes.

At the slit, a photographic plate is darkened to a degree depending upon the amounts of heavy, medium, and light particles in the beam.

Geiger Counters

The Geiger-Müller counter, or GM counter, is a device to detect and indicate the strength of radiant energy and/or particle showers at the upper short-wavelength end of the electromagnetic spectrum. It is essentially a gas-filled chamber constructed of a metal tube charged negatively, through which a thin wire is stretched to serve as a positive electrode. The shell or tube is charged quite heavily as compared with the wire.

On entering the chamber, an atomic particle or radiation short enough in wavelength to exhibit particle properties produces ionization of the gas. Since the wire electrode is charged positive, the electrons which result from the primary ionization and are in the vicinity of the wire become further accelerated. This causes a secondary ionizing process. The secondary ionization in turn results in a third action, and as a consequence the total ionizing process (called *avalanche ionization*) is, in effect, a greatly amplified measure of the number of ions produced by the initial ionizing particle or radiation. And the degree of ionization caused at first by the particle is an indication of its energy and properties.

Fig. 15-44. A portable pistol-grip type of Geiger-Müller counter more properly called the beta-gamma survey meter. Instruments such as these are used for quick checks of possible radiation contamination and field-survey work involving uranium and other radioactive ores.

Geiger counters are designed somewhat differently for specific purposes. That is, those designed for measuring gamma radiation will have different characteristics from those made for cosmic radiation work. In either case, the fundamental operation is the same.

The voltage pulses which occur in Geiger counters as a result of entering particles or radiation are usually amplified to produce audible indications in earphones when used in the field for detection purposes.

FIG. 15-45. Interior view of a radiation counter similar to that shown in Fig. 15-44.

Fig. 15-46.Two types of tubes used in radiation counting instruments. The one on the right (with its cap, center) is used in the portable instruments shown in Fig. 15-44.

FIG. 15-47. A beam of 3-million-volt electrons emerging through a thin aluminum window from a pressurized Van de Graaf accelerator at Massachusetts Institute of Technology. The sterilizing of pharmaceuticals, foods, and even body tissues by beams of high-energy electrons is an established technique. Of greatest commercial value is the volume sterilization of certain perishable foods, including fish, meats, wheat, and other packaged products. There has been a great deal of research of high-energy electrons for sterilizing purposes. (*Courtesy of Dr. John G. Trump, High-voltage Research Laboratory at Massachusetts Institute of Technology.*)

There are other methods of energy detection and measurement which employ somewhat different principles. One is called the *scintilloscope* and is based upon the fact that energy particles will, under the proper conditions, excite certain substances to the emission of visible light. These minute individual pulses of light are amplified and recorded so that the instrument is a highly sensitive and accurate device.

Another method makes use of certain crystals. Such counters are quite rugged and are particularly well adapted to specific types of investigation. Their operation also involves ionization and the consequent release of electrons in the crystal lattice structure. The electrons move toward one surface of the crystal which has been prepared and established as an anode. This rapid migration of electrons within the crystal structure is amplified and recorded with considerable accuracy to determine the nature of the ionizing unit of energy.

Conclusion

It is hoped that the reader, having completed this book, will be urged by his own interest to pursue other less general and more detailed textbooks on radio, illumination, nuclear physics, medicine, or whatever specific branch of the sciences appeals most strongly to him.

We started out in Chapter 1 with an analysis of the relationship between matter and energy and have tried throughout the course of the book to recognize this relationship in descriptions, examples, and explanations. As electron tubes become more complex in our story, and as we reach the upper limits of the electromagnetic spectrum, this relationship becomes apparent to the extent that particles and electromagnetic radiation can be reconciled as one, even though the behavior of each generally manifests itself differently to us.

Acknowledgment

This book is not intended as a complete and finished treatise on the science of electronics or on the various uses and wavelengths of radiant energy, nor is it a first-time presentation of new facts and developments pertaining to these subjects. The author, in preparing the manuscript, has tried to gather together the fundamental and basic principles expressed by many authors, both written and illustrated, and, in fusing them together and sifting out the more complicated technical aspects, produce a digest of general interest and/or a foundation for more advanced study.

The names of scientists and physicists identified with the development and application of electron tubes and radiant energy during the past 10 years number in the hundreds. "Atomic Energy for Military Purposes," by Henry D. Smyth (Princeton University Press), better known popularly as "The Smyth Report," lists 220 individuals whose work was essential to the successful use of atomic energy for both military and civilian purposes. In the field of electronics and others related to it, there are hundreds more who contributed some discovery or development which helped bring the science to its present stage.

To mention each of these men and women at the appropriate place in the text of this book would neither give them adequate credit for their work nor increase the reader's appreciation of it. However, the books listed below were referred to by the author in checking data and obtaining considerable factual information, and since they cover their specific subjects much more completely, the individuals identified with various developments and discoveries are named in these texts.

This book stems from the original "Primer of Electronics"

published by the McGraw-Hill Book Company in 1943. At the time of its publication and until the end of the Second World War, information on many of the subjects was restricted. The story of atomic energy, radar, loran, and others could not be told. In fact, many of them had just about crossed the threshold of the laboratory into practical use.

Since then, applications of electron tubes for the production and control of radiant energy have unfolded, so that this book is, in a sense, an *extension* and *revision* of the original "Primer" rather than a second edition. Those acknowledgments listed in the original apply also to this book, since most of the material in the first has been used, with certain adjustments, in this one.

The author is most grateful to Mr. O. H. Biggs, chief engineer of the General Engineering Laboratory; Mr. W. B. Whalley, chief engineer, Applications Research Section; and Mr. T. C. Sargent, Dr. Ben Kievet, Mr. E. H. Ulm, Mr. R. B. Martenson, and their colleagues, all of the Sylvania Electric Products Inc. engineering staff. The time these men took in reading portions of the manuscript dealing with their particular phase of engineering work was their own, and the author is most appreciative of their assistance and suggestions.

Readers will doubtless recognize the extensive contributions of many other manufacturers to the science of electronics. To assure this recognition a few are mentioned: The Bell Telephone Laboratories, The RCA Manufacturing Company, Inc., The General Electric Company, The Westinghouse Electric Corp., The Corning Glass Works, The Western Electric Company, The Federal Telephone and Radio Corporation, The Columbia Broadcasting Company, The I. E. duPont de Nemours Company, The Union Carbide & Carbon Corporation, the Machlett Laboratories, The Allen B. DuMont Laboratories, Inc., Eastman Kodak Company, Sperry Gyroscope Company, and many others.

There are also certain nonmanufacturing organizations whose contributions have been and are at present essential in electronic and radiant energy work. These include the Massachusetts Institute of Technology, the University of California, and other institutions within whose laboratories many fundamental theories are explored and made ready for commercial development by manufacturers. Of course, the research laboratories of the Atomic Energy Commission and the physicists who work in and with them are responsible for a vast amount of exploration in the atomic-energy field—both theoretical and practical.

The courtesy of those contributing illustrations has been acknowledged in the text.

Credit is due Miss S. W. Murphy, artist and colorist of Sylvania, for producing many of the drawings, diagrams, and rendering used in illustrating this book. Last but certainly not least, the author is grateful to Miss Jan Reynolds, lighting consultant of Sylvania and secretary, who typed the manuscript and maintained some degree of order in assembling the photographs and illustrations. The success of both in translating the author's verbal mumblings and longhand into intelligible copy and pictures has been remarkable.

Listed below are those books to which reference was made in the preparation of this one. It is hoped that their authors will consider the "new Primer" as a basic training for their more advanced treatments.

References

"Atomic Microscope," *Scientific American,* July, 1951.

Bergmann, Ludwig, and H. S. Halfield: "Ultrasonics," John Wiley & Sons, Inc., New York, 1943.

Cathode Press, Machlett Laboratories, Springdale, Conn.

Cramer, J. L., and R. E. Peierls: "Atomic Energy," Penguin Books, Ltd., England, 1950.

Fink, Donald G.: "Television Engineering," McGraw-Hill Book Company, Inc., New York, 1952.

Finkelnburg, W.: "Atomic Physics," McGraw-Hill Book Company, Inc., New York, 1950.

Glasstone, Samuel: "Sourcebook on Atomic Energy," D. Van Nostrand Company, Inc., New York, 1950.

Hahn, Otto: "New Atoms," Elsevier Publishing Co., Inc., 1950.

Hofstad, Lawrence: "Reactors," *Scientific American,* April, 1951.

Hornung, J. L.: "Radar Primer," McGraw-Hill Book Company, Inc., New York, 1948.

"I.E.S. Lighting Handbook," Illuminating Engineering Society, New York, 1947.

Lapp, R. E., and H. L. Andrews: "Nuclear Radiation Physics," Prentice-Hall, Inc., New York, 1948.

Ney, Edward P.: "Heavy Elements from Space," *Scientific American,* May, 1951.

Pollard, Ernest, and William L. Davidson: "Applied Nuclear Physics," John Wiley & Sons, Inc., New York, 1951.

"Reference Data for Radio Engineers," Federal Telephone & Radio Corp., 1950.

Read, Oliver: "The Recording and Reproduction of Sound," Howard M. Sams & Co., Inc., Indianapolis, 1949.

Rothman, S. C., "Constructive Uses of Atomic Energy," Harper & Brothers, New York, 1949.

Smith, Alpheus W.: "The Elements of Physics," McGraw-Hill Book Company, Inc., New York, 1948.

Smyth, Henry D.: "Atomic Energy for Military Purposes," Princeton University Press, Princeton, N. J., 1945.

Index

A

Absolute temperature, 98
Acoustics, 82
Alpha particles, 5, 212
Alternating current, 46
  generators, 46, 47
  motors, 52
Americium, 217
Ampère, André, 42
Ampere, 22
Amplification factor, 239, 240
Amplifiers, 239, 240, 302
  beam-power, 302
Amplitude, 81
Amplitude modulation, 160–162
Angstrom, 83
Angular momentum, 8
Anode, 233
Antennas, radar, 185–187
Anti-TR box, 309, 310
Approach lighting, airport stroboscopic, 283
Argon in incandescent lamps, 246
Armature, 52
Atom, 2, 8
  carbon, 3, 15
  excited, 254
  hydrogen, 8
  size of, 2
  structure, 14–16

Atomic bomb, 220, 223, 224
Atomic energy, 79
Audio frequency, 162
Aurora borealis, 87
Autotransformer, 57
Avalanche ionization, 327

B

Bactericidal tubes, 273, 274
Bactericidal ultraviolet, 132–134
Ballasts in fluorescent lamps, 265–269
Battery, dry-cell, 19, 25, 26
  storage, 77
Beam candlepower, 98
Beam-power tube, 241, 302
Beam relay communication, 199–201
Becquerel, 208
Berkelium, 217
Beta particles, 6, 212
Betatron, 314–319
  "doughnut" tube, 315, 316
Black body, 98
Black-light sources, 274–276
Bohr, Dr. Niels, 2
Bomb, atomic, 223, 224
  hydrogen, 224, 225
Boyce Thompson Institute, 132
Broadcasting, commercial radio, 156
  television, 164–168

335